Pumps

by Perry O. Black

THEODORE AUDEL & CO.
a division of
HOWARD W. SAMS & CO., INC.
4300 West 62nd Street
Indianapolis, Indiana 46206

Contents

CHAPTER 13

CHAPTER 14

CHAPTER 1

Basic Fluid Principles

A fluid is used in many different devices to develop a push or a pull and to control an action. Countless applications of fluid units in modern industry can be cited.

PHYSICS

The branch of science which deals with the properties and changes of matter and energy is called *physics*. Some of the basic principles of fluids must be considered before the succeeding chapters can be understood properly.

Matter

By definition, matter is any substance or material that can be weighed or measured. The three states in which matter may exist are known as:

1. Solid
2. Liquid
3. Gas

Water is the familiar example of a substance that exists in each of the three states of matter (Fig. 1) as: (1) ice (solid); (2) water (liquid); and (3) steam (gas).

Ques. In what three forms does matter exist?
Ans. As a solid, a liquid, or a gas.

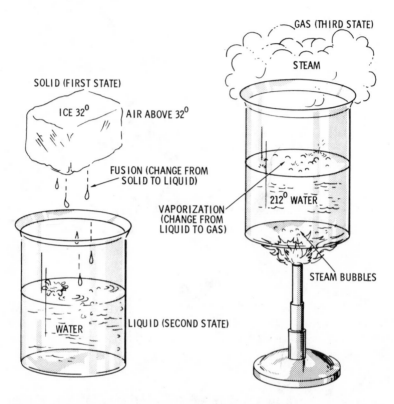

Fig. 1. Illustrating the three states of matter: (1) Solid; (2) Liquid; and (3) Gas. Note that the change of state from a solid to a liquid is called "fusion," and the change of state from liquid to a gas is called "vaporization."

Ques. What is the distinguishing difference between matter and a body?

Ans. A body is a definite quantity of matter.

Ques. How can the quantity of matter in a body be determined?

Ans. By weighing on a lever or platform scale, or on a spring scale.

Ques. Which type of scale gives an accurate reading in all locations?

Ans. The lever or platform scale.

10

Ques. Why does the reading vary on a spring scale?

Ans. Since weight depends on gravity and since gravity decreases with elevation, the reading on a spring scale varies, as shown in Fig. 2.

Energy

Energy is the *capacity for doing work and overcoming resistance.* Two types of energy are: (1) *potential;* and (2) *kinetic* (Fig. 3).

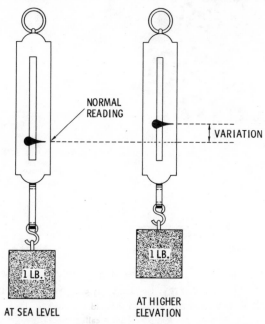

NORMAL READING

VARIATION

1 LB.

1 LB.

AT SEA LEVEL

AT HIGHER ELEVATION

Fig. 2. Illustrating variation in readings of a spring scale for different elevations.

Ques. What is meant by potential energy?

Ans. Energy that is the result of the relative position of a body.

Ques. What is meant by kinetic energy?

Ans. The energy of a body that results from its motion.

Ques. What is another definition for potential energy?

Ans. The *stored capacity* for performing work. This energy is due to the elevation of a body at rest.

11

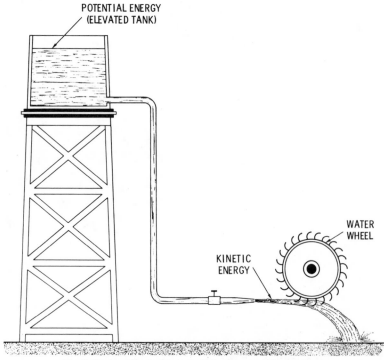

Fig. 3. Diagram illustrating potential energy and kinetic energy.

As shown in Fig. 3, water stored in an elevated reservoir or tank represents potential energy, because it may be utilized to do work as it is liberated to a lower elevation.

Ques. What is another definition for kinetic energy?
Ans. The *dynamic inertia* possessed by a moving body.

Conservation of Energy—It is a doctrine of physics that energy can be transmitted from one body to another or transformed in its manifestations, but *energy may be neither created nor destroyed.* Energy may be dissipated; that is, converted into a form from which it cannot be recovered (the heat that escapes with the exhaust from a locomotive, for example, or the condensed water from a steamship). However, *the total amount of energy in the universe remains constant but variable in form.*

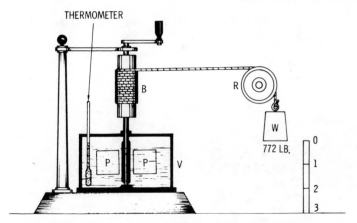

THERMOMETER

Fig. 4. Joule's experiment revealed the mechanical equivalent of heat.

Joule's Experiment—This experiment is a classic illustration (Fig. 4) of the conservation of energy principle. In 1843, Dr. Joule of Manchester, England, performed his classic experiment which demonstrated to the world the *mechanical equivalent of heat*. It was discovered that the work performed by the descending weight (*W* in Fig. 4) was not lost, but appeared as heat in the water—the agitation of the paddles having increased the water temperature by an amount that can be measured by a thermometer. According to Joule's experiment, when 772 foot-pounds of work energy had been expended on the 1 pound of water, the temperature of the water had increased 1°F. This is known as *Joule's equivalent,* that is, 1 unit of heat equals 772 foot-pounds of work.

Experiments by Prof. Rowland (1880) and others provide higher values; a value of 778 ft-lb is generally accepted, but 777.5 ft-lb is probably more nearly correct, the value 777.52 ft-lb being used by Marks and Davis in their steam tables. The value 778 ft-lb is sufficiently accurate for most calculations.

Heat

Heat is a form of energy that is known by its effects. The effect of heat is produced by the accelerated vibration of molecules. Theoretically, all molecular vibration stops at −273°C., and there is no heat formed. There are two types of heat: (1) *sensible* heat; and (2) *latent* heat.

13

Sensible Heat—The effect of this form of heat is indicated by the sense of touch or feeling (Fig. 5).

INDICATED BY
"SENSE" OF FEELING

SENSIBLE HEAT

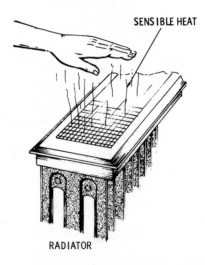

RADIATOR

Fig. 5. The common radiator is an example of sensible heat.

Ques. How is sensible heat measured?
Ans. By means of a thermometer.

Ques. What is a thermometer?
Ans. An instrument consisting of a glass tube that terminates in a bulb which is charged with a liquid, usually mercury or colored alcohol.

Ques. What is the basic working principle of the thermometer?
Ans. The liquid in the glass tube either contracts or expands with changes in temperature, falling or rising within the tube which is placed against a graduated scale. The Fahrenheit, Centigrade, and Reaumur thermometer scales are shown in Fig. 6.

Ques. How are extremely high temperatures measured?
Ans. By means of a pyrometer. A diagram illustrating the basic principle of a thermocouple pyrometer is shown in Fig. 7.

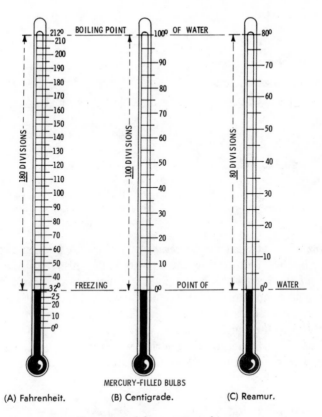

Fig. 6. Three types of thermometer scales.

Latent Heat—This form of heat is that quantity of heat which becomes concealed or hidden inside a body while producing some change in the body other than an increase in temperature.

When water at atmospheric pressure is heated to 212°F., a further increase in temperature does not occur, even though the supply of heat is continued. Instead of an increase in temperature, vaporization occurs, and a considerable quantity of heat must be added to the liquid to transform it into steam. The total heat consists of *internal* and *external* latent heats. Thus in water at 212°F. and at atmospheric pressure, considerable heat is required to cause the water to begin boiling (*internal* latent heat). The additional heat that is required

15

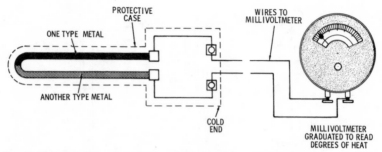

Fig. 7. Basic principle of a thermocouple pyrometer. A thermocouple is used to measure high temperatures. In principle, when heat is applied to the junction of two dissimilar metals, a current of electricity begins to flow in proportion to the amount of heat applied. This current is brought to a meter and translated in terms of heat.

to boil the water is called *external* latent heat. A familiar example of both internal and external latent heat is shown in Fig. 8.

Unit of Heat—The heat unit is the amount of heat required to raise the temperature of 1 pound of water 1 degree Fahrenheit at the maximum density of the water. The *British thermal unit,* abbreviated *Btu,* is the standard for heat measure or for the heat unit. A unit of heat *Btu* is equal to 252 calories, which is the quantity of heat required to raise the temperature of 1 pound of water from 62° F. to 63°F.

INTERNAL LATENT HEAT   EXTERNAL LATENT HEAT

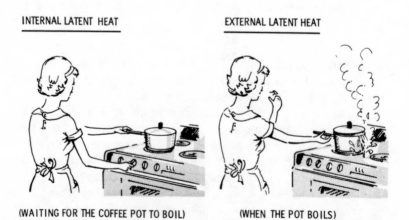

(WAITING FOR THE COFFEE POT TO BOIL)   (WHEN THE POT BOILS)

Fig. 8. Domestic setting for illustrating internal (left) and external (right) latent heat.

Assuming no loss of heat, 180 heat units are required to raise the temperature of 1 pound of water from 32°F. to 212°F. If the transfer of heat occurs at a uniform rate and if six minutes are required to increase the temperature of the water from 32°F. to 212°F., 1 heat unit *Btu* is transferred to the water in (6 × 60) ÷ 180, or 2 seconds.

Specific Heat—This is the ratio of the amount of heat *Btu* required to raise the temperature of a substance 1 degree Fahrenheit to the amount of heat *Btu* required to raise the temperature of an equal quantity of water 1 degree (1°) Fahrenheit. Some substances can be heated more quickly than other substances. Metal, for example, can be heated more quickly than glass, wood, or air. If a given substance requires one-tenth the amount of heat to bring it to a given temperature that is required for an equal weight of water, the number

Table 1. Specific Heat of Common Substances

Solids

Copper	0.0951
Wrought iron	0.1138
Glass	0.1937
Cast iron	0.1298
Lead	0.0314
Tin	0.0562
Steel, Hard	0.1175
Soft	0.1165
Brass	0.0939
Ice	0.5040

Liquids

Water	1.0000
Sulfuric acid	0.3350
Mercury	0.0333
Alcohol	0.7000
Benzene	0.9500
Ether	0.5034

Gases

	At constant pressure	At constant volume
Air	0.23751	0.16847
Oxygen	0.21751	0.15507
Hydrogen	3.40900	2.41226
Nitrogen	0.24380	0.17273
Ammonia	0.50800	0.29900
Alcohol	0.45340	0.39900

17

of heat units *Btu* required is 1/10 (0.1); and its specific heat is 1/10 (0.1).

Ques. What standard is taken for the specific heat of a substance?
Ans. The standard is water from 62°F. to 63°F.

Example: The quantity of heat required to raise the temperature of 1 pound (1 lb.) of water 1 degree (1°) Fahrenheit is equal to the quantity of heat required to raise the temperature of 8.4 lbs. of cast iron 1 degree Fahrenheit. Since the specific heat of water is 1.0, the specific heat of cast iron is (1.0 ÷ 8.4), or 0.1189.

Thus, the specific heat is the ratio between the two quantities of heat. The specific heat of some common substances is shown in Table 1.

Transfer of Heat—Heat may be transferred from a body to another body which is at a lower temperature (Fig. 9) by:

1. Radiation
2. Conduction
3. Convection

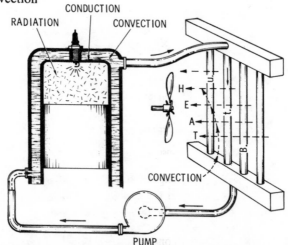

Fig. 9. Diagram illustrating transfer of heat by radiation, conduction, and convection. It should be noted that the air, not the water, is the cooling agent; the water is only the medium for transferring the heat to the point where it is extracted and dissipated by the air.

When heat is transmitted by radiation, the hot material, such as burning fuel, sets up waves in the ether. In a boiler-type furnace, the heat is given off by *radiation*—the heat rays radiating in straight lines in all directions. The heat is transferred to the crown sheet and the sides of the furnace by means of radiation.

Contrary to popular opinion, heat is transferred through solids, such as boiler plate, by *conduction* (Fig. 10). The temperature of the

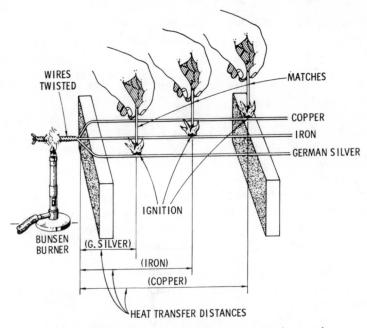

Fig. 10. Illustrating differences in heat conductivity of various metals.

furnace boiler plate is only slightly higher than the temperature of the water that is in contact with the boiler plate. This is due to the extremely high conductivity of the boiler plate.

Ques. What is meant by conduction of heat?

Ans. The transfer of heat from the heated portions of a body to the cooler portions.

Ques. On what condition is conduction dependent?

19

Ans. Conduction depends on unequal temperatures in the various portions of a given body.

Ques. How is heat transferred by convection?
Ans. By motion occurring within the heated matter.

Ques. In what states of matter can heat be transmitted by means of convection?
Ans. In liquids and in gases.

Effects of Heat—Nearly all substances expand with an increase in temperature, and they contract or shrink with a decrease in temperature.

Ques. What substance is an exception to the above statement for all temperature changes?
Ans. Water is an exception. It is a remarkable characteristic of water that at its point of maximum density (39.1°F.) water expands as heat is added and that it also expands slightly as the temperature decreases from that point.

Ques. Why does heat cause a substance to expand?
Ans. An increase in heat results from an increase in the velocity of molecular motion. Since the molecules become more separated in distance by their more frequent violent collisions, the body expands.

Ques. What is meant by linear expansion?
Ans. That is the expansion in a longitudinal direction of solid bodies.

Ques. What is meant by volumetric expansion?
Ans. That is the expansion in volume of a substance.

Ques. Define the coefficient of linear expansion of a solid substance.
Ans. It is the ratio of the increase in length of a body to its original length, produced by an increase in temperature of 1 degree Fahrenheit (1°F.). If a bar of length L at $N°F$. is heated to $N° + 1°F$. and it expands a distance F, the coefficient of expansion is $F \div L$ (as shown in Fig. 11).

BASIC FLUID PRINCIPLES

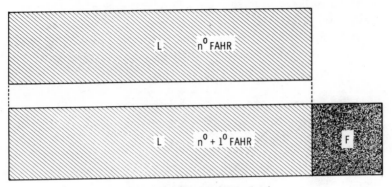

COEFFICIENT OF EXPANSION = F ÷ L

Fig. 11. Illustrating coefficient of expansion.

Ques. What are some of the advantages and disadvantages of expansion and contraction resulting from heat?

Ans. Red-hot rivets are used to fasten boiler plate. As the rivets cool, they contract, binding the plates together with great force. Iron rims are first heated and then placed on the wheel. As the iron cools,

Table 2.   Linear Expansion of Common Metals
(between 32° and 212° F.)

	Linear expansion per unit length per degree F.
aluminum	0.00001234
antimony	0.00000627
bismuth	0.00000975
brass	0.00000957
bronze	0.00000986
copper	0.00000887
gold	0.00000786
iron, cast	0.00000556
iron, wrought	0.00000648
lead	0.00001571
nickel	0.00000695
steel	0.00000636
tin	0.00001163
zinc, cast {	0.00001407
zinc, rolled {	

volumetric expansion = 3 times linear expansion.

the rim contracts and binds the wheel. It is common practice to leave a small space between the ends of the steel rails of a railroad to allow for longitudinal expansion and contraction of the rails. Values that can be used in calculations of linear expansion are indicated in Table 2.

Pressure

Pressure (symbol P) is a force exerted against an opposing body; or a thrust distributed over a surface. It is a force which tends to compress a body when it is applied.

If a force is applied in the direction of its axis, a spring is compressed (Fig. 12). The resistance of the spring constitutes an opposing force, equal and opposite in direction to the applied force.

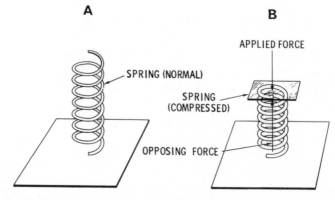

Fig. 12. Illustrating the nature of pressure: (A) spring in its normal state; and (B) pressure system in state of equilibrium.

Ques. If a given force (2 lb.) is applied to a spring, to what extent is the spring compressed?

Ans. Since the resistance of a spring is increased with the degree of compression, it is compressed to the point where its resistance is equal to 2 lb., or the pressure applied.

Ques. What is the condition of the pressure system, as shown in Fig. 12B?

Ans. It is said to be in a state of equilibrium.

It should be noted that pressure is considered to be distributed over a unit area of the surface. The pressure distributed over an entire surface is usually stated in pounds per square inch (lb. per sq. in.), or *psi*.

Problem: If the total working area of the plunger of a pump is 10 sq. in., what is the total pounds of pressure on the plunger when pumping against 125 lb. per sq. in. (Fig. 13)?

Solution: Since 125 lb. of pressure is exerted on each square inch of the working face of the plunger and since the area of the working face of the plunger is 10 sq. in., the total pressure exerted on the plunger face is 1250 lb., as:

$$10 \text{ sq. in.} \times 125 \text{ lb. per sq. in.} = 1250 \text{ lb.}$$

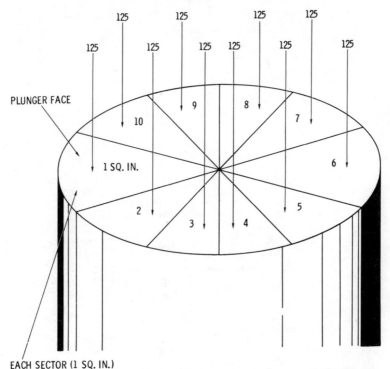

EACH SECTOR (1 SQ. IN.)

Fig. 13. The distribution of pressure over a surface. A pressure of 125 lbs. per sq. in. is exerted on each sector (1 sq. in.).

The ball-peen hammer is used for peening and riveting operations. The peening operation indents or compresses the surface of the metal, expanding or stretching that portion of the metal adjacent to the indentation. As shown in Fig. 14, the contract area is nearly zero if the flat and special surfaces are perfectly smooth. However, perfectly smooth surfaces do not exist. The most polished surfaces (as seen under a microscope) are similar to emery paper; therefore, the contact area is very small. As shown in Fig. 15, the pressure, in lb. per sq. in., is multiplied when applied through a spherical contact surface.

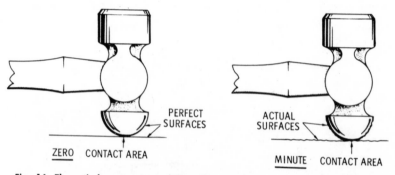

Fig. 14. Theoretical contact area (left) and actual contact area (right) of flat and spherical surfaces.

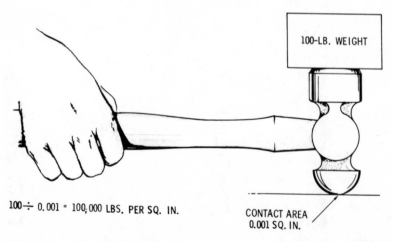

Fig. 15. The pressure (lb. per sq. in.) is multiplied when it is applied to the flat surface through a spherical contact area.

Problem: If the ball peen of a machinist's hammer is placed in contact with a flat surface (see Fig. 15) and a weight of 100 lb. is placed on the hammer (not including the weight of the hammer), how many pounds of pressure are exerted at the point of contact if the contact area is 0.01 sq. in.?

Solution: If the contact area were 1 sq. in. in area, the pressure would equal 100 lb. on the 1 sq. in. of flat surface. Now, if the entire 100-lb. weight or pressure is borne on only 0.01 sq. in. (as in Fig. 15), the pressure in lb. per sq. in. is equal to (100 ÷ 0.01), or 10,000 lb. per sq. in.

Perhaps, another example (Fig. 16) may illustrate this point more clearly.

Problem: Lay out the entire surface *ABCD* equal to 1 sq. in., and divide the surface into 16 small squares (1/16 sq. in.), placing a 5-lb. weight on each small square. Then the area of each small square is $(1/16)^2$, or 0.0625 sq. in. If all the 5-lb. weights are

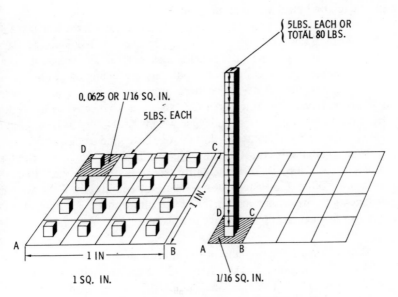

Fig. 16. Diagram illustrating pressure per sq. in. of flat surface.

25

placed on one small square (as in the diagram), the total weight or pressure on that small square is (5 × 16), or 80 lb., on 0.0625 sq. in. of surface.

In the left-hand diagram (see Fig. 16), the 5-lb. weights are distributed over the entire 1 sq. in. of area, the pressure totaling (5 × 16), or 80 lb. of pressure per sq. in. of surface. In the right-hand diagram, the sixteen 5-lb. weights (80 lb.) are borne on only 0.0625 sq. in. of surface. Thus, the total weight or pressure, if each of the sixteen small squares were to bear 80 lb., would be (16 × 80), or 1280 lb. per sq. in. of surface.

Ques. How is pressure indicated if each square inch of surface bears an equal weight or pressure?

Ans. If the given pressure is 100 lb., for example, the pressure is indicated as 100 lb. per sq. in.

Atmospheric Pressure—Usually, unless stated otherwise, the term *pressure* indicates pressure per sq. in. The various qualifications of pressure are: initial pressure; mean effective pressure; terminal pressure; back pressure; and total pressure.

The atmospheric pressure is due to the weight of the earth's atmosphere; at sea level it is equal to approximately 14.69 lb. per sq. in. The pressure of the atmosphere does not remain constant at a given location, because weather conditions are changing continually.

A diagram illustrating atmospheric pressure is shown in Fig. 17. If a piston having a surface area of 1 sq. in. is connected to a weight by a string passing over a pulley, a weight of 14.69 lb. is required to raise the weight from the bottom of the cylinder (assuming airtightness and no friction) against the atmosphere which distributes a pressure of 14.69 lb. over the entire face area of the piston (area = 1 sq. in.). Then the system is in a "state of equilibrium," the weight balancing the resistance or weight of the atmosphere. A slight excess pressure is then required to move the piston.

Ques. What is the pressure of the atmosphere?

Ans. The pressure of the "standard atmosphere" is 14.69 lb. per sq. in. at sea level. The standard value (14.7 lb. per sq in.) is used for most calculations.

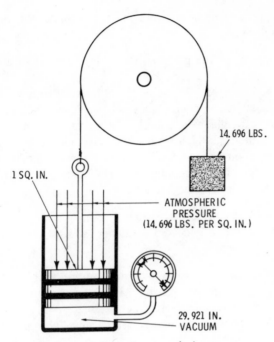

14.696 LBS.

1 SQ. IN.

ATMOSPHERIC
PRESSURE
(14.696 LBS. PER SQ. IN.)

29.921 IN.
VACUUM

Fig. 17. Diagram illustrating atmospheric pressure.

Ques. Why does a person not "feel" the pressure of the atmosphere?

Ans. The air exerts pressure on the body both externally and internally; therefore, the pressures in all directions are balanced.

Ques. Does the atmospheric pressure remain constant at a given location?

Ans. No. Depending on the weather conditions, the atmospheric pressure changes continually.

Ques. Does atmospheric pressure vary with the elevation?

Ans. Yes. It decreases approximately 0.5 lb. for each 1000-ft. increase in elevation.

Ques. Does the decrease in atmospheric pressure, as elevation increases, affect gasoline-engine operation?

27

Ans. Yes. In climbing a mountain, for example, the engine gradually loses power.

Ques. Why does the gasoline engine lose power, as elevation increases?

Ans. The air expands at the higher altitudes; therefore, the volume of air taken in by the engine does not weigh as much at the higher altitudes as it weighs at sea level. The mixture becomes too rich at the higher altitudes, which results in poor combustion of fuel. Thus, a supercharger on an automobile, especially in mountain driving, can be advantageous in overcoming the inherent inability of the gasoline engine to take in a full charge of air.

Ques. What is a perfect vacuum?

Ans. A space that is devoid of matter, and in which the pressure is "zero."

Gauge Pressure—Pressure measured *above* that of atmospheric pressure is called "gauge pressure." Pressure measured *above* that of a perfect vacuum is called "absolute pressure." A diagram illustrating the difference between "gauge pressure" and "absolute pressure" is shown in Fig. 18.

In the cylinder containing the piston (see left-hand diagram in Fig. 18), a perfect vacuum exists below the piston, as registered by the

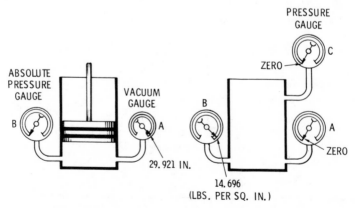

Fig. 18. Illustrating absolute pressure (left) and gauge pressure (right).

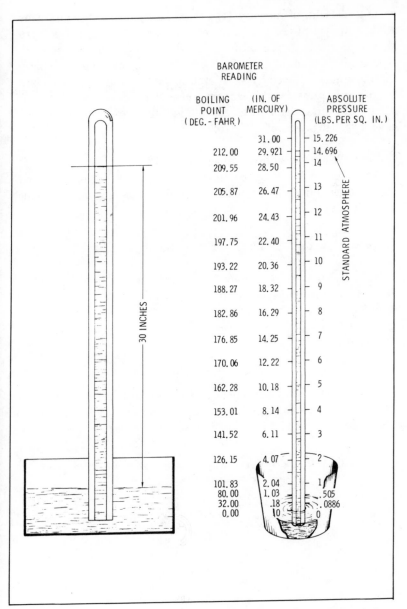

BAROMETER
READING

BOILING POINT (DEG. - FAHR.)	(IN. OF MERCURY)	ABSOLUTE PRESSURE (LBS. PER SQ. IN.)
	31.00	15.226
212.00	29.921	14.696
209.55	28.50	14
205.87	26.47	13
201.96	24.43	12
197.75	22.40	11
193.22	20.36	10
188.27	18.32	9
182.86	16.29	8
176.85	14.25	7
170.06	12.22	6
162.28	10.18	5
153.01	8.14	4
141.52	6.11	3
126.15	4.07	2
101.83	2.04	1
80.00	1.03	.505
32.00	.18	.0886
0.00	0	0

30 INCHES

STANDARD ATMOSPHERE

Fig. 19. Illustrating the basic principle of the barometer and the relation of the Fahrenheit scale, barometric pressure reading, and absolute pressure.

value 29.921 in. of mercury (explained later) on the vacuum gauge *A*. The equivalent reading on the absolute pressure gauge *B* is "zero" lb. per sq. in. If the piston is removed from the cylinder (as in the right-hand diagram in Fig. 18), air rushes into the cylinder. That is, the vacuum is replaced by air at atmospheric pressure. At "standard" atmospheric pressure, the vacuum gauge *A* drops to "zero," the absolute pressure gauge *B* reads 14.696 and the pressure gauge *C* indicates a "gauge pressure" of "zero."

Ques. What is meant by "gauge pressure"?

Ans. That is the effective pressure for doing work against the pressure of the atmosphere, as measured by the pressure gauge (see gauge *C* in Fig. 18).

Ques. How can "absolute pressure" be expressed as "gauge pressure"?

Ans. By subtracting 14.696 lb. from the absolute pressure reading. In comparing readings on the absolute pressure gauge *B* and the gauge *C* in Fig. 18, it may be noted that the reading on the absolute pressure gauge *B* minus 14.696 lb. is equal to the reading on gauge *C*, or "gauge pressure."

Barometer

A *barometer* is an instrument that is used to measure atmospheric pressure. The instrument can be used to determine height or altitude above sea level, and it can be used in forecasting weather.

Table 3. Conversion of Barometer Reading to Absolute Pressure

Barometer (in. of mercury)	Pressure lb. per sq. in.	Barometer (in. of mercury)	Pressure lb. per sq. in.
28.00	13.75	29.921	14.696
28.25	13.88	30.00	14.74
28.50	14.00	30.25	14.86
28.75	14.12	30.50	14.98
29.00	14.24	30.75	15.10
29.25	14.37	31.00	15.23
29.50	14.49		
29.75	14.61		

The barometer reading is expressed in terms of "inches of mercury." This can be illustrated, as in Fig. 19, by filling a 34-in. length of glass tubing with mercury and then inverting the tubing in an open cup of mercury. The mercury inside the glass tubing falls until its height above the level of the mercury in the cup is approximately 30 in. (standard atmosphere). The weight of the 30-in. column of mercury is equivalent to the weight of a similar column of air approximately 50 miles in height.

The barometer reading in "inches of mercury" can be converted to "lb. per sq. in." by multiplying the barometer reading by 0.49116. This value corresponds to the weight of a 1-in. column of mercury that has a cross-sectional area of 1 sq. in.

The barometer readings (inches of mercury) are converted to atmospheric pressure (lb. per sq. in.) in Table 3. The table calculations are based on the "standard" atmosphere (29.92 in. of mercury) and pressure (14.696 lb. per sq. in.). Thus, 1 in. of mercury is equivalent to (14.696 ÷ 29.921), or 0.49116 lb. per sq. in.

Ques. How does the barometer measure atmospheric pressure?
Ans. In terms of "inches of mercury."

Ques. Why does the column of mercury remain suspended at 30 in. above the level of the mercury (see Fig. 19)?
Ans. The weight of the 30-in. column of mercury is the same as that of a similar column of air approximately 50 miles in height.

Ques. How can the barometric pressure reading in "inches of mercury" be converted to absolute pressure in "lb. per sq. in."?
Ans. To convert the barometer reading in "inches of mercury" to absolute pressure in "lb. per sq. in.," multiply the barometer reading by 0.49116 (see Table 3).

Problem: What absolute pressure reading corresponds to a barometer reading of 20 inches of mercury?
Solution: The absolute pressure reading can be calculated by means of the formula:

barometer reading (in. of mercury) × 0.49116 = lb. per sq. in.

Therefore, the absolute pressure reading is (20×0.49116), or 9.82 lb. per sq. in.

Ques. How are pressure values lower than the pressure of the atmosphere usually expressed?

Ans. As absolute pressure, in lb. per sq. in., for calculations; or in actual practice, as the equivalent in "inches of mercury."

In an engine room, for example, the expression "28-in. vacuum" signifies an absolute pressure in the condenser of (14.696 − 13.75), or 0.946 lb. per sq. in. This indicates that the mercury in a column connected to a condenser having a 28-in. vacuum rises to a height of 28 inches, which represents the difference in the atmospheric pressure and the pressure inside the condenser (14.73 − 0.946), or 13.804 lb.

Gravity

The force that tends to attract all bodies in the earth's sphere toward the center point of the earth is known as *gravity*. The rate of acceleration of gravity is approximately 32 ft. per second per second.

Ques. What is the symbol for gravity?
Ans. The symbol for gravity is g (no period).

Ques. What is the effect of gravity on a free-falling body?

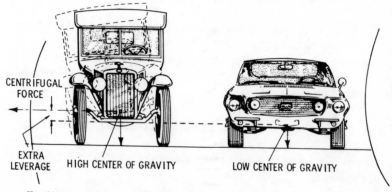

CENTRIFUGAL FORCE

EXTRA LEVERAGE   HIGH CENTER OF GRAVITY

LOW CENTER OF GRAVITY

Fig. 20. Comparison of the height of the center of gravity in an early-model automobile (left) and later model (right).

Ans. Starting from a state of rest, a free-falling body falls 32.16 ft. during the first second; at the end of the next second, the body is falling at a velocity of (32.16 + 32.16), or 64.32 ft. per second.

Center of Gravity—That point in a body about which all its weight or parts are evenly distributed or balanced is known as its "center of gravity," abbreviated *c.g.* If the body is supported at its center of gravity, the entire body remains at rest, even though it is attracted by gravity. A higher center of gravity and a lower center of gravity are compared in Fig. 20, as related to the center of gravity in automobiles.

Centrifugal Force—The force that tends to move rotating bodies *away from* the center of rotation is called "centrifugal force." It is due to inertia. A body moving in a circular path tends to be forced *farther from* the axis or center point of the circle described by its path.

If the centrifugal force balances the attraction of the mass around which it revolves, the body continues to move in a uniform path. The operating principle of the centrifugal pump (Fig. 21) is based on centrifugal force.

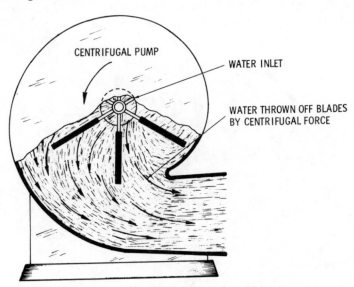

Fig. 21. Illustrating the use of centrifugal force in the basic operation of a centrifugal pump.

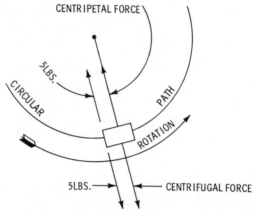

Fig. 22. Illustrating the state of equilibrium between centrifugal and centripetal forces.

Centripetal Force—The force that tends to move rotating bodies *toward* the center of rotation is called "centripetal force." Centripetal force resists centrifugal force, and the moving body revolves in a circular path when these opposing forces are equal (Fig. 22)—that is, the system is in a *state of equilibrium*.

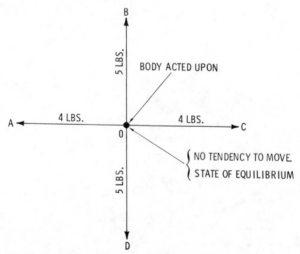

Fig. 23. State of equilibrium existing as a resultant of directly opposed forces.

34

If a body *O* (Fig. 23) is acted upon by two directly opposed forces *OA* and *OC* that are equal and if it is also acted upon by another pair of directly opposed forces *OB* and *OD,* the various forces balance, and the resultant reaction on the body *O* is "zero," that is, the body remains in a state of rest.

Ques. What is meant by a "state of equilibrium"?

Ans. This condition is present when two or more forces are so proportioned and so directed that the resultant reaction on a body is that there is no tendency to move the body.

Force

A force is completely defined only when its *direction, magnitude,* and *point of application* are defined. All three of these requirements can be represented by a line or vector, so that its direction, length, and location correspond to given conditions.

As shown in Fig. 24, a force of 4000 lb. can be represented by drawing a line to a convenient scale (1 in. = 1000 lb.), which requires a line *AB* 4 in. in length, drawn in the direction of and to the point where the force is applied. Note that the arrowhead is placed at the point where the force is applied.

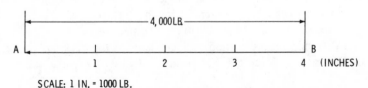

SCALE: 1 IN. = 1000 LB.

Fig. 24. A line or vector is used to represent a force and its intervals, its direction, and its point of application. The arrowhead indicates the point of application of the force.

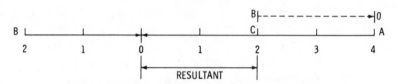

Fig. 25. Diagram used to determine the resultant of two directly opposed forces.

35

Resultant of Directly Opposed Forces—If the lines *OA* and *OB* (Fig. 25) are used to represent two directly opposed forces acting on the point *O*, and the forces *OA* and *OB* are equal to 4000 lb. and 2000 lb., respectively, these opposed forces can be represented by a single line *OC* or force, which is equal to (4000 − 2000), or 2000 lb. Thus, the resultant of forces *OA* and *OB* is a single force *OC*. The broken line in the illustration indicates the subtraction of the smaller force *OB*.

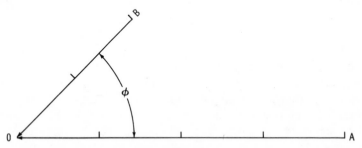

Fig. 26. Diagram of two forces acting on a common point at an angle to each other.

Resultant of Forces at an Angle—If two forces *OA* and *OB* are acting on a common point *O*, an angle is formed (Fig. 26) in which the two forces can be represented by the lines *OA* and *OB* whose lengths represent 4000 lb. and 2000 lb., respectively.

To determine the direction and intensity of the *resultant* force, a parallelogram of force can be constructed (Fig. 27). The parallelo-

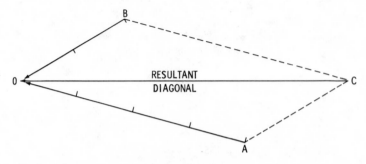

Fig. 27. Determining the resultant of two angular forces by the parallelogram-of-forces method.

gram can be constructed from the diagram in Fig. 26. The broken line *BC* is constructed parallel to line *OA*, and the broken line *AC* is drawn parallel to line *OB*. The diagonal *OC* represents the direction and intensity (by measuring its length) of the *resultant* force which is equivalent to the two forces *OA* and *OB*.

Components of a Force—The components of a force can be determined by reversing the process of determining the resultant of two forces. A component of force is a single force that was used to compound the resultant force derived by the parallelogram-of-forces principle.

For example, the reaction due to the thrust of a connecting rod on the crank pin (Fig. 28) may be considered. The thrust can be divided into two component forces.

One component force acts in a direction tangent to the circle described by the crank pin, which causes the crank to turn; the other component force acts in the direction of the axis of the crank arm, which causes the shaft to press against its bearing. A diagram (see Fig. 28) can be constructed to determine the components of a force.

From point *O*, project a line *OC* equal in length to the thrust of the connecting rod (see Fig. 28). Complete the parallelogram of forces

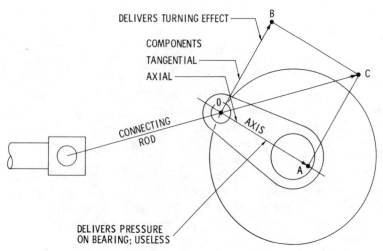

Fig. 28. Determining the components of a force by means of the parallelogram-of-forces method.

to obtain points B and A, their lengths OB and OA representing the components of force in direction and intensity.

Motion

Motion is usually described as *a change in position* in relation to an assumed fixed point. Motion is strictly a *relative* matter. Motion is a relative matter because there can be no motion unless some point or object is regarded as stationary (Fig. 29).

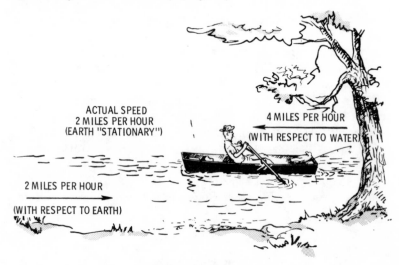

ACTUAL SPEED
2 MILES PER HOUR
(EARTH "STATIONARY")

4 MILES PER HOUR

(WITH RESPECT TO WATER)

2 MILES PER HOUR

(WITH RESPECT TO EARTH)

EARTH "STATIONARY"

Fig. 29. Illustrating motion.

As shown in the illustration (see Fig. 29), the man is rowing the boat at a speed of 4 miles per hour against a current flowing at 2 miles per hour in the opposite direction. The boat is moving at 4 miles per hour with respect to the water, and the water is moving at 2 miles per hour with respect to the earth.

The familiar example of the ferryboat crossing the river, pointing upstream to counteract the motion of the water, is used to illustrate *apparent* and *actual* motion (Fig. 30). The line OA represents the apparent motion (both distance and direction) of the boat; but regarding the earth as stationary, the line OB represents the actual motion of the boat. If the water is regarded as stationary, the boat is moving in the direction represented by the line OA.

Newton's Laws of Motion—The noted physicist, Sir Isaac Newton, announced the three laws of motion. They are:

1. *First Law of Motion.* If a body is at rest, it tends to remain at rest; or if a body is in motion, it tends to remain in motion in a straight line until acted upon by a force.

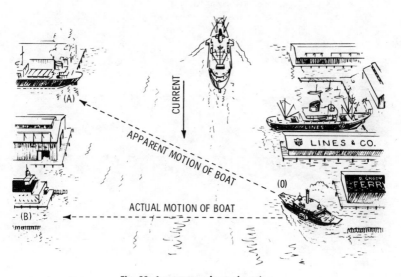

Fig. 30. Apparent and actual motion.

2. *Second Law of Motion.* If a body is acted on by several forces, it tends to obey each force as though the other forces do not exist, whether the body is at rest or in motion.
3. *Third Law of Motion.* If a force acts to change the state of a body with respect to rest or motion, the body offers a resistance that is equal and directly opposed to the force; or, to every action there is an equal and opposite reaction.

Types of Motion—The *rate of change* of position in relation to time is termed *velocity*. Velocity is also the rate of motion in a given direction, as the rotation of a sphere, in relation to time. The *rate of increase in velocity* or the average increase of velocity in a given unit of time is called *acceleration*.

A train traveling at a rate of 30 miles per hour is an example of *linear* velocity; and a line shaft rotating at a rate of 125 revolutions per minute is an example of *rotary* velocity. *Linear* motion and *rotary* motion are illustrated in Fig. 31.

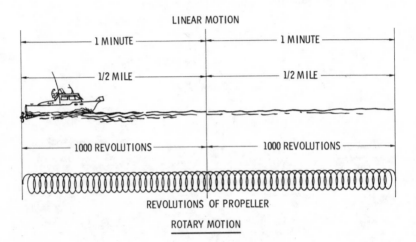

Fig. 31. Linear motion and rotary motion.

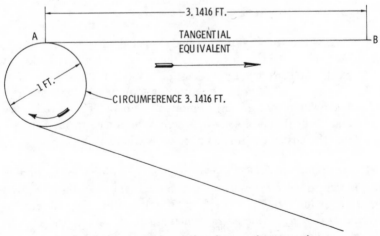

Fig. 32. The tangential equivalent distance of rotary motion.

Tangential motion is the equivalent of rotary motion, but is regarded as moving in a straight line or tangential direction. Tangential motion or velocity is commonly used in belting calculations. As shown in Fig. 32, the circumference of a 1-ft. diameter pulley is 3.1416 ft. Thus, for each revolution of the pulley, the belt travels the tangential equivalent distance *AB*, or 3.1416 ft.

Example: If a 4-ft. diameter pulley is rotating at 100 rpm, what is the tangential speed of the belt? The calculation is:

$$\text{tangential speed} = \text{circumference} \times rpm$$
$$= 4 \times 3.1416 \times 100$$
$$= 12.566 \times 100$$
$$= 1256.6 \text{ ft. per minute}$$

Vibrating motion that describes a path similar to the arc of a circle is called *oscillating* motion. A familiar example of oscillating motion is the pendulum of a clock. Vibrating motion that makes a path simi-

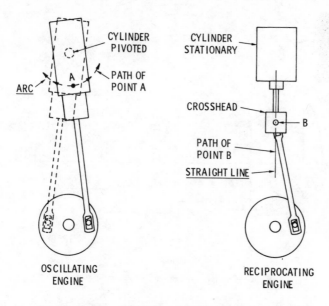

Fig. 33. Diagrams illustrating oscillating type of engine (left) and reciprocating type of engine (right).

41

lar to a straight line is called *reciprocating* motion. The movement of the crosshead of an engine is an illustration of reciprocating motion. Oscillating and reciprocating motion are illustrated in Fig. 33.

The oscillating-type engine (see Fig. 33) is sometimes used on board ships as a capstan engine. It can be noted that the to-and-fro path of point *A* is similar to the arc of a circle whose center point is the center point of the pivot about which the cylinder oscillates. In the right-hand diagram, note that the point *B* on the crosshead moves up and down or reciprocates in a straightline path.

The movement of a point through equal space in equal intervals of time is called *constant* motion. The movement of a point through unequal spaces in equal intervals of time is called *variable* motion. A diagram illustrating both constant motion and variable motion is shown in Fig. 34.

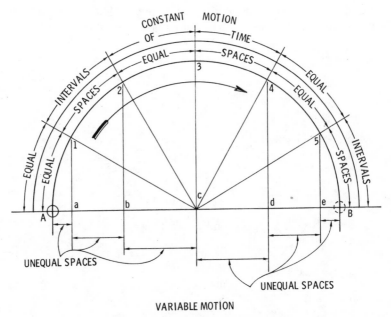

Fig. 34. Constant motion and variable motion.

In the movements of the crank pin and piston of an engine (see Fig. 34), the rate of motion from the position of the crank pin at the beginning of the stroke (position *A*) is constant as it rotates to position *B*. This means that it passes through equal arcs in equal intervals of time. Perpendiculars from points *1, 2, 3*, etc., locate the corresponding positions *a, b, c,* etc., of the piston. As shown in the diagram, the traversed spaces (*Aa, ab,* etc.) are unequal; therefore, the motion is variable. The diagram represents the true relation where there is no distortion, as with a Scotch-yoke mechanism; but when a connecting rod is used, there is distortion due to the "angularity" of the connecting rod.

Momentum—The power of a body to overcome resistance by virtue of its motion is termed *momentum*. Momentum is the quantity of motion in a moving body.

Momentum is measured by multiplying the quantity of matter in a body by its velocity. For a numerical value of momentum—it is the force in pounds steadily applied that can stop a moving body in 1 second. Therefore, momentum is equal to the mass of a body multiplied by its velocity in feet per second or:

$$\text{momentum} = \frac{\text{weight}}{32.16} \times \text{velocity (ft. per second)}$$

The formula for determining momentum is:

$$M = \frac{WV}{g}$$

in which;

   W is the weight, in lb.

   V is velocity, in ft. per second

   g is attraction due to gravity (32.16)

Inertia—The property of matter which causes a body to tend to remain at rest, if it is already at rest; or, if it is moving, to keep moving in the same direction unless affected by an outside force, is called inertia (symbol I). This gives rise to two states of inertia known as: (1) *static inertia;* and (2) *dynamic inertia.* These two types of inertia are illustrated in Fig. 35.

43

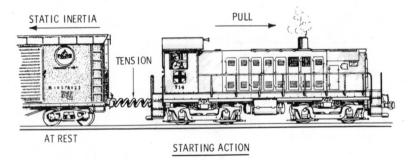

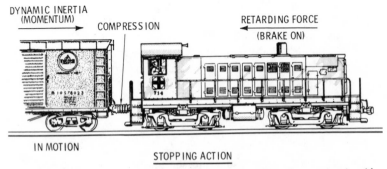

Fig. 35. Static inertia with respect to a body at rest (top) and dynamic inertia with respect to a body in motion (bottom).

Friction

The resistance to motion of two moving objects that touch is called *friction*. Friction is caused partially by the natural adhesion of one body to another; but its chief cause is the roughness of surfaces that are in contact. Even a glossy, polished surface is not smooth when viewed with a powerful magnifying glass or microscope (Fig. 36).

Coefficient of Friction—The ratio of the force required to slide a body along a horizontal plane surface to the weight of the body is the "coefficient of friction." The coefficient of friction is equivalent to the tangent of the "angle of repose."

The angle of repose is the largest angle with the horizontal at which a mass of material, such as an embankment or pile of coal, can remain at rest without sliding (Fig. 37). This angle varies with different materials.

44

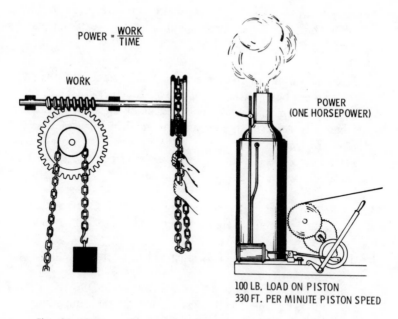

$$POWER = \frac{WORK}{TIME}$$

WORK

POWER
(ONE HORSEPOWER)

100 LB. LOAD ON PISTON
330 FT. PER MINUTE PISTON SPEED

Fig. 36. Diagrams showing the difference between work (left) and power (right).

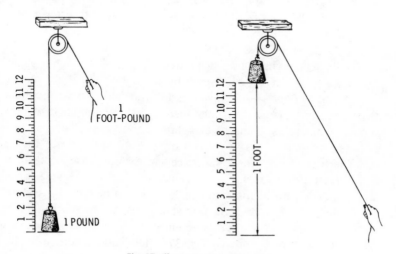

1
FOOT-POUND

1 FOOT

1 POUND

Fig. 37. Illustrating 1 foot-pound.

45

Laws of Friction—The first laws of friction were given by Morin about 1830, but they have been modified by later experiments. As summarized by Kent, the laws of friction are:

1. Friction varies approximately as the normal pressure with which the rubbing surfaces are pressed together.
2. Friction is approximately independent of the area of the surfaces, but it is slightly greater for smaller surfaces than for larger surfaces.
3. Friction decreases with an increase in velocity, except at an extremely low velocity and with soft surfaces.

As applied to lubricated surfaces, the laws of friction for *perfect lubrication* (surfaces completely separated by a film of lubricant) are:

1. The coefficient of friction is independent of the materials making up the surfaces.
2. The coefficient of friction varies directly with the viscosity of the lubricant, which varies inversely with the temperature of the lubricant.
3. The coefficient of friction varies inversely as the unit pressure and varies directly as the velocity.
4. The coefficient of friction varies inversely as the mean film thickness of the lubricating medium.
5. Mean film thickness varies directly with velocity and inversely as the temperature and unit pressure.

As applied to *imperfect lubrication,* that is, surfaces partially separated (which may range from nearly complete separation to nearly complete contact) by a film of lubricant, the laws of friction are:

1. The coefficient of friction increases with an increase in pressure between the surfaces.
2. The coefficient of friction decreases with an increase in relative velocity between the surfaces.

Machinery cannot be operated without lubrication, notwithstanding the alleged "antifriction" metals, because of the tiny irregularities in a smooth metal surface. A lubricant is used to keep the rubbing parts separated by a thin film of oil, thus preventing actual contact so far as possible.

Ques. What causes friction?
Ans. It is due primarily to the roughness of the contacting surfaces.

Ques. What are the characteristics of friction?
Ans. It may be either useful or harmful. In most instances, friction is harmful, because the power necessary to overcome friction in any mechanism is wasted.

Ques. What is an example of a harmful effect of friction?
Ans. The wearing action on bearings.

Ques. What is meant by the angle of repose?
Ans. The largest angle with the horizontal at which a mass of material can remain at rest without sliding (see Fig. 37).

Ques. What is meant by "antifriction" metals?
Ans. The term is misleading. Metals without a small amount of friction do not exist.

Ques. What is the purpose of a lubricant?
Ans. A lubricant keeps the rubbing parts separated by means of a thin film of oil, thus preventing actual contact as nearly as possible.

Ques. What is a peculiar characteristic of graphite?
Ans. It does not lubricate, but it fills the tiny pores in the bearing surface.

Work and Power

The expenditure of energy to overcome resistance through a certain distance is *work*. It is difficult to understand horsepower without an understanding of the difference between work and power (Fig. 36). *Power* is the rate at which work is done, that is, work divided by the "time" in which it is done.

The standard unit for measuring work is the *foot-pound* (ft-lb). The foot-pound is the amount of work that is done in raising a weight

47

of 1 lb. through a distance of 1 ft., or in overcoming a pressure of 1 lb. through a distance of 1 ft. (Fig. 37).

The term *horsepower* is believed to have been adopted by James Watt, the inventor of the steam engine, to represent the power or capacity of a strong London draft-type horse for doing work during a short time interval, and the term was used as a power rating for his steam engines. The standard unit for measuring power is the horsepower (*hp*), which is defined as *33,000 foot-pounds per minute*. In other words, one horsepower is required to raise a weight of:

$$33,000 \text{ lb. a height of} \ldots\ldots\ldots\ldots 1 \text{ ft. in one minute}$$
$$3,300 \text{ lb. a height of} \ldots\ldots\ldots 10 \text{ ft. in one minute}$$
$$33 \text{ lb. a height of} \ldots\ldots 1000 \text{ ft. in one minute}$$
$$3.3 \text{ lb. a height of} \ldots\ldots 10,000 \text{ ft. in one minute}$$
$$1 \text{ lb. a height of} \ldots\ldots 33,000 \text{ ft. in one minute}$$

A formula that is generally used to calculate engine horsepower is:

$$hp = \frac{2\,PLAN}{33,000}$$

in which;

P is the mean effective pressure in lb. per sq. in.

L is the length of stroke, in ft.

A is the area of piston, in sq. in. ($0.7854 \times d^2$)

N is the number of revolutions per minute (*rpm*)

Since the stroke of an engine is usually given in inches, rather than in feet, and the revolutions per minute are given, rather than the piston speed, the above formula involves extra calculations for these items as well as the extra multiplication and division introduced because of the constants. Therefore, the formula can be reduced to its lowest terms, as follows:

$$hp = \frac{2\,PLAN}{33,000}$$

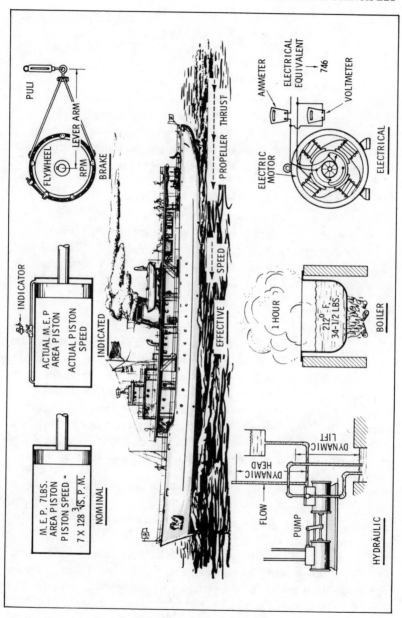

Fig. 38. Various types of horsepower.

$$= \frac{2 \times P \times \frac{L}{12} \times (0.7854 \times d^2) \times N}{33,000}$$

$$= \frac{0.1309 \times PLd^2N}{33,000}$$

$$= 0.000003967 \ PLd^2N$$

Thus, the constant 0.000004 can be used for most calculations; by changing the order of the factors, the formula is simplified to:

$$hp = 0.000004 \ d^2LNP$$

According to its definitions and the manner in which it is derived, the various types of horsepower are: (1) *nominal;* (2) *indicated;* (3) *brake;* (4) *effective;* (5) *hydraulic;* (6) *boiler;* and (7) *electrical.* The various types of horsepower are illustrated in Fig. 38.

Basic Machines

For many years the basic mechanical contrivances that enter into the composition or formation of machines were referred to as "mechanical powers." Since these mechanical contrivances are regarded in a more static than dynamic sense—that is, the consideration of opposing forces in equilibrium rather than tending to produce motion—it is more correct to refer to them as basic machines. Strictly speaking, the term "power" is a dynamic term relating to the "time rate of doing work." When the elements of a machine are in equilibrium, no work is done; therefore, it is incorrect to refer to the basic machines as "mechanical powers."

It should be understood that the action of all the basic machines depends on the principle of work, which is "the applied force, multiplied by the distance through which it moves, equals the resistance overcome, multiplied by the distance through which it is overcome."

The basic machines are: (1) *lever;* (2) *wheel and axle;* (3) *pulley;* (4) *inclined plane;* (5) *screw;* and (6) *wedge.* These machines can be reduced further to three classes of machines, as follows: (1) a solid body turning on an axis; (2) a flexible cord; and (3) a hard and smooth inclined surface.

50

The *Principle of Moments* is important in studying the basic machines. This important principle can be stated as follows: "When two or more forces act on a rigid body and tend to turn it on an axis, equilibrium exists if the sum of the moments of the forces which tend to turn the body in one direction equals the sum of the moments of those forces which tend to turn the body in the opposite direction about the same axis."

Lever—A "lever" is a bar of metal, wood, or other substance that is used to exert a pressure or to sustain a weight at one point in its length by receiving a force at a second point, and is free to turn at a third or fixed point called the *fulcrum*. Its application is based on the principle of moments. The following general rule can be applied to all classes of levers.

Rule: The force P, multiplied by its distance from the fulcrum F, is equal to the load W, multiplied by its distance from the fulcrum.

Thus, the formula for calculation involving the three classes of levers is:

$$F \times \text{distance} = W \times \text{distance}$$

As shown in the illustration (Fig. 39), there are three classes of levers.

Problem: What force P is required at a point 3 ft. from the fulcrum F to balance a weight of 112 lb. applied at a point 6 in. from the fulcrum?

Solution: The distances or lengths of the levers are 3 ft. and 6 in., respectively. Since the distances must be of the same denomination, the 3 ft. must be reduced to inches (3×12), or 36 inches. Then, applying the rule:

$$P \times 36 = 112 \times 6$$

$$P = \frac{112 \times 6}{36}$$

$$= 18.67 \text{ lb.}$$

51

Wheel and Axle—A comparison of the wheel and axle with the "first-class lever" (see Fig. 39) indicates that they are similar in principle. The same formula can be used for calculations involving the wheel and axle. The "Chinese wheel and axle" is illustrated in Fig. 40. This is a modification of the wheel and axle and can be used to ob-

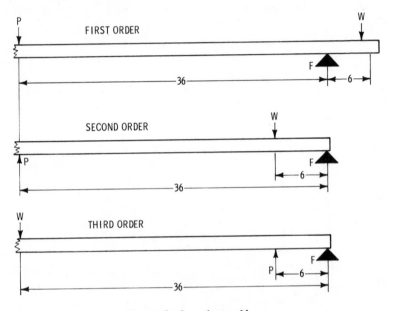

Fig. 39. The three classes of levers.

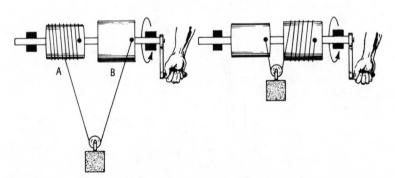

Fig. 40. The principle of the differential hoist, cranking clockwise to lift the weight (left), and the lifting operation completed (right).

tain extreme leverage. This is also the basic principle of the differential hoist. As the crank is turned clockwise, the cable winds onto drum *B* and unwinds from drum *A*; since drum *B* is larger in diameter, the length of cable between the two drums is gradually taken up, lifting the load. Thus, if the difference in the diameters of the two drums is small, an extreme leverage is obtained, enabling heavy weights to be lifted with little effort. Also, the load remains suspended at any point, because the difference in diameters of the two drums is too small to overbalance the friction of the parts.

Pulley—The two types of pulleys are *fixed* and *movable*. No mechanical advantage is obtained from the fixed pulley; its use is important in accomplishing work that is appropriate—raising water from a well, for example.

The "movable" pulley, by distributing its weight into separate portions, is attended by mechanical advantages proportional to the num-

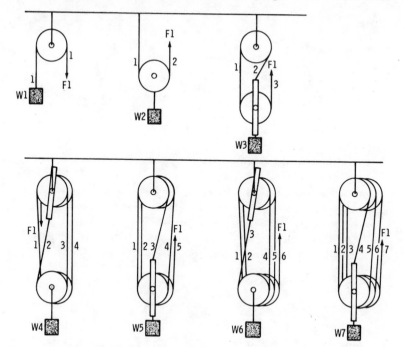

Fig. 41. Relation between force applied and load lifted in the various basic pulley combinations.

bers of points of support. As illustrated in Fig. 41, the relation between the force applied and the load lifted is changed by the various basic pulley combinations. Of course, an even greater range may be obtained by additional pulleys, but there is a practical limit to which this is mechanically expedient. The following rule states the relation between force and load.

Rule: The load W that can be lifted by a combination of pulleys is equal to the force F times the number of ropes supporting the lower or movable block.

Inclined Plane—If a sloping path or incline is substituted for a direct upward line of ascent, a given weight can be raised by a smaller weight. Thus, the inclined plane is a basic machine, because a lesser force can be applied to lift a load (Fig. 42).

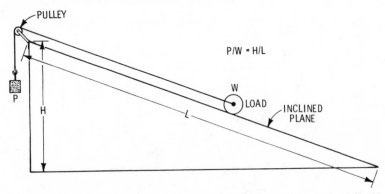

Fig. 42. Inclined plane. A smaller weight (P) can be used to lift a load or weight (W), because the load is partially supported by the inclined plane.

Rule: As the applied force P is to the load W, so is the height H to the length of the inclined plane L.

Thus, the calculation is:

$$\text{force} : \text{load} = \text{height} : \text{length of plane}$$

Problem: What force P is required to lift a load of 10 lb. if the height is 2 ft. and the plane is 12 ft. in length?

Solution: Substituting in the above equation:

$$P : 10 = 2 : 12$$

$$P \times 12 = 2 \times 10$$

$$P = \frac{10 \times 2}{12} = \frac{20}{12} = \ 1\text{-}2/3 \ \text{lb.}$$

Screw—This type of basic machine is merely "an inclined plane wrapped around a cylinder." The screw is used to exert a severe pressure through a small space. Since it is subject to a high loss from friction, the screw usually exerts a small amount of power in itself, but a large amount of power may be derived when combined with the lever or wheel.

Rule: As the applied force *P* is to the load *W*, so is the pitch to the length of thread per turn.

Thus, the calculation is:

applied force *P* : load *W* = pitch : length of thread per turn

Problem: If the pitch or distance between threads is 1/4 in. and a force *P* of 100 lb. is applied, what load or weight *W* can be moved by the screw if the length of thread per turn of the screw is 10 inches?

Solution: Substituting in the above equation:

$$100 : \text{load } W = 1/4 : 10$$

$$\text{load } W \times 1/4 = 10 \times 100$$

$$\text{load } W = \frac{10 \times 100}{1/4}$$

$$= 4000 \text{ lb.}$$

Wedge—The "wedge" is virtually a pair of inclined planes that are placed back-to-back or in contact along their bases. (Fig. 43).

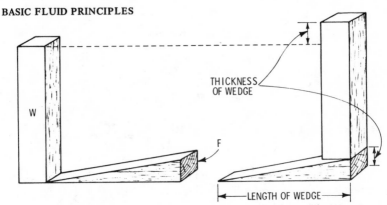

THICKNESS OF WEDGE

W

F

LENGTH OF WEDGE

Fig. 43. Application of a wedge (P) to raise a heavy load or weight (W)

Rule: As the applied force *P* is to the load *W*, so is the thickness of the wedge to its length.

Thus, the calculation is:

applied force *P* : load *W* = thickness of wedge : length of wedge

Problem: What applied force *P* is required to raise a load *W* of 2000 lb., using a wedge that is 4 in. in thickness and 20 in. in length?

Solution: Substituting in the equation:

$$\text{applied force } P : 2000 = 4 : 20$$
$$P \times 20 = 4 \times 2000$$
$$P = \frac{4 \times 2000}{20}$$
$$= 400 \text{ lb.}$$

WATER

In the study of hydraulics and pumps, it is important that water and its characteristics be understood. Water is *a most remarkable substance.* By definition, water is a *compound* of hydrogen and oxygen in the proportion of two parts by weight of hydrogen to sixteen parts by weight of oxygen.

The behavior of water under the influence of temperature is extraordinary. When subjected to low temperatures, water is converted to a solid (ice) which, because of its peculiar characteristic of expanding during its change of state, causes pipes to burst and other types of damage. At higher temperatures, water is converted to a gas (steam); thus, water is used as a medium for developing power, as in steam for a steam engine.

Ques. What is a most remarkable characteristic of water?

Ans. At maximum density (39.1°F.), water expands as heat is added, and it expands slightly as the temperature drops from this point, as shown in Fig. 44.

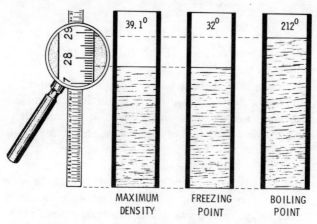

MAXIMUM DENSITY   FREEZING POINT   BOILING POINT

Fig. 44. Illustrating a remarkable property of water—expansion at temperatures both "above" and "below" its temperature at "point of maximum density" (39.1°F.) (A) If one lb. of water is placed in a cylinder having a cross-sectional area of one sq. in. at 39.1°F., the water rises to a height of 27.68 in.; (B) As the temperature drops to 32°F., the water rises to a height of 27.7 in.; and (C) As the temperature is increased to 212°F., the water rises to a height of 28.88 in. in the tube.

Ques. What are the freezing and boiling points of water at atmospheric pressure at sea level?

Ans. It freezes at 32°F. and boils at 212°F., when the barometer reads 29.921 in. of mercury.

Ques. What is the importance of the reading 29.921 in. of mercury?

Ans. It is the standard atmosphere.

Ques. What is the equivalent of 29.921 in. of mercury in lb. per sq. in.?

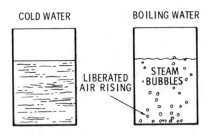

Fig. 45. Diagrams showing boiling of water to liberate air that is "mechanically mixed" in the water.

Ans. 14.696 lb. per sq. in.

Ques. What substance, in addition to hydrogen and oxygen, is contained in water?

Ans. Water contains approximately 5 percent of air by volume (Fig. 45), mechanically mixed with it. It is for this reason that steam engines that condense moisture should have air pumps attached to the condenser; otherwise, the necessary vacuum cannot be maintained.

Ques. What is a striking example of air contained in the water?

Ans. The operation of steam heating plants. Since the air is liberated when the water boils, it passes into the radiators with the steam; therefore, automatic air valves must be provided to rid the system of the air, which may cause the radiators to become airbound and rendered ineffective.

Ques. How does pressure affect the boiling point of water?

Ans. The boiling point rises as the pressure increases. Thus, the boiling point is 212°F. for standard atmospheric pressure at sea level; the boiling point is 327.8°F. at 100 lb. (absolute) pressure.

Ques. Why is the water "boiling" in Fig. 46A and not boiling in Fig. 46B?

Ans. Fig. 46A shows water boiling (as in a tea kettle) by the addition of heat. If the vessel were closed, the water would continue to boil, causing the pressure to rise. Now, if no more heat is added when the pressure reaches 100 lb., for example, the water would cease boiling and the pressure would remain constant if no heat were lost. The temperature of the water, steam, and pressure are said to be

58

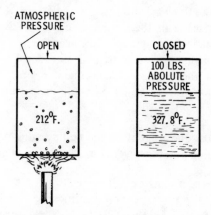

Fig. 46. The effect of pressure on the temperature at which water boils:
(A) at atmospheric pressure; (B) at 100 lbs. (absolute pressure).

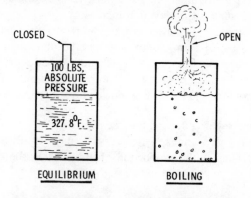

Fig. 47. Showing state of equilibrium (left) between
temperature and pressure. The equilibrium is upset
(right) by reducing the pressure, resulting in boiling.

in a state of equilibrium. The least variation in temperature (either
upward or downward) destroys the "state of equilibrium" and causes
a change.

Ques. How can the water (Fig. 47) be made to boil again?

Ans. By permitting some of the confined steam to escape, as in
the right-hand diagram.

59

Ques. Why does the water boil (see Fig. 47)?

Ans. On the escape of the steam, a reduction in pressure occurs and the equilibrium of the system is disturbed. The water (containing excess heat) immediately begins to boil and tends to keep the pressure constant. If the process is continued, a gradual reduction in temperature and pressure results until all the heat originally introduced into the system is used up.

Ques. How does elevation affect the boiling point of water?

Ans. The boiling point is lowered as the elevation increases.

Ques. Why is the boiling point lowered?

Ans. Because the pressure of the atmosphere is lowered as the elevation increases. At an elevation of 5000 ft., for example, water boils at a temperature of 202°F.

Ques. What annoying effect is experienced by the decreasing atmospheric pressure as the elevation increases?

Ans. The gradual reduction in the power output of an automobile engine as it ascends a mountain. The charge of fuel mixture is decreased, because the total (sea level) atmospheric pressure is not available to force the charge of fuel into the cylinders—an inherent defect of a gasoline engine that is not equipped with a supercharger.

Ques. What other condition may be noticed?

Ans. The reduced atmospheric pressure may disturb the quality of the mixture. That is, the proportion of air entering the carburetor is reduced.

Ques. What common domestic practice is impossible at high altitudes?

Ans. Eggs cannot be boiled.

Ques. What type of cooking utensil depends on the effect of pressure on the boiling point for its basic operation?

Ans. The pressure cooker.

Ques. Is it essential that water be "hot" before it can be brought to a boil?

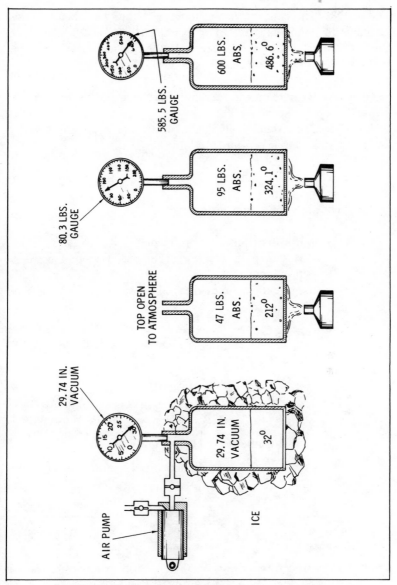

Fig. 48. The boiling point (temperature) of water varies with a change in pressure. Entirely different values are obtained for other liquids.

Ans. No. The concept that a liquid must be "hot" before it can be made to boil is incorrect. For example, water at 28-in. vacuum pressure boils at 100°F.; however, if the vacuum pressure is increased to 29.74 in., the water boils at 32°F. (Fig. 48).

Ques. At what temperature can water be made to boil and to freeze?

Ans. At 32°F., water boils at 29.74-in. vacuum pressure, and it freezes at atmospheric pressure (14.7 lb.).

Ques. What cooking utensil depends on a variation in pressure for its basic operation?

Ans. The glass coffee brewing apparatus.

Ques. What is its basic operating principle?

Ans. Water is placed in the lower globe and ground coffee is placed in the upper container, (Fig. 49). When heat is applied, the pressure that is generated forces the boiling water through the filter

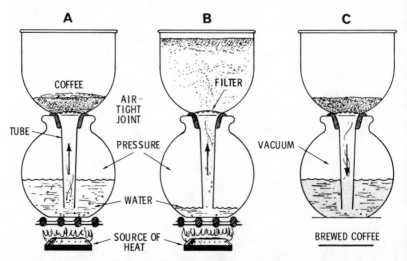

Fig. 49. The glass-type of coffee-brewing apparatus depends on the variation in pressure for its operation: (A) When heat is applied, pressure increases and forces the water into the upper container; (B) The upflow portion of the cycle is completed; and (C) The cooling period produces a vacuum in the lower globe, and the excess pressure of the atmosphere forces the liquid downward into the lower container.

and into the upper container. When the heat is turned off, the cooling of the lower globe causes a vacuum to form therein, and the pressure of the atmosphere forces the brewed coffee downward through the filter and into the lower globe.

Ques. Why does the tube not extend to the bottom of the lower globe?

Ans. For two reasons: (1) to leave a reserve of water in the lower globe, the boiling of which forces steam into the container and cooks the coffee; (2) to prevent the lower globe becoming entirely dry with probable breakage resulting from temporary inattention.

Ques. Why does impure water cause considerable trouble in boiler operation?

Ans. Impure water often contains ingredients that form scale which is precipitated on heating and adheres to the heating surfaces of the boiler. Scale in boilers may be hard and rock-like in nature; or it may be soft, greasy, or powdery in nature, depending on its chemical and mechanical composition or formation.

Ques. What is the effect of scale on a boiler?

Ans. It is an extremely poor conductor of heat, which results in wasting of fuel and in overheating of the metal in the heating surface. Thus, boilers should be cleaned frequently and, in most instances, special chemical treatment should be applied to the feed water before it passes into the boiler.

Ques. On which property of water is the basic operation of hot-water heating systems dependent?

Ans. Expansion and contraction resulting from the rise or fall of temperature, respectively. In a U-shaped glass tube, for example (Fig. 50), water poured into the tube rises to the same level in each leg of the tube, because the water is at the same temperature in each leg of the tube. Then heat the water in one leg of the tube and cool the water in the other leg, as shown. The hot water in the heated leg of the tube expands and rises above the level AB, while the cold water in the opposite leg contracts and recedes below the normal level AB.

63

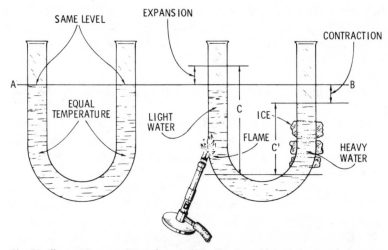

Fig. 50. Illustrating expansion and contraction of water with variation in temperature, resulting in a change in weight per unit volume.

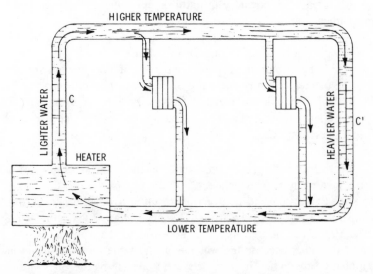

Fig. 51. Thermocirculation in a hot-water heating system.

Ques. How can equilibrium occur within the tube when the water is at different levels?

Ans. The longer column *C* (see Fig. 50) consisting of expanded and lighter water weighs the same as the shorter column consisting of contracted and heavier water.

Ques. Explain why the expansion and contraction property of water is the basic operating principle of hot-water heating systems.

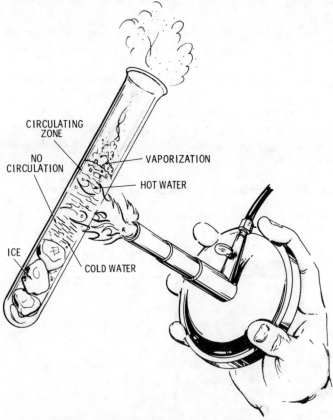

CIRCULATING ZONE

NO CIRCULATION

VAPORIZATION

HOT WATER

ICE

COLD WATER

Fig. 52. Experiment illustrating effect of no circulation. If ice is placed in the bottom of the test tube and heat is applied near the surface of the water, the water boils at that point; however, the heat does not melt the ice, because the cold water around the ice is heavier than the hot water at the top, which prevents thermocirculation. If the heat is applied at the bottom of the tube, the ice melts and all the water is vaporized if the heat is applied long enough.

65

Ans. The weight of the hot and expanded water in the upflow column *C* (Fig. 51), being less than that of the cold and contracted water in the downflow column, upsets the equilibrium of the system and results in a continuous circulation of the water, as indicated by the arrows.

Ques. What is this type of circulation in a hot-water heating system called?

Ans. Thermocirculation, which is another term for circulation resulting from application of heat.

Ques. What is the result if there is no circulation of the water (Fig. 52) in a boiler?

Ans. Practically no generation of steam results, except for a film of steam which separates the water from the heating surface. The latter surface becomes red hot and the boiler may be damaged or destroyed.

Ques. What is the state or condition described above called?

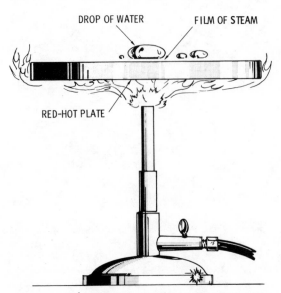

DROP OF WATER   FILM OF STEAM

RED-HOT PLATE

Fig. 53. The spheroidal state in which a drop of water on a red-hot plate changes to steam.

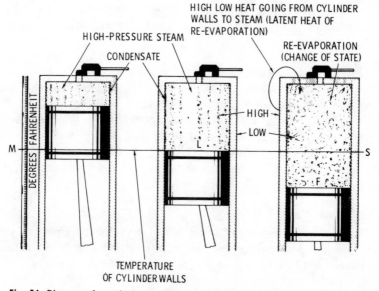

Fig. 54. Diagram of a cylinder in a steam engine, illustrating the cooling action by 'change of state.' The line (MS) represents the average temperature of the cylinder walls. In actual operation, when steam is admitted to the cylinder and during a portion of its stroke, its temperature is higher than that of the cylinder walls (left). If the point (L) is assumed to be the position of the piston at equal temperatures (center), condensation takes place; as the piston advances beyond point (L), the temperature of the steam is lower than that of the cylinder walls. The excess heat in the cylinder walls causes the condensate to boil; that is, re-evaporation occurs, which robs the cylinder walls of some of their heat.

Ans. The spheroidal state (Fig. 53). As shown in the illustration, a small quantity of water poured on a red-hot plate separates into drops and moves all around the plate, being supported by a thin film of steam. Since the water (after steam has formed) is not in contact with the plate, there is practically no cooling effect on the plate.

Ques. What is a typical example of cooling by re-evaporation?
Ans. In steam engine operation, as shown in Fig. 54.

Ques. What is a mistaken concept of re-evaporation, even among some engineers?

Ans. Re-evaporation is regarded as a loss which, in fact, is incorrect. Since the area of the indicator diagram from the point L (Fig. 54) to the point of prerelease is increased, re-evaporation represents a gain.

Ques. Why is this concept of re-evaporation incorrect?

Ans. It is the price or cost of re-evaporation that is a loss, and not the re-evaporation process itself. That is, re-evaporation robs the cylinder walls of a quantity of heat corresponding to the latent heat of re-evaporation. This additional cooling of the cylinder walls increases condensation during the first portion of the stroke, which is the loss. Since this loss exceeds the gain due to re-evaporation, re-evaporation is erroneously considered a loss.

Weight of Water

An important property of water is that it varies in weight (lb. per unit volume) with changes in temperature, giving rise to circulation in boilers and heating systems, as has been explained previously.

Ques. Is the statement that 1 U.S. gallon of water (231 cu. in.) weighs 8.33111 lb. (commonly expressed as 8-1/3 lb.) accurate?

Ans. No.

Ques. Why is the statement not accurate?

Ans. The U. S. gallon of water weighs 8.33111 lb. only at the standard temperature of 62°F.; at any other temperature reading, its weight is different. For calculations at most temperature readings, the weight of a gallon of water is considered to be 8-1/3 lb., which is near enough in most instances. However, it should be understood that this is an approximate value. For precision calculations, the weight of a gallon of water at the given temperature should be used. The weight of water per cu. ft. at various temperatures is given in Table 4. The relative volume of water at various temperatures compared with its volume at 4°C. is given in Table 5.

Properties of Water With Respect to Pump Design

Experience in the design of pumps has shown that water is nearly an unyielding substance when it is confined in pipes and pump passages, which necessitates substantial construction for withstanding the

Table 4. Weight of Water per Cu. Ft. at Various Temperatures

Temp., deg. F	Lb. per cu. ft.	Temp., deg. F	Lb. per cu. ft.	Temp., deg. F	Lb. per cu. ft.	Temp., deg. F	Lb. per cu. ft.	Temp., deg. F	Lb. per cu. ft.	Temp., deg. F	Lb. per cu. ft.	Temp., deg. F	Lb. per cu. ft.	Temp., deg. F	Lb. per cu. ft.
32	62.41	62	62.35	91	62.10	121	61.69	150	61.19	180	60.57	208	59.92	440	51.87
33	62.41	63	62.34	92	62.08	122	61.68	151	61.17	181	60.55	209	59.90	450	51.28
34	62.42	64	62.34	93	62.07	123	61.66	152	61.15	182	60.53	210	59.87	460	51.02
35	62.42	65	62.33	94	62.06	124	61.64	153	61.13	183	60.51	211	59.85	470	50.51
36	62.42	66	62.32	95	62.05	125	61.63	154	61.11	184	60.49	212	59.82	480	50.00
37	62.42	67	62.32	96	62.04	126	61.61	155	61.09	185	60.46	214	59.81	490	49.50
38	62.42	68	62.31	97	62.02	127	61.60	156	61.07	186	60.44	216	59.77	500	48.78
39	62.42	69	62.30	98	62.01	128	61.58	157	61.05	187	60.42	218	59.70	510	48.31
40	62.42	70	62.30	99	62.00	129	61.56	158	61.03	188	60.40	220	59.67	520	47.62
41	62.42	71	62.29	100	61.99	130	61.55	159	61.01	189	60.37	230	59.42	530	46.95
42	62.42	72	62.28	101	61.98	131	61.53	160	60.99	190	60.35	240	59.17	540	46.30
43	62.42	73	62.27	102	61.96	132	61.51	161	60.97	191	60.33	250	58.89	550	45.66
44	62.42	74	62.26	103	61.95	133	61.50	162	60.95	192	60.30	260	58.62	560	44.84
45	62.42	75	62.25	104	61.94	134	61.48	163	60.93	193	60.28	270	58.34	570	44.05
46	62.41	76	62.25	105	61.93	135	61.46	164	60.91	194	60.26	280	58.04	580	43.29
47	62.41	77	62.24	106	61.91	136	61.44	165	60.89	195	60.23	290	57.74	590	42.37
48	62.41	78	62.23	107	61.90	137	61.43	166	60.87	196	60.21	300	57.41	600	41.49
49	62.41	79	62.22	108	61.89	138	61.41	167	60.85	197	60.19	310	57.08	610	40.49
50	62.40	80	62.21	109	61.87	139	61.39	168	60.83	198	60.16	320	56.75	620	39.37
51	62.40	81	62.20	110	61.86	140	61.37	169	60.81	199	60.14	330	56.40	630	38.31
52	62.40	82	62.19	111	61.84	141	61.36	170	60.79	200	60.11	340	56.02	640	37.17
53	62.39	83	62.18	112	61.83	142	61.34	171	60.77	201	60.09	350	55.65	650	35.97
54	62.39	84	62.17	113	61.81	143	61.32	172	60.75	202	60.07	360	55.25	660	34.48
55	62.38	85	62.16	114	61.80	144	61.30	173	60.73	203	60.04	370	54.85	670	32.89
56	62.38	86	62.15	115	61.78	145	61.28	174	60.71	204	60.02	380	54.47	680	31.06
57	62.38	87	62.14	116	61.77	146	61.26	175	60.68	205	59.99	390	54.05	690	28.82
58	62.37	88	61.13	117	61.75	147	61.25	176	60.66	206	59.97	400	53.62	700	25.38
59	62.37	89	62.12	118	61.74	148	61.23	177	60.64	207	59.95	410	53.19	706.1	19.16
60	62.36	90	62.11	119	61.72	149	61.21	178	60.62			420	52.74		......
61	62.35			120	61.71			179	60.60		......	430	52.33		

Table 5. Expansion of Water

C.°	F.°	Volume	C.°	F.°	Volume	C.°	F.°	Volume
4	39	1.00000	35	95	1.00586	70	158	1.02241
5	41	1.00001	40	104	1.00767	75	167	1.02548
10	50	1.00025	45	113	1.00967	80	176	1.02872
15	59	1.00083	50	122	1.01186	85	185	1.03213
20	68	1.00171	55	131	1.01423	90	194	1.03570
25	77	1.00286	60	140	1.01678	95	203	1.03943
30	86	1.00425	65	149	1.01951	100	212	1.04332

pressure—especially periodic shocks or water hammer. Accordingly, in pump design, a liberal factor of safety should be used.

Pressure at Different Depths—The pressure of water varies with the head; this is equal to 0.43302 lb. per sq. in. for each foot of static head. Thus, a head of 2.31 ft. exerts a pressure of (2.31 × 0.43302), or 1 lb. per sq. in., as shown in Table 6.

Compressibility of Water—Water is only slightly compressible. According to Kent, its compressibility ranges from 0.00004 to 0.000051 in. for one atmosphere of pressure, decreasing with an increase in temperature. For each 1 cubic foot distilled water diminishes in volume from 0.0000015 to 0.0000013 in. Water is so incompressible that, even at a depth of 1 mile, 1 cubic foot of water weighs approximately 1/2 lb. more than at the surface.

AIR

Air is a gas that is a mixture of oxygen, 23.2 percent (by weight); nitrogen, 75.5 percent; and argon, 1.3 percent. Other substances present in the air or atmosphere in small amounts are carbonic acid, or carbon dioxide, 0.03 to 0.04 percent; krypton, 0.01 percent; and small amounts of several other gases. The air or atmosphere is a mixture of the following gases by volume: oxygen, 21.0 percent; nitrogen, 78.0 percent; and argon, 0.94 percent.

The term *free air* refers to the air at atmospheric pressure. It does *not* refer to air under identical conditions. Barometer and temperature readings vary with the altitude of a locality and at different times. Thus, "free air" is not necessarily the air at sea level conditions—or an absolute pressure of 14.7 lb. per sq. in. at a temperature of 60°F. It is correct to refer to the air at atmospheric condition at the point where a compressor is installed as "free air."

Table 6. Pounds per Square Inch to Feet (Head) of Water

(Based on water at its greatest density)

Pressure Pounds Per Square Inch	Feet Head	Pressure Pounds Per Square Inch	Feet Head	Pressure Pounds Per Square Inch	Feet Head	Pressure Pounds Per Square Inch	Feet Head	Pressure Pounds Per Square Inch	Feet Head	Pressure Pounds Per Square Inch	Feet Head	Pressure Pounds Per Square Inch	Feet Head
1	2.31	53	122.43	105	242.55	157	362.67	209	482.79	261	602.91	365	843.15
2	4.62	54	124.74	106	244.86	158	364.98	210	485.10	262	605.22	370	854.70
3	6.93	55	127.05	107	247.17	159	367.29	211	487.41	263	607.53	375	866.25
4	9.23	56	129.36	108	249.48	160	369.60	212	489.72	264	609.84	380	877.80
5	11.55	57	131.67	109	251.79	161	371.91	213	492.03	265	612.15	385	899.35
6	13.86	58	133.98	110	254.10	162	374.22	214	494.34	266	614.46	390	900.90
7	16.17	59	136.29	111	256.41	163	375.53	215	496.65	267	616.77	395	912.45
8	18.48	60	138.60	112	258.72	164	378.84	216	498.96	268	619.08	400	924.00
9	20.79	61	140.91	113	261.03	165	381.15	217	501.27	269	621.39	405	931.55
10	23.10	62	143.22	114	263.34	166	383.46	218	503.58	270	623.70	410	947.10
11	25.41	63	145.53	115	265.65	167	385.77	219	505.89	271	626.01	415	958.65
12	27.72	64	147.84	116	267.96	168	388.08	220	508.20	272	628.32	420	970.20
13	30.03	65	150.15	117	270.27	169	390.39	221	510.51	273	630.63	425	981.75
14	32.34	66	152.46	118	272.58	170	392.70	222	512.82	274	632.94	430	993.30
15	34.65	67	154.77	119	274.89	171	395.01	223	515.13	275	635.25	435	1004.85
16	36.96	68	157.08	120	277.20	172	397.32	224	517.44	276	637.56	440	1016.40
17	39.27	69	159.39	121	279.51	173	399.63	225	519.75	277	639.87	445	1027.95
18	41.58	70	161.70	122	281.82	174	401.94	226	522.06	278	642.18	450	1039.50
19	43.89	71	164.01	123	284.13	175	404.25	227	524.37	279	644.49	455	1051.05
20	46.20	72	166.32	124	286.44	176	406.56	228	526.68	280	646.80	460	1062.60
21	48.51	73	168.63	125	288.75	177	408.87	229	528.99	281	649.11	465	1074.15
22	50.82	74	170.94	126	291.06	178	411.18	230	531.30	282	651.42	470	1085.70
23	53.13	75	173.25	127	293.37	179	413.49	231	533.61	283	653.73	475	1097.25
24	55.44	76	175.56	128	295.68	180	415.80	232	535.92	284	656.04	480	1108.80
25	57.75	77	177.87	129	297.99	181	418.11	233	538.23	285	658.35	485	1120.35
26	60.06	78	180.18	130	300.30	182	420.42	234	540.54	286	660.66	490	1131.90
27	62.37	79	182.49	131	302.61	183	422.73	235	542.85	287	662.97	495	1143.45
28	64.68	80	184.80	132	304.92	184	425.04	236	545.16	288	665.28	500	1155.00
29	66.99	81	187.11	133	307.23	185	427.35	237	547.47	289	667.59	525	1212.75
30	69.30	82	189.42	134	309.54	186	429.66	238	549.78	290	669.90	550	1270.50
31	71.61	83	191.73	135	311.85	187	431.97	239	552.09	291	672.21	575	1328.25
32	73.92	84	194.04	136	314.16	188	434.28	240	554.40	292	674.52	600	1386.00
33	76.23	85	196.35	137	316.47	189	436.59	241	556.71	293	676.83	625	1443.75
34	78.54	86	198.66	138	318.78	190	438.90	242	559.02	294	679.14	650	1501.50
35	80.85	87	200.97	139	321.09	191	441.21	243	561.33	295	681.45	675	1559.25
36	83.16	88	203.28	140	323.40	192	443.52	244	563.64	296	683.76	700	1617.00
37	85.47	89	205.59	141	325.71	193	445.83	245	565.95	297	686.07	725	1674.75
38	87.78	90	207.90	142	328.02	194	448.14	246	568.26	298	688.38	750	1732.50
39	90.09	91	210.21	143	330.33	195	450.45	247	570.57	299	690.69	775	1790.25
40	92.40	92	212.52	144	332.64	196	452.76	248	572.88	300	693.00	800	1848.00
41	94.71	93	214.83	145	334.95	197	455.07	249	575.19	305	704.55	825	1905.75
42	97.02	94	217.14	146	337.26	198	457.38	250	577.50	310	716.10	850	1963.50
43	99.33	95	219.45	147	339.57	199	459.69	251	579.81	315	727.65	875	2021.25
44	101.64	96	221.76	148	341.88	200	462.00	252	582.12	320	739.20	900	2079.00
45	103.95	97	224.07	149	344.19	201	464.31	253	584.43	325	750.75	925	2136.75
46	106.26	98	226.38	150	346.50	202	466.62	254	586.74	330	762.30	950	2194.50
47	108.57	99	228.69	151	348.81	203	468.93	255	589.05	335	773.85	975	2252.25
48	110.88	100	231.00	152	351.12	204	471.24	256	591.36	340	785.40	1000	2310.0
49	113.19	101	233.31	153	353.43	205	473.55	257	593.67	345	796.95	1500	3465.
50	115.50	102	235.62	154	355.74	206	475.86	258	595.98	350	808.50	2000	4620.
51	117.81	103	237.93	155	358.05	207	478.17	259	598.29	355	820.05	3000	6930.
52	120.12	104	240.24	156	360.36	208	480.48	260	600.60	360	831.60		

The average condition of the atmosphere in a temperate climate is referred to as *normal air*. This term is used to indicate air with 36-percent relative humidity at 68°F.

Humidity

Water vapor is always present in the atmosphere. The actual quantity of water present in the air is referred to as *absolute* humidity, and it is usually expressed as "grains of moisture per cu. ft. of air." A "grain" is 1/7000 part of 1 pound. The temperature of the air determines the amount of water that the air is capable of holding—the warmer the air, the more moisture it can hold. For example, the air at 80°F. can hold nearly twice as much moisture as it can hold at 60°F.

The actual amount of moisture in the air as compared with the maximum amount of moisture that the air is capable of holding at a given temperature, expressed as a percentage, is called the *relative humidity*. Two thermometers (a wet-bulb and a dry-bulb thermometer) are required to determine relative humidity. This is a form of "hydrometer," and it consists of two thermometers mounted side by side; the bulb of one thermometer is kept moist by means of a loose cotton wick tied around its bulb, the lower end of the wick dipping into a vessel that contains water. The wet bulb is cooled by evaporation of water from the bulb; therefore, the wet-bulb thermometer indicates a lower temperature reading than the dry-bulb thermometer —the difference depending on the rate of evaporation which, in turn, is determined by the amount of water vapor in the atmosphere. If the air is saturated with moisture, its relative humidity is 100 percent; air at the same temperature, but holding one-half the saturation amount, has a relative humidity of 50 percent. A table can be used to determine the percentage of relative humidity after the wet-bulb and dry-bulb readings have been obtained.

Ques. What is meant by "free air"?

Ans. Air at atmospheric pressure. In regard to air compressors, it is the atmospheric condition of the air at the point where the compressor is installed.

Ques. What is "normal air"?

72

Ans. It is the average condition of the atmosphere in a temperate climate, but actually refers to air with 36 percent relative humidity at 68°F.

Ques. What is humidity?
Ans. The water vapor that is always present in the atmosphere.

Ques. What is "absolute humidity"?
Ans. The actual quantity of water in the air, expressed in grains of moisture per cu. ft. of air.

Ques. What is "relative humidity"?

Table 7. Volume and Weight of Air at Atmospheric Pressure For Different Temperatures

Temperature, Degrees F.	Volume of 1 Pound of Air, in Cubic Feet	Weight per Cubic Foot, Pounds	Temperature, Degrees F.	Volume of 1 Pound of Air, in Cubic Feet	Weight per Cubic Foot, Pounds
0	11.57	0.0864	325	19.76	0.0506
12	11.88	0.0842	350	20.41	0.0490
22	12.14	0.0824	375	20.96	0.0477
32	12.39	0.0807	400	21.69	0.0461
42	12.64	0.0791	450	22.94	0.0436
52	12.89	0.0776	500	24.21	0.0413
62	13.14	0.0761	600	26.60	0.0376
72	13.39	0.0747	700	29.59	0.0338
82	13.64	0.0733	800	31.75	0.0315
92	13.89	0.0720	900	34.25	0.0292
102	14.14	0.0707	1000	37.31	0.0268
112	14.41	0.0694	1100	39.37	0.0254
122	14.66	0.0682	1200	41.84	0.0239
132	14.90	0.0671	1300	44.44	0.0225
142	15.17	0.0659	1400	46.95	0.0213
152	15.41	0.0649	1500	49.51	0.0202
162	15.67	0.0638	1600	52.08	0.0192
172	15.92	0.0628	1700	54.64	0.0183
182	16.18	0.0618	1800	57.14	0.0175
192	16.42	0.0609	2000	62.11	0.0161
202	16.67	0.0600	2200	67.11	0.0149
212	16.92	0.0591	2400	72.46	0.0138
230	17.39	0.0575	2600	76.92	0.0130
250	17.89	0.0559	2800	82.64	0.0121
275	18.52	0.0540	3000	87.72	0.0114
300	19.16	0.0522	....	....	....

volumetric expansion = linear expansion.

Ans. The relation between the actual amount of water in the air as compared with the maximum amount of moisture that the air is capable of holding at a given temperature, expressed as a percentage.

Ques. What factor determines whether the air "feels" moist or dry?

Ans. The relative humidity (not absolute humidity) determines this "feeling."

Ques. What does the term "humidity" generally mean?

Ans. It refers to relative humidity or percentage of saturation of the air.

Ques. What is the effect of moisture in the air on an air compressor?

Ans. Its efficiency is decreased because the presence of water vapor in the air being compressed increases the total heating capacity of the air; this is due to the latent heat of the water vapor. The increased temperature increases the pressure and power required for compression.

Weight of Air

Pure air, at 32°F. and a barometric pressure of 14.696 lb. per sq. in., weighs 0.08071 lb. per cu. ft. The weight and volume of air changes with variations in temperature and pressure (Table 7).

SUMMARY

The three states in which matter may exist are known as: (1) *solid;* (2) *liquid;* and (3) *gas.* Water is a familiar example of a substance that exists in each of the three states of matter as ice, water, and steam, respectively.

Energy is the capacity for doing work and for overcoming resistance. The two types of energy are: (1) *potential;* and (2) *kinetic.*

The two types of heat are: (1) *sensible;* and (2) *latent.* The effect of heat is produced by the accelerated vibration of molecules. Heat is transferred from one body to another by radiation, conduction, and convection.

Pressure (P) is a force exerted against an opposing body or a thrust distributed over a surface. Pressure is considered to be distributed over a unit area of the surface.

Atmospheric pressure is due to the weight of the earth's atmosphere; at sea level it is equal to about 14.69 lb. per sq. in. The pressure of the atmosphere does not remain constant at a given location, because weather conditions vary continually.

Pressure measured *above* that of atmospheric pressure is termed "gauge pressure." Pressure measured *above* that of a perfect vacuum is termed "absolute pressure."

The barometer is used to measure atmospheric pressure. The barometer reading is expressed in "inches of mercury." At standard atmospheric pressure, the barometer reads approximately 30 in. of mercury. The barometer reading in "inches of mercury" can be converted to "lb. per sq. in." by multiplying the barometer reading by 0.49116.

The force that tends to draw all bodies in the earth's sphere toward the center of the earth is known as *gravity*. The rate of acceleration of gravity is approximately 32 ft. per second per second. Centrifugal force tends to move a rotating body *away from* its center of rotation. Centripetal force tends to move a rotating body *toward* its center of rotation.

A force is defined completely only when its direction, magnitude, and point of application are defined. All these factors can be represented by a line or vector with an arrowhead.

Motion is described as a change in position in relation to an assumed fixed point. Motion is strictly a relative matter. *Velocity* is the rate of change of position in relation to time, and *acceleration* is the rate of increase or average increase in velocity in a given unit of time.

The resistance to motion of two moving objects that touch is called *friction*. The ratio of the force required to slide a body along a horizontal plane surface to the weight of the body is called the *coefficient of friction*.

The expenditure of energy to overcome resistance through a distance is *work*. The standard unit for measuring work is the *foot-pound (ft-lb)*. The foot-pound is the amount of work that is done in raising 1 lb. a distance of 1 ft., or in overcoming a pressure of 1 lb. through a distance of 1 ft.

Power is the rate at which work is done; or work divided by the "time" in which it is done. The standard unit for measuring power is the *horsepower (hp)*, which is defined as *33,000 foot-pounds per minute*. The formula that can be used to calculate engine horsepower is:

$$hp = \frac{2\ PLAN}{33,000}$$

The basic machines are: (1) *lever;* (2) *wheel and axle;* (3) *pulley;* (4) *inclined plane;* (5) *screw;* and (6) *wedge*. The Principle of Moments is important in studying the basic machines.

An important property of water is that it varies in weight (lb. per unit volume) with changes in temperature, giving rise to circulation in boilers and heating systems. A U. S. gallon of water (231 cu. in.) weighs 8.33111 lb. at 62°F.

Air is a gas that is a mixture of oxygen, 23.2 percent (by weight); nitrogen, 75.5 percent; and argon, 1.3 percent. Other substances present are carbonic acid, or carbon dioxide, 0.03 to 0.04 percent; krypton, 0.01 percent; and small quantities of several other gases. Air is a mixture (by volume) of oxygen, 21.0 percent; nitrogen, 78.0 percent; and argon, 0.94 percent.

Humidity is the water vapor that is always present in the atmosphere. The actual quantity of water present in the air is *absolute* humidity, and it is usually expressed as "grains of moisture per cu. ft. of air." A "grain" is 1/7000 part of 1 pound. The actual amount of moisture in the air as compared with the maximum amount of moisture that the air is capable of holding, expressed as a percentage, is called *relative humidity*.

REVIEW QUESTIONS

1. What is the definition of matter?
2. What are the three states of matter?
3. What is the definition of energy?
4. What are the two forms of energy?
5. State the Law of Conservation of Energy?
6. What are the two forms of heat?
7. What is the unit of heat?
8. What is meant by the specific heat of a substance?

9. What are three methods of transferring heat?
10. What is meant by pressure?
11. What is the value for standard atmospheric pressure?
12. What is the difference between "gauge pressure" and "absolute pressure"?
13. How is atmospheric pressure measured?
14. What is the definition of gravity?
15. What is the difference between centrifugal force and centripetal force?
16. What is the definition of motion?
17. Explain the difference between momentum and inertia.
18. What is friction, and what is its cause?
19. Explain the difference between *work* and *power*.
20. What is the standard unit of work? Of power?
21. State the "Principle of Moments."
22. What elements are found in air?
23. What is the definition of humidity?

CHAPTER 2

Principles of Hydraulics

An understanding of hydraulics is necessary before the basic principles of the various types of pumps can be understood. *Hydraulics* is the branch of physics that deals with the mechanical properties of water and other liquids and with the application of these properties in engineering.

BASIC PRINCIPLES

As aforementioned, water is a truly remarkable substance. At its maximum density (39.1°F.), water expands as heat is applied, and it also expands slightly as the temperature decreases from that point. Under the influence of temperature and pressure, water can exist as: a solid (ice); a liquid (water); and as a gas (steam).

The pressure exerted by a liquid on a surface is proportional to the area of the surface. This hydraulic principle is illustrated in Fig. 1. Two cylinders with different diameters are joined by a tube and filled with water. If the area of the larger piston *M,* for example, is 30 times the area of the smaller piston *S,* and a 2-lb. weight is placed on the smaller piston, then pressure is transmitted to the water and to the larger piston. That pressure is equal to 2 pounds for each portion of the piston's surface that is equal in area to the total area of the surface of the smaller piston—the larger piston is exposed to an upward pressure equal to 30 times that of the smaller piston, or 60 pounds. Also, if a 60-lb. weight is placed on the larger piston, the two pistons remain in equilibrium. This equilibrium is destroyed if either a greater or a lesser weight is applied.

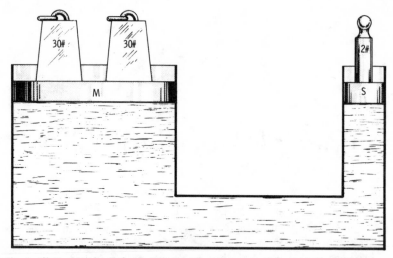

Fig. 1. Illustrating the hydraulic principle that the pressure exerted by a liquid on a surface is proportional to the area of the surface.

A small quantity of water can be made to balance a much larger weight. As shown in Fig. 2, a locomotive weighing 101,790 lb. can be balanced on a hydraulic lift against a smaller quantity of water,

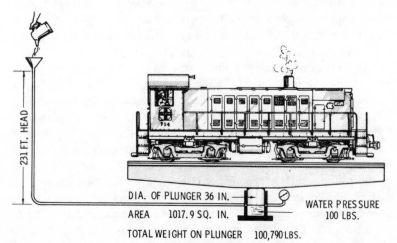

Fig. 2. Illustrating the principle that a smaller quantity of water can be made to balance a much larger weight.

assuming no leakage nor friction and that the vertical pipe leading to the plunger clyinder is exceedingly small in its diameter. For example, if the area of the plunger requires 100 lb. per sq. in. pressure on the plunger to balance the 101,790-lb. locomotive, the load is balanced when the pipe is filled with water to a height of (100 × 2.31), or 231 ft.

The pressure on any portion of a fluid having uniform density is proportional to its depth below the surface (Fig. 3). As illustrated in

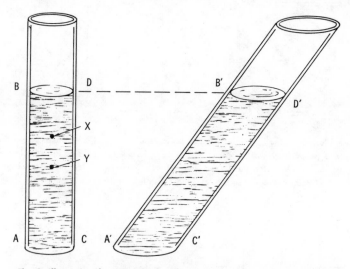

Fig. 3. Illustrating the principle that the pressure on any portion of a liquid having uniform density is proportional to its depth below the surface.

Fig. 4, the number of 1-lb. weights placed on a scale totals 11 lb., which gives a total weight or pressure of 11 lb. per sq. in., if resting on 1 sq. in. of surface. Likewise, a column of water 1 sq. in. in cross-sectional area and 2.31 ft. in height weighs 1 pound (see Fig. 4). A gauge placed at the bottom of the column which is (2.31 × 2), or 4.62 ft. in height indicates a pressure of 2 lb. per sq. in. Therefore, the pressure of water at any depth is equal to:

$$\text{pressure} = \frac{\text{depth in ft.}}{2.31}$$

81

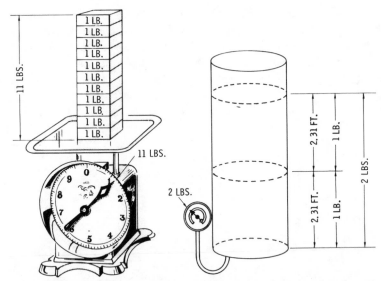

Fig. 4. Illustrating the principle that the pressure of water at any point below the surface is proportional to the depth of the point below the surface. Pressure in lbs. per sq. in. is illustrated (left), and the relation between water pressure at any point below the surface and the depth in feet is shown (right).

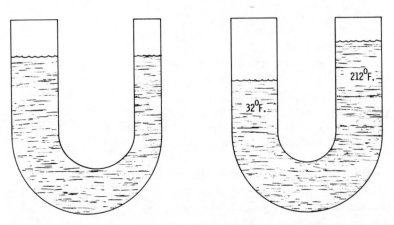

Fig. 5. Fluids rise to the same level in each arm of a U-tube when the temperature of the liquid is the same in each arm (left), and they rise to different levels when the temperature is different in each arm.

As shown in Fig. 5, *fluids rise to the same level in each arm of a U-tube when the temperature of the liquid is the same in each arm* (at rest) of water and other liquids is known as *hydrostatics*. Water different in each arm (right).

Primary considerations in hydraulics are "head" and "lift." The *head* is the depth of the water in a vessel, pipe, or conduit—which is a measure of the pressure on any given point below the surface. Therefore, the term "head" indicates the difference in the level of water between two points, and is usually expressed in feet. The two types of head are "static head" and "dynamic head" (Fig. 6).

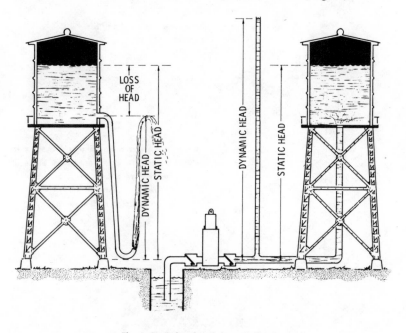

Fig. 6. Static head and dynamic head.

Hydraulically, *lift* is the height to which atmospheric pressure forces or "lifts" water above the elevation of its source of supply. In respect to pump operation, the height, measured from the elevation of the source of supply to the center point of the inlet opening of the pump, is termed "lift" (see Figs. 7 and 8). The two types of lift are "static lift" and "dynamic lift."

83

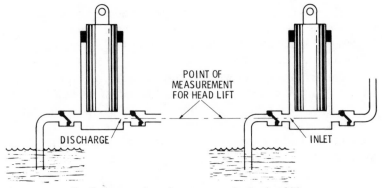

Fig. 7. Correct points of measurement for head and lift.

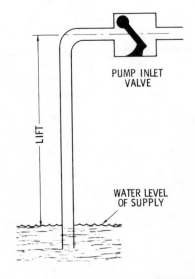

Fig. 8. Correct measurement for static lift with respect to pump operation. Static lift is measured from the surface of the water supply to the center point of the inlet opening of the pump.

HYDROSTATICS

The branch of hydraulics dealing with the pressure and equilibrium (at rest) of water and other liquids is known as *hydrostatics*. Water is the liquid that is most often considered in studying the basic principles of hydraulics, but other liquids are also included.

Static Head

The height above a given point of a column or body of water at rest, the weight of the water causing pressure, is termed *static head*.

In respect to pump operation, the head is measured from the center point of the pump outlet connection (see Fig. 7).

In most calculations it is common practice to estimate the pressure per foot of head at 0.5 lb. of pressure per sq. in. The correct value for calculating pressure of water per foot of static head is 0.43302 lb. per sq. in. This value is accurate for a water temperature of 62°F.

Ques. What is static head?
Ans. The height above a given point of a body of water at rest—the weight of the water thereby causing pressure.

Ques. With respect to pump operation, from what point is head measured?
Ans. From the center point of the pump outlet connection.

Ques. What approximate value is commonly used in calculations for estimating pressure per foot of head?
Ans. One-half pound (0.5 lb.) of pressure per sq. in.

Ques. What is the accurate value for pressure of water per foot of head?
Ans. The pressure of water per ft. of static head is 0.43302 lb. per sq. in.

Static Lift

The height to which atmospheric pressure causes a column of water to rise above the source of supply to restore equilibrium is termed *static lift*. The weight of the column of water (1 sq. in.) of cross-sectional area required to restore equilibrium is equal to the pressure exerted by the atmosphere (lb. per sq. in.).

The pressure of the atmosphere can be made available for lifting water from the source of supply to an elevated pump by removing air from the inlet pump (Fig. 9). In the left-hand diagram, the inlet pipe (before connection with the pump) presses downward on the surface of the water with equal pressure (lb. per sq. in.) on both the inside and outside of the pipe, because the pipe is open at the top. If the end of the pipe is connected to a pump which removes air from the pipe to create a partial vacuum, the water rises to a height

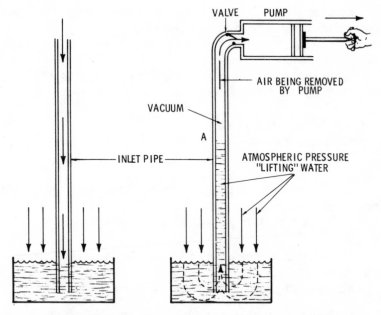

VALVE   PUMP

AIR BEING REMOVED
BY PUMP

VACUUM

A

INLET PIPE

ATMOSPHERIC PRESSURE
"LIFTING" WATER

Fig. 9. Diagrams illustrating the method of making the atmospheric pressure available for "lifting" water from the source to an elevated pump.

A (see diagram) that is determined by the available atmospheric pressure.

When the barometer indicates 30 in. of mercury at sea level, the atmospheric pressure at sea level is 14.74 lb. per sq. in., which is the atmospheric pressure that can maintain or balance a 34.042-ft. column of water, if the column is completely devoid of air and the water temperature is 62°F. (maximum density). Thus, the atmospheric pressure "lifts" the water to a height that establishes equilibrium between the weight of the water and the pressure of the atmosphere.

When the water temperature is warmer than 62°F., the height to which the water can be lifted decreases because of the increased vapor pressure. A boiler feed pump taking water at 153°F., for example, cannot produce a vacuum higher than 21.78 in., because the water begins to boil at that point and the pump chamber fills with steam. Therefore, the theoretical "lift" is:

$$34 \times \frac{21.78}{30} = 24.68 \text{ ft. (approximately)}$$

The result is approximate because no correction is made for the 34-ft. column of water at 62°F. At 153°F., of course, the column length would be increased slightly.

The maximum height to which water at standard temperature (62°F) can be lifted is determined by the barometric pressure. As

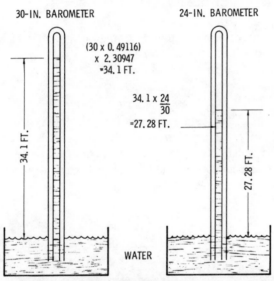

30-IN. BAROMETER   24-IN. BAROMETER

(30 x 0.49116)
x 2.30947
=34.1 FT.

34.1 x $\frac{24}{30}$
=27.28 FT.

34.1 FT.

27.28 FT.

WATER

Fig. 10. Illustrating the maximum lift of water at standard temperature (62°F.) when barometric pressure is 30 in. (left) and 24 in. (right).

shown in Fig. 10, the water rises to a height of 34.1 ft. when the barometric pressure is 30 inches, and it rises to 27.28 ft. when the barometric pressure is 24 inches (using 0.49116 lb. per sq. in. and 2.30947 ft. as head of water for each lb. per sq. in.).

Ques. How can atmospheric pressure be used to raise water from the source to an elevated pump?

Ans. By removing the air from the inlet pipe to the pump.

Ques. What is meant by a "vacuum"?

Ans. A "vacuum" is a space that is devoid of matter and in which the pressure is "zero." The word "vacuum" is often used to designate a space in which the pressure is less than atmospheric pressure; however, this is actually only a "partial vacuum."

Ques. What is the maximum height to which atmospheric pressure can lift water?

Ans. Approximately 34 ft., when the barometric pressure is 30 in. and the water temperature is 62°F.

Ques. What determines the maximum height to which water is lifted at standard temperature (62°F.)?

Ans. Barometric pressure.

Displacement

The weight of the water pushed aside (displaced) by the flotation of a vessel is termed *displacement*. The term *draft* is used to indicate the depth to which an object or vessel sinks in the water—the depth at which the weight of the water displaced is equal to the weight of the object or vessel.

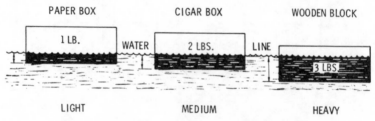

Fig. 11. Displacement or "draft" of objects placed in a liquid.

Displacement and draft are illustrated in Fig. 11. If a paper box, a cigar box, and a solid block of wood (all of same dimensions) are placed in a pan of water, each sinks to a depth proportional to its weight. Each object sinks until the weight of the water that it displaces is equal to the weight of the object. Thus, the cigar box (2 lb.) sinks to twice the depth of the paper box (1 lb.) and the wooden block (3 lb.) sinks to three times the depth that the paper box (1 lb.) sinks.

The resultant pressure of a fluid on an immersed body acts upward vertically through the center of gravity of the displaced fluid, and it is equal to the weight of the fluid displaced. This is known as *Archimedes' Principle*. The center point of pressure for any plane surface acted upon by a fluid is the point of action of the resultant pressure acting upon the surface.

Ques. To what depth does an object or vessel sink in water?

Ans. It sinks in water until the weight of the water occupied or displaced is equal to the weight of the object or vessel.

Ques. What is meant by "draft"?

Ans. It is a marine term that refers to the depth that an object or vessel sinks in water—the depth at which the weight of the water displaced is equal to the weight of the vessel.

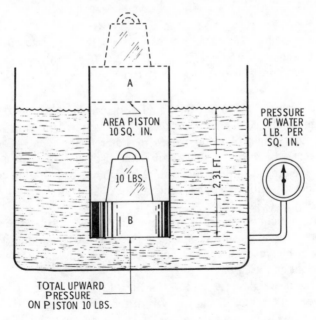

Fig. 12. Buoyancy is illustrated by submerging a cylinder containing a frictionless piston in water.

Ques. Why is the draft of a boat less in salt water than in fresh water?

Ans. Because salt water is heavier than fresh water.

Buoyancy

The power or tendency of a liquid to keep a vessel afloat is termed *buoyancy*. It is the upward pressure exerted by a fluid on a floating body. Buoyancy is illustrated in Fig. 12. In the diagram a cylinder open at both ends is submerged in water to a depth of 2.31 ft. If an airtight and frictionless piston were inserted in the cylinder at point *A* and released, it would sink to point *B* and remain suspended at that point.

During the descent of the piston (see Fig. 12), the upward pressure of the water on the lower face of the piston increases gradually. The piston does not descend past point *B,* because the total upward pressure on the piston at point *B* is equal to its weight and the entire system (piston and displaced water) is in a state of equilibrium:

>weight of piston .... 10 lb.
>pressure of water .... 1 lb. per sq. in.
>area of piston .... 10 sq. in.
>total pressure on piston (1 × 10) = 10 lb.

The center of gravity of the liquid displaced by the immersed body is termed the *center of buoyancy.* As illustrated in Fig. 13A, a rectangular block of wood placed in water floats evenly (or on an even keel), because the volume of water displaced aft is proportional to the volume displaced forward. A weight placed at the center of buoyancy C_B submerges the wooden blocks at points *A* and *B* to the same depths (Fig. 13B).

If the weight is placed in an aft position (Fig. 13C), the block is immersed to a greater depth than the forward position. Thus the center of buoyancy shifts to a point which depends on the position of the weight and its size.

If equal weights (*A* and *B* in Fig. 13D) are placed at equal distances, the center of buoyancy is at the center point and the block remains level. In actual practice, it is not practical to place equal weights at equal distances from the center of buoyancy. Thus, a

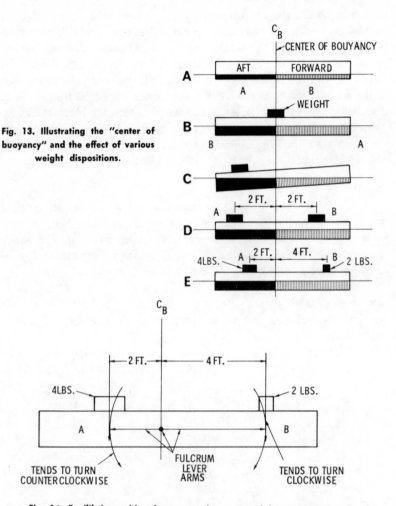

Fig. 13. Illustrating the "center of buoyancy" and the effect of various weight dispositions.

Fig. 14. Equilibrium with reference to the center of buoyancy (C_B) and proper distribution of weights.

4-lb. weight (see *A* in Fig. 13E) is placed 2 ft. aft, and a 2-lb. weight *B* is placed 4 ft. foward to prevent shifting the center of buoyancy. This is also illustrated in Fig. 14, in which the same wooden block is pivoted through its center of buoyancy C_B. The pivot forms the fulcrum or "origin of moments."

91

A *moment* is the measure of a force (or weight) by its effect in producing rotation about a fixed point or fulcrum, and it is measured in foot-pounds when the force is measured in pounds and the distance is measured in feet. The 4-lb. weight placed on a 2-ft. lever arm (see Fig. 14) tends to rotate the wooden block counterclockwise with a force of (4 lb. × 2 ft.), or 8 foot-pounds. Opposed to this force, the 2-lb. weight on a 4-ft. lever arm tends to turn the block clockwise with a force of (2 lb. × 4 ft.), or 8 foot-pounds. Since the moments are then equal and opposite, there is no resultant tendency to rotate the wooden block—it is in a state of equilibrium.

Stability

The capacity of an object to return to equilibrium or its original pisition after having been displaced is termed *stability*. With respect to a floating vessel, it is the characteristic (due to its shape) which gives the vessel the capacity to right itself and to assume its normal position after a roll or oscillation caused by a heavy sea.

The cross-sectional shape of the immersed surface of the body determines stability. Thus, the stability of a round-bottomed yacht's tender or dinghy is low in comparison to the stability of a flat-bottomed rowboat.

In a floating body at rest on water, the line joining the center of gravity or buoyancy of the immersed hull bottom, because the

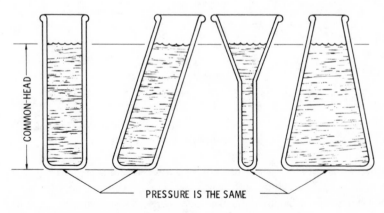

Fig. 15. Illustrating the hydraulic principle that the pressure, in lbs. per sq. in., is identical for containers that have different shapes.

known as the *axis of equilibrium*. If an external force moves the axis of equilibrium to an inclined position, a vertical line drawn upward from the new center of buoyancy intersects the axis of equilibrium at a point called *the metacenter*. Thus, the metacenter of the hull of a vessel is determined by the location of the center of gravity or buoyancy of the immersed hull bottom, because the metacenter is the point of the transverse section of a hull where a vertical line from its center of gravity or buoyancy intersects a line passing through the center of gravity of the hull. Therefore, if the metacenter is located *above* the center of gravity, equilibrium is *stable;* if it coincides with the center of gravity, equilibrium is maintained; and if the metacenter is located *below* the center of gravity, equilibrium is *unstable*.

Hydrostatic Paradox

When water is placed in containers having different shapes (Fig. 15), the intensity of the pressure, in lb. per sq. in., is the same at the bottom of each container, but the total liquid pressure against the bottom of each container is proportional to the area of the bottom of the container. This is related to the hydraulic principle that: *A small quantity of fluid can be made to balance a much larger weight.*

The quantity of liquid, or its total weight, has no effect either on the intensity of pressure or on the total pressure, if the "head" remains the same. The fact that the total liquid pressure against the bottom of a vessel may be many times greater (or many times less) than the total weight of the liquid is termed a *hydrostatic paradox*.

Hydrostatic Balance

Archimedes stated: *A body immersed in a fluid loses an amount of weight that is equivalent to the weight of the fluid displaced.* When a body is immersed in a liquid, it is acted upon by two forces: (1) *gravity,* which tends to lower the body; and (2) *buoyancy,* which tends to raise the body.

This principle is illustrated in Fig. 16. An assembly consisting of a hollow brass cylinder and a solid cylinder of the same size is suspended from one pan of the balance, and a counterweight is placed on the other pan to balance the assembly. If the hollow cylinder is filled with water, equilibrium is disturbed. However, if the balance

93

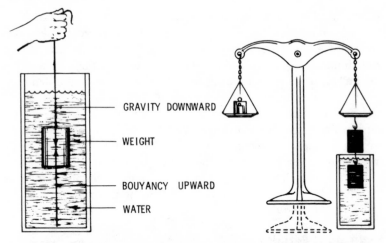

GRAVITY DOWNWARD

WEIGHT

BOUYANCY UPWARD

WATER

Fig. 16. Illustrating Archimede's principle that: A body immersed in a fluid loses
an amount of weight that is equivalent to the weight of the fluid displaced.

is lowered to submerge the solid cylinder, equilibrium is restored. Thus, when the solid cylinder is submerged, a portion of its weight equal to the weight of the water in the hollow cylinder is lost.

HYDRODYNAMICS

The branch of physics dealing with the *motion and action* of water and other liquids is called *hydrodynamics*. Various forces act upon a liquid, causing it to be in a state of motion.

Dynamic Head

The *dynamic head* of water is an equivalent or virtual head of water in motion, which represents the resultant pressure necessary to force the water from a given point to a given height and to over-come all frictional resistance. The dynamic head operating to cause *flow* of a liquid is divided into three parts: (1) *velocity head;* (2) *entry head;* and (3) *friction head.*

Velocity Head—The height through which a body must fall in a vacuum to acquire the velocity with which the water flows into the pipe is equal to ($v^2 \div 2g$), in which v is velocity in *ft. per second* and $2g = 64.32$.

94

Entry Head—this is the head required to overcome the frictional resistance to entrance to the pipe. With a sharp-edged entrance, the entry head is equal to approximately one-half the velocity head; with a smooth, rounded entrance, the entry head is negligible.

Friction Head—This is due to the frictional resistance to flow inside the pipe. In most pipes of considerable length, the sum of the entry head and the velocity head required barely exceeds one foot. In a long pipe with a small head, the sum of the velocity head and entry head is usually so small that it can be omitted. The loss of head due to the friction of water in pipes and elbows of various sizes and for various rates of flow can be obtained from tables that are used in pump calculations.

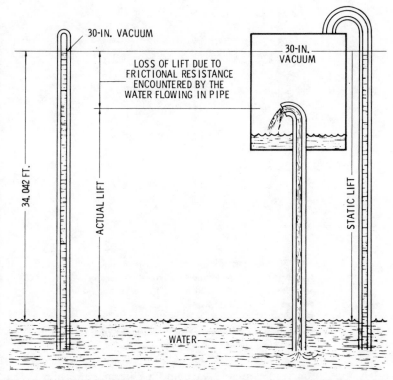

Fig. 17. Theoretical lift (left), for a pump, which corresponds to static lift for a given barometer reading, but is not obtained in actual practice; the dynamic lift (right) is actual lift, plus all frictional resistance.

95

Dynamic Lift

The *dynamic lift* of water is an equivalent or virtual lift of water in motion, which represents the resultant pressure necessary to lift the water from a given point to a given height and to overcome all frictional resistance (Fig. 17). The practical limit of actual lift in pump operation ranges from 20 to 25 feet. The practical limit of lift is reduced by longer inlet lines, by a larger number of elbows, and by pipes that are too small. Higher altitudes also reduce the practical limit of lift.

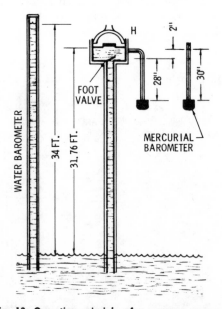

Fig. 18. Operating principle of a common vacuum-type lift pump as measured by "inches of mercury" and "feet of water." The distance 31.76 ft. is the approximate height that the water can be lifted with the atmospheric pressure at 14.74 lbs. (30 in. of mercury). In actual practice, 25 ft. is considered the maximum lift for satisfactory operation.

The operation of a common vacuum-type lift pump is illustrated in Fig. 18. When the mercury in the barometer *0* is at 30 in. (corresponding to atmospheric pressure at 14.74 lb.), the head of water is

2.30947 ft. for each lb. per sq. in. Therefore, if water, rather than mercury, were used in the barometer, the height of the column of water (at atmospheric pressure of 14.74 lb., or 30 in. of mercury) is (14.74 × 2.30947), or 34.042 ft. The piston of the pump in the illustration is located at 31.76 ft. above the water level, and an attached mercurial gauge *H* would read 28 in., leaving a margin of only 2 in. of available pressure to overcome friction and to lift the foot valve *M*. The distance 31.76 ft. is the approximate height that the water can be lifted at atmospheric pressure of 14.74 lb. (30 in. of mercury). The maximum practical lift for satisfactory pump operation is approximately 25 ft.

The term "negative lift" is applied when the level of the water supply is higher than the pump inlet; or it is the vertical distance from the water supply level to the pump inlet at a lower level. This is sometimes called "suction head" (Fig. 19).

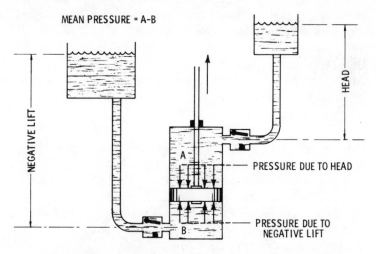

Fig. 19. Illustrating "negative lift," sometimes called "suction head." The pump shown is double-acting, but the second set of valves is not shown for the sake of simplicity.

As shown in the illustration, the standard measurement for negative lift is from the surface of the water supply to the lower center point of the pump inlet, but the pressure due to negative lift varies, depending on the position of the piston. It should be noted that the column to the piston balances a portion of the total column; therefore, the actual amount of negative lift at a given instant is the difference between the two columns.

Ques. What is the practical limit of lift for pump operation?

Ans. From 20 to 25 feet. Since dynamic lift is greater than static lift and if the pump were located at a distance of 25 ft. above the water level, only 30 − (25 × 1.113) or 2.2 in. of the barometer would be available (at atmospheric pressure of 14.74 lb. or 30 in. of mercury) to cover the frictional resistance due to water in motion. Therefore, the location of the pump should be lowered to a distance of not more than 20 ft. above the level of the water supply.

Ques. What conditions require a shorter lift or reduce the practical limit of lift?

Ans. Longer inlet lines, a larger number of inlet elbows, smaller pipes, and higher altitudes reduce the practical limit of lift.

Ques. What is the effect of negative lift?

Ans. It assists the pumping operation, because it exerts a pressure on the piston, which opposes the pressure on the other side of the piston due to the head (see Fig. 19).

Ques. Is it correct to measure the lift from the center point of the outlet to the level in the tank (as in Fig. 19)?

Ans. No. The "instantaneous" lift for a given instant extends from the level in the tank to the upper face of the piston (vertical distance). This principle also applies to negative lift (supply level above lower face of piston). Thus, the strictly correct definitions are not conveniently applied to actual practice.

Effect of Temperature on Theoretical Lift—When the water is warm, the height to which it can be lifted decreases because of the increased vapor pressure. A boiler feed pump receiving water at 201.96°F., for example, could not produce a vacuum greater than 5.49 in., because the water at that temperature begins to *boil,* filling the pump chamber with steam. Therefore, the corresponding theoretical lift is:

Table 1. Theoretical Life for Various Temperatures
(leakage not considered)

Temp. (°F.)	Absolute pressure of vapor (lb. per sq. in.)	Vacuum (in. of mercury)	Lift (ft.)	Temp. (°F.)	Absolute pressure of vapor (lb. per sq. in.)	Vacuum (in. of mercury)	Lift (ft.)
102.1	1	27.88	31.6	182.9	8	13.63	15.4
12*.3	2	25.85	29.3	188.3	9	11.60	13.1
141.6	3	23.83	27.0	193.2	10	9.56	10.8
153.1	4	21.78	24.7	197.8	11	7.52	8.5
162.3	5	19.74	22.3	202.0	12	5.49	6.2
170.1	6	17.70	20.0	205.9	13	3.45	3.9
176.9	7	15.67	17.7	209.6	14	1.41	1.6

$$34 \times \frac{5.49}{30} = 6.22 \text{ ft.}$$

The theoretical maximum lift for various temperatures, leakage not considered, is given in Table 1. A rise in temperature causes expansion—the column of water that can be supported by atmospheric pressure is lengthened (Fig. 20).

At 62°F., the atmosphere can support a 34-ft. column of water at a barometer reading of 30 in. of mercury. As the temperature rises, the water expands, which lengthens the column of water.

As shown in Fig. 20, a 34-ft. column of water at a temperature of 60°F. is placed in a tube that is closed at the bottom and is open at the top. If the water is heated to 180°F., the weight of the water per cu. ft. decreases from 62.36 lb., at 60°F., to 60.57 lb. at 180°F. (from Table 5 in Chapter 1). Thus, from expansion of the water, the length of the 34-ft. column (see Fig. 20) becomes:

$$34 \times \frac{62.36}{60.57} = 35 \text{ ft.}$$

The properties of water with respect to temperature changes are given in Table 2. Pressure, specific volume, density, and specific heat all vary with temperature changes.

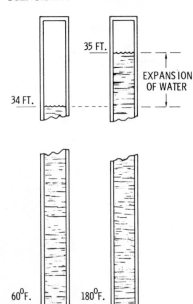

Fig. 20. Illustrating the increase in maximum theoretical lift with an increase in water temperature.

When a liquid is placed in a closed chamber (which is otherwise empty and at a uniform temperature), evaporation occurs more or less rapidly at first. After a time, however, the space outside the liquid becomes partially filled with stray molecules which have escaped through the surface film. These molecules move about inside the chamber, and they are deflected from its walls and from each other. Some molecules may return to the surface of the liquid, and they may be attracted to the interior portion of the liquid. Ultimately, as many molecules may be returned to the liquid as are leaving it, and an equilibrium may be attained—at which stage evaporation may be said to have ceased. There is no further loss to the liquid, or gain to the vapor outside it; however, a continued exchange of molecules occurs as new molecules are projected from the surface and other molecules are falling into the liquid in equal numbers. Thus, the chamber is filled with saturated vapor; or the vapor is said to be *saturated*. In any state before this final stage is arrived at, the vapor is said to be *nonsaturated*. A saturated vapor is a vapor that is in equilibrium with its own liquid.

100

Table 2. Properties of Water With Respect to Change in Temperature

Temp. (°F.)	Pressure, (lb. per sq. in.)	Specific volume, (cu. ft. per lb.)	Density, (lb. per cu. ft.)	Specific heat	(°F.) Temp.	Pressure, (lb. per sq. in.)	Specific volume, (cu. ft. per lb.)	Density, (lb. per cu. ft.)	Specific heat
20	0.06	0.01603	62.37	1.0168	240	24.97	0.01692	59.11	1.012
30	0.08	0.01602	62.42	1.0098	250	29.82	0.01700	58.83	1.015
40	0.12	0.01602	62.43	1.0045	260	35.42	0.01708	58.55	1.018
50	0.18	0.01602	62.42	1.0012	270	41.85	0.01716	58.26	1.021
60	0.26	0.01603	62.37	0.9990	280	49.18	0.01725	57.96	1.023
70	0.36	0.01605	62.30	0.9977	290	57.55	0.01735	57.65	1.026
80	0.51	0.01607	62.22	0.9970	300	67.00	0.01744	57.33	1.029
90	0.70	0.01610	62.11	0.9967	310	77.67	0.01754	57.00	1.032
100	0.95	0.01613	62.00	0.9967	320	89.63	0.01765	56.66	1.035
110	1.27	0.01616	61.86	0.9970	330	103.00	0.01776	56.30	1.038
120	1.69	0.01620	61.71	0.9974	340	118.00	0.01788	55.94	1.041
130	2.22	0.01625	61.55	0.9979	350	135.00	0.01800	55.57	1.045
140	2.89	0.01629	61.38	0.9986	360	153.00	0.01812	55.18	1.048
150	3.71	0.01634	61.20	0.9994	370	173.00	0.01825	54.78	1.052
160	4.74	0.01639	61.00	1.0002	380	196.00	0.01839	54.36	1.056
170	5.99	0.01645	60.80	1.0010	390	220.00	0.01854	53.94	1.060
180	7.51	0.01651	60.58	1.0019	400	247.00	0.01870	53.50	1.064
190	9.34	0.01657	60.36	1.0029	410	276.00	0.01890	53.00	1.068
200	11.52	0.01663	60.12	1.0039	420	308.00	0.01900	52.60	1.072
210	14.13	0.01670	59.88	1.0050	430	343.00	0.01920	52.20	1.077
220	17.19	0.01677	59.63	1.0070	440	381.00	0.01940	51.70	1.082
230	20.77	0.01684	59.37	1.0090					

Effect of Temperature on Dynamic Lift—Pumps handling water at high temperatures must work on reduced actual lift, because the boiling point is related to the pressure. At 212°F., a pump cannot lift any water, because the cylinder fills with steam on the admission stroke.

Theoretically, a pump (with no leakage) can draw or "lift" water to a height of 34.042 ft. when the barometer reads 30 in. of mercury, but the pump cannot attain a perfect vacuum because of valve leakage, air in the water, and water vapor; the actual height of the water is usually less than 30 ft., and it is considerably less for warm or hot water.

When the water is warm, the height that it can be lifted decreases, due to increased vapor pressure. A boiler feed pump receiving water at 153°F., for example, can produce a vacuum not larger than 21.78 in., because the water begins to boil at that point and the pump chamber is filled with steam. The corresponding theoretical lift then is:

$$34 \times \frac{21.78}{30} = 24.68 \text{ ft., approximately}$$

The result is approximate because no correction has been made for the 34-ft. column of water at 62°F., which is lengthened slightly. Also, the practical lift is considerably less.

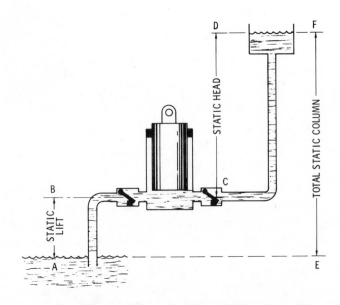

Fig. 21. Illustrating "static total column," which is "static lift" plus "static head," extending vertically from the level of the water supply to the point of discharge or surface level of the water in the tank.

Total Column

The term *total column* has been coined to avoid the term "total head." The "total column" is *head plus lift*. The term "total head" means *head plus lift;* "lift" should never be called "head." The two types of "total column" are: (1) *static;* and (2) *dynamic.*

Static Total Column—The *static lift plus the static head,* or the height or distance from the level of supply to the level in the tank, in feet, is termed the *static total column.* It is the column that is causing pressure resulting from its weight (Fig. 21). Thus in the illustration:

static lift *AB* + static head *CD* = static total column *EF*

Dynamic Total Column—*The dynamic lift plus the dynamic head,* or the equivalent total column of water in motion, is termed the *dynamic total column.* It represents the pressure resulting from the

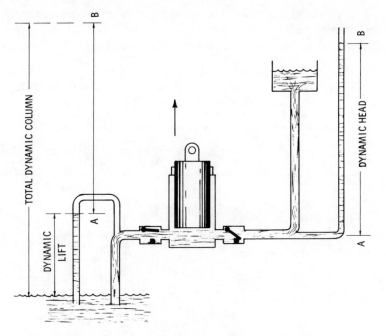

Fig. 22. Illustrating the "dynamic total column", which is "dynamic lift" plus "dynamic head". Note that the length of AB (left) is equal to the dynamic head AB (right).

static total column, plus the resistance to flow caused by friction (Fig. 22).

Problem: If static lift is 20 ft.; lift friction, 10 percent; static head, 200 ft.; and head friction is 20 percent, what is the dynamic total column? What is the corresponding pressure?
Solution:

$$\text{dynamic lift} = 20 \times 1.10 = 22 \text{ ft.}$$
$$\text{dynamic head} = 200 \times 1.20 = 240 \text{ ft.}$$
$$\text{total dynamic column} = 262 \text{ ft.}$$

$$\text{corresponding pressure} = 262 \times 0.43302 = 113.5 \text{ lb. per sq. in.}$$

Friction of Water in Pipes

In the plumbing trade, there has been wide misunderstanding concerning the laws governing rates of discharge of water from faucets and the relations of pressure and discharge. This misunder-

Table 3. Loss in Pressure by Friction per 100-Ft. Length of Wrought Iron Pipe
(in lb. per sq. in.)

Gallons per Minute	Nominal Diameter in Inches					
	½	¾	1	1¼	1½	2
1	0.9	0.2	....	....	....	....
2	3.2	0.8	....	....	....	....
3	6.9	1.8	0.6	....	....	....
4	11.7	3.2	0.9	0.3	0.1	....
5	17.8	4.5	1.4	0.4	0.2	....
6	24.8	6.4	2.0	0.5	0.3	0.1
8	42.6	10.9	3.4	0.9	0.4	0.1
10	64.0	16.5	5.1	1.4	0.6	0.2
12	90.0	23.1	7.1	1.9	0.9	0.3
14	120.0	30.4	9.6	2.5	1.2	0.4
16	....	40.0	12.2	3.2	1.5	0.5
18	....	48.7	15.2	4.0	1.8	0.7
20	....	59.2	18.3	4.8	2.3	0.8
30	....	120.0	38.7	10.2	4.8	1.7
40	....	....	66.0	17.4	8.2	2.9
50	....	....	98.0	26.1	12.4	4.3

standing has produced waste. Table 3 can be valuable in calculating the loss of pressure due to friction in pipes of various sizes which deliver various volumes of water per minute.

In addition to the friction encountered in pipes, friction occurs in the faucets. The friction varies with the type and make of faucet. The friction losses in Table 4 refer to a single type and make of faucet. Allowances should be made for other types of faucets.

Table 4.   Loss in Pressure of Water Through a Faucet

(½-in. commercial faucet)

Rate of Flow (gal. per min.)	Loss in Pressure (lb. per sq. in.)
4	2
5	3-½
8	9
10	15
15	33
20	60

A plumber should be able to estimate the losses in pressure due to the several factors that are involved, and thus be able to determine the pressure required at the fixtures to deliver water at a given rate of flow. The following problems are used to illustrate methods of calculation.

Problem: What pressure is required for a flow of 10 gal. per minute through a 3/4-in. pipe line that is 350 ft. long?

Solution: From Table 3, the drop in pressure is 16.5 lb. per 100 ft. of 3/4-in. pipe for a flow of 10 gal. per minute; for 350 ft. of pipe, the required pressure is:

$$\frac{16.5 \times 350}{100} = 16.5 \times 3.5 = 57.8 \text{ lb.}$$

Problem: The height of the water in a windmill tank is 60 ft. How many gal. per min. can flow through 500 ft. of 1-1/2" pipe with a vertical rise of 23 ft.?

105

Solution: 2.3 ft. head = 1 lb. pressure.

Hence;

pressure due to tank elevation = (60 ÷ 2.3) = 26.1 lb.
pressure loss due to 23-ft. rise = (23 ÷ 2.3) = 10.0 lb.
total pressure available to cause flow = 16.1 lb.

pressure available per 100 ft. of pipe = (16.1 ÷ 5) = 3.2 lb.

From Table 3; the two values nearest 3.2 lb. for 1-1/2″ pipe are: 2.3 lb. pressure for 20 gal. per min. and 4.8 lb. pressure for 30 gal. per min. Thus, by interpolation, the 3.2 lb. pressure corresponds to a flow of:

$$20 + \frac{(3.2 - 2.3)}{(4.8 - 2.3)} \times 10 = 23.6 \text{ gal. per min.}$$

Problem: A 3/4-in. pipe extends 75 ft. with a vertical rise of 23 ft. What pressure is required at the water mains in the street to deliver 10 gal. per min. through a 1/2-in. faucet?

Solution:

From Table 3:

friction loss through 75 ft. of 3/4-in. pipe = (16.5 × 75/100)
= 12.4 lb.
loss due to 23-ft. rise (23 ÷ 2.3) = 10.0 lb.

From Table 4:

loss in flow through faucet at 10 gal. per min. = 15.0 lb.
total pressure required = 37.4 lb.

In most installations, a pressure loss due to flow through the meter must be considered (Table 5). At a given rate of flow (30 gal. per min.), it may be noted that the loss in pressure in passing through the meter decreases rapidly as the size of the meter increases.

Problem: Water in a 3/4-in. pipe passes through a meter and extends 125 ft. from a main to a faucet. The faucet is 23 ft. above the

106

Table 5. Pressure Loss in Flow Through Meter

Meter Size (in.)	Gal. per Min.	Pressure Loss (lb.)
⅝	10	2 - 7
⅝	30	16 - 65
¾	30	14 - 30
1	30	4 - 7

street main, and must deliver 10 gal. per min. What pressure is required at the main?

Solution:

From Table 3:
    friction loss in 125 ft. of pipe = (16.5 × 1.25 = 20.6 lb.
        pressure loss due to 23-ft. rise (23 ÷ 2.3) = 10.0 lb.
        From Table 4: friction loss through faucet = 15.0 lb.
        From Table 5: pressure loss through meter =   3.0 lb.
        total pressure required at street main = 48.6 lb.

In the above calculations, loss in pressure due to the fittings has not been considered. Unless numerous fittings have been used, this loss may be either omitted or estimated. Roughly, the loss in pressure due to an elbow in small pipes may be estimated at 1/4 to 1/2 lb., which indicates that it is desirable to use as few fittings as possible. The loss in head due to friction in terms of head (in feet) for various sizes of smooth 90° elbows and for 100 ft. of smooth pipe is given in Table 6.

FLOW OF WATER

The quantity of water discharged through a pipe is determined by: (1) *head;* (2) *length of pipe;* (3) *character of interior surface;* and (4) *number and sharpness of bends.* The head is measured vertically between the surface level at the pipe inlet and the level at the center point of the discharge end. Flow is independent of the position of the pipe, regardless of whether it is horizontal or inclined.

Measurement of Water Flow

The most accurate methods that can be used to measure water flow are either to measure the volume or to weigh the liquid delivered,

Table 6. Loss of Head Due to Friction

Loss of Head in Feet in Various Sizes of Smooth 90° Elbows							Loss of Head in Feet per 100 Feet of Smooth Pipe						
Gallons Per Min. Delivered	PIPE SIZES, INCHES—INSIDE DIAMETER						Gallons Per Min. Delivered	PIPE SIZES, INCHES—INSIDE DIAMETER					
	1	1¼	1½	2	2½	3		1	1¼	1½	2	2½	3
20	2.52	0.89	0.42	0.146	0.067	0.038	20	42.0	11.1	5.2	1.82	0.61	0.25
25	3.84	1.33	0.62	0.218	0.101	0.057	25	64.0	16.6	7.8	2.73	0.92	0.38
30	5.44	1.88	0.88	0.307	0.142	0.083	30	89.0	23.5	11.0	3.84	1.29	0.54
35	7.14	2.50	1.18	0.408	0.189	0.107	35	119.0	31.2	14.7	5.10	1.72	0.71
40	9.12	3.20	1.50	0.528	0.242	0.137	40	152.0	40.0	18.8	6.60	2.20	0.91
45	……	4.00	1.86	0.656	0.308	0.173	45	……	50.0	23.2	8.20	2.80	1.15
50	……	4.80	2.27	0.792	0.365	0.207	50	……	60.0	28.4	9.90	3.32	1.38
70	……	9.04	4.24	1.430	0.683	0.286	70	……	113.0	53.0	18.40	6.21	2.57
75	……	……	4.80	1.670	0.781	0.458	75	……	……	60.0	20.90	7.10	3.05
90	……	……	6.72	2.320	0.991	0.600	90	……	……	84.0	29.40	9.81	4.01
100	……	……	8.16	2.860	1.320	0.744	100	……	……	102.0	35.80	12.00	4.96
125	……	……	……	4.320	2.060	1.140	125	……	……	……	54.00	18.20	7.60
150	……	……	……	6.080	2.810	1.580	150	……	……	……	76.00	25.50	10.50
175	……	……	……	8.160	3.720	2.100	175	……	……	……	102.00	33.80	14.00
200	……	……	……	10.320	4.740	2.670	200	……	……	……	129.00	43.10	17.80
250	……	……	……	……	7.260	4.080	250	……	……	……	……	66.00	27.20

Fig. 23. A typical weir. It is used to measure the water flow in small streams.

The chief disadvantage of these methods lies in the fact that they can be used only in measuring small quantities of water. Large quantities of water can be measured by the following methods: (1) *weir;* (2) *pitot tubs;* and (3) *venturi meter.*

Weir—The weir is a device that is commonly used to measure water flow. It consists of a notch in the vertical side of a tank or reservoir through which water may flow to be measured. The weir is especially adaptable for measuring the flow of small streams (Fig. 23).

To construct a weir, a notched board is placed across a small stream at some point, allowing a small pond to form. The notch in the board should be beveled on both side edges and on the bottom. The bottom of the notch is called the "crest" of the weir. The crest should be level and sides should be vertical.

A stake should be driven near the bank in the pond above the weir at a distance less than the width of the notch. The top of the stake should be level with the crest. The depth of the water above the

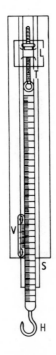

Fig. 24. Hook gauge, used to measure the depth of water above a weir.

top of the stake can be measured with a graduated rule (see Fig. 23); or it can be measured with a "hook gauge" for precision (Fig. 24).

The *hook gauge* consists of a graduated slide arranged to slide in the frame. It can be finely adjusted by means of the screw T (see Fig. 24) which passes through a lug L with a milled nut. A vernier V is also provided.

The hook gauge is first set to "zero" at which point the hook is level with the crest, and the slide is raised until the hook pierces the surface of the water. The hook gauge is located behind the weir to avoid the curvature effect as the water approaches the weir.

All formulas for weirs do not obtain the same results. The Francis formula has been used widely. It was derived from a series of experiments on 10-ft. weirs as follows:

$$Q = 3.33 \ (L - 0.14) \ H \frac{3}{2} \text{, for one end contracted}$$

110

$$Q = 3.33 \ (L - 0.24) \ H^{\frac{3}{2}}, \text{ for both ends contracted}$$

$$Q = 3.33 \ (L - H^{\frac{3}{2}}), \text{ without end contractions}$$

In the formulas;

Q is cu. ft. per second
L is length of weir, in ft.
H is head over crest, in ft.

A formula used for the V-notched weir (for small flows is):

$$Q = 2.544 \ H^{\frac{5}{2}}$$

In the formula;

H is head, in ft., above the apex of the triangle.

A weir table (see Table 7) can be used to determine the amount of water flowing over the weir. The first vertical column represents the depth of flow over the notch, and the first horizontal line represents the fractional parts of an inch. The body of the table indicates the cu. ft. of water per minute per inch (or fractional inch) of weir. The result for a 1-in. weir must be multiplied by the total horizontal length of the weir.

Pitot Tube—A pitot tube is a bent tube that is used to determine the velocity of running water by placing the curved end underneath the surface of the water and observing the height to which the water rises in the tube. It is a type of current meter, and the basic feature is the thin-edged orifice at the curved end of the tube (Fig. 25). The basic principle of the pitot tube is—when it is placed in running water, with the orifice turned upstream, the impact of the fluid causes an excess pressure in the tube that is equal to the velocity head.

The pitot tube formula is derived as follows: The head of water in the tube due to impact is v^2/g, the head due to velocity is v, and the water should rise a height h above the surface. Experiments have

111

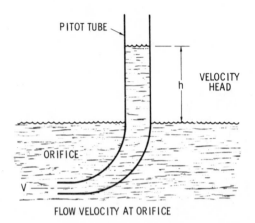

Fig. 25. Basic principle of a pitot tube, used for
measuring the flow of water.

Table 7. Weir Table for Cu. Ft. of Water per Inch of Depth Above Notch

(for 1-in. horizontal width of weir)

inches		⅛	¼	⅜	½	⅝	¾	⅞
0	0.00	0.01	0.05	0.09	0.14	0.19	0.26	0.32
1	0.40	0.47	0.55	0.64	0.73	0.82	0.92	1.02
2	1.13	1.23	1.35	1.46	1.58	1.70	1.82	1.95
3	2.07	2.21	2.34	2.48	2.61	2.76	2.90	3.05
4	3.20	3.35	3.50	3.66	3.81	3.97	4.14	4.30
5	4.47	4.64	4.81	4.98	5.15	5.33	5.51	5.69
6	5.87	6.06	6.25	6.44	6.62	6.82	7.01	7.21
7	7.40	7.60	7.80	8.01	8.21	8.42	8.63	8.83
8	9.05	9.26	9.47	9.69	9.91	10.13	10.35	10.57
9	10.80	11.02	11.25	11.48	11.71	11.94	12.17	12.41
10	12.64	12.88	13.12	13.36	13.60	13.85	14.09	14.34
11	14.59	14.84	15.09	15.34	15.59	15.85	16.11	16.36
12	16.62	16.88	17.15	17.41	17.67	17.94	18.21	18.47
13	18.74	19.01	19.29	19.56	19.84	20.11	20.39	20.67
14	20.95	21.23	21.51	21.80	22.08	22.37	22.65	22.94
15	23.23	23.52	23.82	24.11	24.40	24.70	25.00	25.30
16	25.60	25.90	26.20	26.50	26.80	27.11	27.42	27.72
17	28.03	28.34	28.65	28.97	29.28	29.59	29.91	30.21
18	30.54	30.86	31.18	31.50	31.82	32.15	32.47	32.80
19	33.12	33.45	33.78	34.11	34.44	34.77	35.10	35.44
20	35.77	36.11	36.45	36.78	37.12	37.46	37.80	38.15

shown that the actual height that the water rises is more nearly equal to the velocity head $v^2/2g$ than to v^2/g, thus the head h is usually considered to be:

$$h = \frac{cv^2}{2g}$$

The coefficient c is fairly constant for any given tube. The quantity of fluid discharged can be calculated by the formula:

$$Q = ca\sqrt{2gh}$$

in which;

    Q = quantity, in cu. ft. per second
    c = coefficient of discharge for orifice (0.95 to 0.98)
    a = area of the orifice, in sq. ft.
    h = velocity head, in feet

Venturi Meter—A venturi meter is an instrument that is similar to an hour glass for accurately measuring the discharge of fluid or gas through a pipe. It consists of a conical nozzle-like reducer followed by a more gradual enlargement to the original size which is the size of the pipe in which the meter is laid (Fig. 26).

In the illustration, the pressure heads (r_1 h_2 and h_3) are shown by the vertical tubes A, B, and C as they appear when measured by open water columns. The pressure head h_2 is less than h_1 by approximately the same difference as the difference in velocity heads as:

$$\frac{(v_2)^2}{2g} - \frac{(v_1)^2}{2g}$$

The pressure h_3 at tube C is approximately the same as that at tube A, or h_1, being slightly less because of loss due to friction of the flowing water. An equation for discharge past the meter is:

$$Q = (cAa\sqrt{2gh}) \div \sqrt{A^2 - a^2}$$

in which;

    Q = discharge, in. cu. ft. per second

113

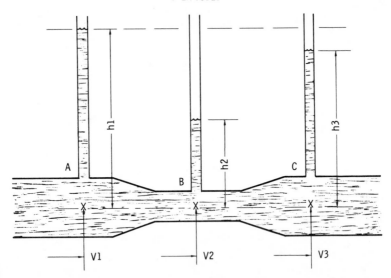

Fig. 26. Basic principle of a venturi meter showing relative pressure heads at points A, B, and C.

A = area at A, in sq. ft.
a = area at B, in sq. ft.
c = coefficient (varies between 0.97 and 1.0)

Siphon

Several types of siphons are in use as: (1) A U-shaped pipe acting on the principle of hydrostatic balance, so that the pressure in one leg tends to equalize the pressure in the other leg; (2) A bent tube or pipe used to transfer liquids from a barrel, etc., in which the flow is due to the difference in weight of the liquid; and (3) A U-shaped tube fitted to steam gauges, etc., so that only water can enter the gauge.

As shown in Fig. 27, the water flows because the height h of the column at A above the surface of the water is less than height h_1 of column B. The flow is due to the weight of a column of water of length $(h_1 - h)$.

If the water in beaker B is at a higher elevation than that in beaker A, the flow is reversed (see Fig. 27). Then the column h is longer

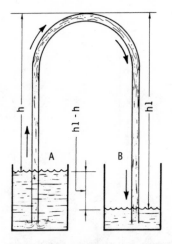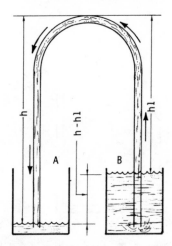

Fig. 27. Basic operation of a siphon. Flow is from the shorter column to the longer
column (left), and is reversed when the column length is reversed (right).

than column h_1, and the motive force is due to the weight of a column
having the length $(h - h^1)$. The atmosphere presses equally on the
surface of the water in the beaker, tending to force the water upward
in the columns. The unequal weight of water in the two columns
upsets equilibrium and causes the water to flow from the beaker
having the shorter column to the beaker having the longer column.

Flow Through Orifices

If an orifice is cut through either the flat side or the bottom of a
vessel, leaving sharp edges (Fig. 28), the stream lines of force set
up in the water approach the orifice in all directions; the direction of
flow of the particles of water converge, except for those near the
center point, producing a contraction of the jet when the orifices are
not shaped properly.

If the approaches are rounded properly to the orifices and constant-diameter short tubes, the diameter of the jet is equal to the area
of the orifice or tube (Fig. 29). An initial contraction takes place in
the short tube, because the tube does not have a rounded entrance,
as shown in the illustration.

The general equation for velocity of water flowing from an orifice
or tube is:

115

CONTRACTED JETS

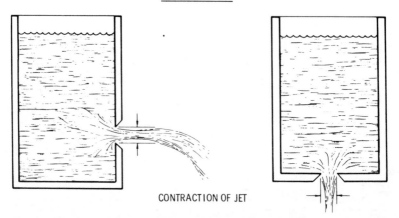

CONTRACTION OF JET

Fig. 28. Directions of flow of water particles through orifices in the side (left) and bottom (right) of a vessel to form a contraction of the jet.

$$v = \sqrt{2gH}$$

in which;

    v = theoretical velocity, in ft. per sec., corresponding to head H

    H = head of water, in ft., on center line of jet

    g = acceleration due to gravity (32.2 ft. per sec.)

If friction and contraction of the jet are considered, the general equation for discharge of water is:

$$Q = CA \sqrt{2\,gH}$$

in which;

    Q = discharge, in cu. ft. per sec.

    C = coefficient of discharge, which is the product of coefficient of friction C_1 and coefficient of contraction C_2.

    a = area, in sq. ft., of the orifice or tube

The path of a jet issuing from a horizontal orifice or a tube describes a *parabola* (Fig. 30). A parabola is a plane curve; every point on the curve is equidistant from a fixed point called the "focus" and

116

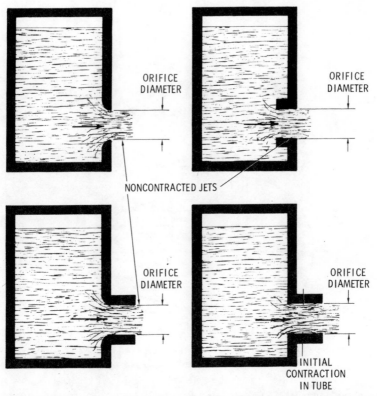

Fig. 29. Illustrating noncontraction jets in flow of water through properly rounded approaches to orifices (left) and a constant-diameter short tube (upper right). The diameter of the jet equals the area of the orifice or tube. Initial contraction occurs inside the tube (lower right), because the tube does not have a rounded approach.

from a fixed line called the "directrix." A parabola is generated by a plane cutting a cone parallel to one of its elements.

As shown in Fig. 30, the plane *MS* cuts the element *AB* at point *L* and at point *F* on the base. The point *F* is projected downward, cutting the curve at the two points *F′* and *F″*. With point *F* as the center point and radius *LF*, swing point *L* around and project downward to the axis *OG*, obtaining point *L′*, on the curve.

Any other point *R*, for example, can be obtained as follows: swing point *R* around with point *F* as center point and project down-

117

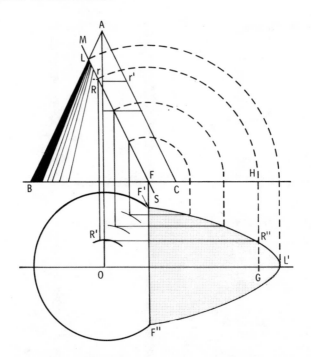

Fig. 30. A parabola. The path described by a jet of liquid issuing from a horizontal orifice or jet is illustrated by a parabola.

ward with line *HG*. Describe an arc (radius = *rr'* of cone at elevation of point *R*), and where the arc cuts the projection of point *R* at *R'*, project the point *R'* to lone *HG* to obtain point *R''*, which is a point on the curve. The other points can be obtained in a similar manner. The curve can be traced through points F' R'', L', etc., and similar points on the opposite side of the axis, ending at point F'' to form the curve, or parabola.

As shown in Fig. 31, a jet of water issuing from the side of a vessel is drawn downward on leaving the orifice by the force of gravity, describing a parabola.

The distance of any point *P* on the curve from the focus *S* is equivalent to its distance to the directrix (point *M*), or *PS = PM,* as indicated by the arc *SM*, having point *P* as its center point.

118

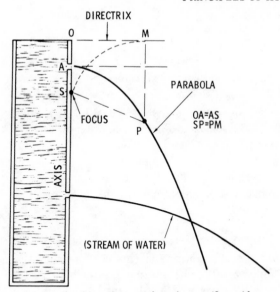

Fig. 31. The flow of water through an orifice with a horizontal axis.

If the side AD of the vessel is inclined to vertical at an angle θ (Fig. 32), the jet issues normally with respect to side AD, rises to a highest point C, and then curves downward. If the distances x and y are the horizontal abscissa and vertical ordinate, measured from the orifice A, the equation for the curve, which is also the equation for a common parabola, is:

$$y = x \tan \theta - \frac{x^2 \sec^2 \theta}{4 h}$$

When a stream of water impinges on a solid surface, it presses on the surface with a force equal and opposite to the force which changes the velocity and direction of motion of the water (Fig. 33). When the orifice is opened at point A, the head h of water causes a pressure P which acts in the direction indicated by the arrow; this causes the car supporting the vessel to move in the same direction. The equation for the reaction of the jet is:

$$P = 2 \, ahw$$

119

in which;

P = reaction
a = area of orifice
h = head of water on orifice
w = weight per unit volume of water

The head h of water on the jet (see Fig. 33) causes a pressure which acts in the left-hand direction and causes W pounds of water to move during each second with a velocity v feet per second; this is called *impulse*. The effect of "impulse" is to produce a pressure which reacts in the right-hand direction, causing the dolly supporting the vessel to move in a direction opposite the direction of jet flow, which is called *reaction*.

Specific Gravity

The ratio of the weight of a given volume of a substance to that of an equal volume of another substance, which is used as a standard of comparison (water for liquids and solids; air or hydrogen for gases) is known as *specific gravity* (sp. gr.). Water is the standard that is considered here.

When dealing with solids, the specific gravity is the ratio of the weight in the air of a given substance to the weight of an equal volume of water. That is, the specific gravity (sp. gr.) is a number that indicates how many times a given volume of a substance is heavier than an equal volume of water.

Since the weight of water varies with temperature, comparisons should be made with water at 62°F. One cubic inch of pure water weighs 0.0361 lb. at 62°F. Therefore, if the specific gravity of a material is known, its weight per cu. in. can be calculated by multiplying its specific gravity by 0.0361. To calculate the weight of one cu. ft. of a given material, multiply its specific gravity by 62.35 (the weight of one cu. ft. of water at 62°F.). This can be illustrated by a typical problem.

Problem: If the specific gravity of wrought iron is 7.85, what is its weight per cu. in.?

Solution: Since water at 62°F. weighs 0.0361 lb., the weight of one cu. in. of wrought iron is:

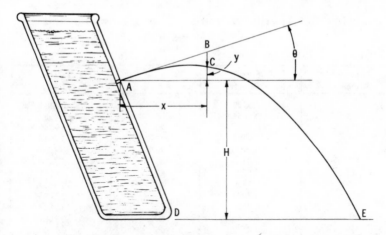

Fig. 32. The flow of water through an orifice whose axis is inclined to the horizontal.

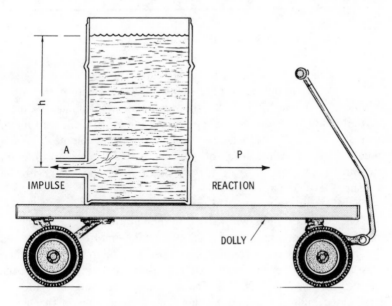

Fig. 38. Illustrating "impulse" and "reaction" of water flowing through an orifice.

121

Table 8. Specific Gravities, Degrees Baume and Degrees A.P.I.

(at 60° Fahrenheit)

Degrees Baume	Specific Gravity	Degrees A.P.I.	Specific Gravity
10	1.0000	10	1.0000
15	0.9655	15	0.9659
20	0.9333	20	0.9340
25	0.9032	25	0.9042
30	0.8750	30	0.8762
35	0.8485	35	0.8498
40	0.8235	40	0.8251
45	0.8000	45	0.8017
50	0.7777	50	0.7796
55	0.7568	55	0.7587
60	0.7368	60	0.7389
65	0.7179	65	0.7201
70	0.7000	70	0.7022
75	0.6829	75	0.6852
80	0.6666	80	0.6690
85	0.6511	85	0.6536
90	0.6363	90	0.6388

$$7.85 \times 0.036 = 0.2826 \text{ lb.}$$

The specific gravity of a liquid indicates the weight of a given volume of the liquid in comparison with the weight of an equal volume of water at 62°F. Since the *density* of a substance is "mass per unit of volume" and weight is considered to be equivalent to mass, then density can be defined as "weight per unit of volume." This is indicated in the illustration of the density of steam at different pressures (Fig. 34), in which the weight of steam increases with the pressure.

The effect of temperature on density of water is illustrated in Fig. 35. The water expands with a rise in temperature. As the temperature rises, the original volume at lower temperature increases and occupies more space, becoming lighter per unit volume, or in density.

A *hydrometer* is an instrument that is used for determining the specific gravity of liquids. It is a closed glass tube containing air with a weighted bulb at one end causing it to float upright in the liquid. The depth to which the hydrometer sinks can be read off on the

DENSITY OF STEAM AT VARIOUS PRESSURES

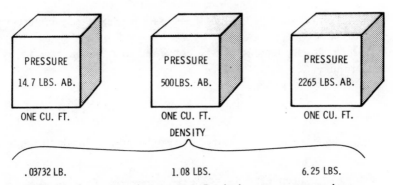

Fig. 34. Density of steam at various pressures. Density increases as pressure increases.

DENSITY OF WATER AT VARIOUS TEMPERATURES

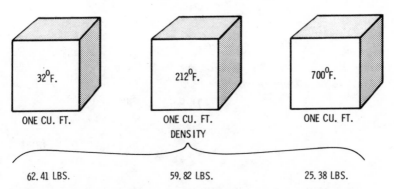

Fig. 35. Illustrating density of water at various temperatures. Density is less as temperature increases.

graduated scale to obtain the specific gravity. The lighter, or less dense, the liquid, the lower the tube sinks.

Baume scale hydrometers for testing the specific gravity of oil are known as "for liquids lighter than water" and marked accordingly. Baume scales are also available "for liquids heavier than water."

123

The comparison is made with distilled water at 60°F.—the oil is also tested at 60°F.

Either a Baume scale hydrometer or an *A.P.I.* (*American Petroleum Institute*) hydrometer can be used to test the specific gravity of a fuel oil or a lubricating oil. Temperature is extremely important in determining specific gravity.

Specific gravity reading can be converted to a Baume reading by the formula:

$$\text{degress Baume} = \frac{140}{\text{sp. gr.}} - 130$$

Baume reading can be converted to specific gravity by the formula:

$$\text{specific gravity} = \frac{140}{130 + \text{degrees Baume}}$$

Example: If the Baume reading for an oil is 26°, the specific gravity of the oil can be calculated by the formula:

$$\text{sp. gr.} = \frac{140}{130 + 26} = 0.897$$

A rule for roughly converting the specific gravity at any temperature to the standard 60°F. is: *For every 10°F. above 60°F., subtract one degree (1°) from the Baume reading, and for every 10°F. below 60°F., add one degree (1°).* The rule can be applied as follows:

$$\text{degrees Baume (60°F.)} = \text{degrees Baume} - \frac{(\text{indicated °F.} - 60°F.)}{10}$$

Example: If a hydrometer indicates a specific gravity of 27.5° Baume at an oil temperature of 75°F., what is the Baume reading at 60°F.?

$$\text{degrees Baume (60°F.)} = 27.5° - \frac{(75°F. - 60°F.)}{10}$$

$$= 27.5° - 1.5° = 26° \text{ Baume}'$$

Example: If the hydrometer indicates 24° Baume at an oil temperature of 40°F., what is the Baume reading at 60°F.?

$$\text{degrees Baume } (60°F.) = 24° - \frac{(40°F. - 60°F.)}{10}$$

$$= 24° - (-2°)$$

$$= 24° + 2° = 26° \text{ Baume}$$

The *A.P.I. (American Petroleum Institute)* specific gravity measurement is similar to Baume, except in scale divisions. Specific gravity can be converted to degrees *A.P.I.* by the formula:

$$\text{degrees } A.P.I. = \frac{141.5}{\text{sq. gr.}} - 131.5$$

Degrees *A.P.I.* can be converted to specific gravity by the formula:

$$\text{sp. gr.} = \frac{141.5}{131.5 + \text{degrees } A.P.I.}$$

Hydrometers are widely used for testing antifreeze solutions for automobile radiators. Typically, a hydrometer for finding the specific gravity of heavy liquids is provided with a Baume scale reading 0-70 and a specific gravity scale ranging from 1.000 to 2.000. For lighter liquids, a Baume scale reading 70-10 and specific gravity scale ranging from 0.7000 to 1.000 is provided. Use only those hydrometers which are calibrated to read the gravity and temperature, and have a table or other means available for converting the freezing point at various solution temperatures. Care must be exercised to use the correct float or table for a given antifreeze solution. It is not practical to mix various types of antifreeze in the same solution as it is impossible to determine the freezing point with a hydometer.

SUMMARY

Hydraulics is the branch of physics that deals with the mechanical properties of water and other liquids and with the application of these properties in engineering. The basic principles of hydraulics are:

1. The pressure exerted by a liquid on a surface is proportional to the area of the surface.
2. A smaller quantity of water can be made to balance a much larger weight.
3. The pressure on any portion of a fluid having uniform density is proportional to its depth below the surface.
4. Fluids rise to the same level in each arm of a U-tube when the temperature of the liquid is the same throughout.

The branch of hydraulics dealing with the pressure and equilibrium (at rest) of water and other liquids is known as *hydrostatics*. Water is most often considered in the study of hydraulics, but other liquids are included.

Static head is the height of a column or body of water at rest above a given point—the weight of the water causing pressure. The head is measured from the center point of the pump outlet connection. In most calculations, the pressure per foot of static head can be estimated at 0.5 lb. per sq. in. For more accurate calculations, the pressure of water per foot of static head is 0.43302 lb. per sq. in. at 62°F.

The height to which atmospheric pressure causes a column of water to rise above the source of supply to restore equilibrium is termed *static lift*. The weight of the column of water (1 sq. in. of cross-sectional area) required to restore equilibrium is equal to the pressure exerted by the atmosphere (lb. per sq. in.). The maximum height to which water at standard temperature (62°F.) can be lifted is determined by the barometric pressure. Water rises to a height of 34.1 ft. when the barometric pressure is 30 inches.

The weight of the water pushed aside (displaced) by the flotation of a vessel is termed *displacement*. The term *draft* indicates the depth to which the vessel or object sinks in the water; it is the depth at which the weight of the water displaced is equal to the weight of the vessel or object.

Buoyancy is the power or tendency of a liquid to keep a vessel afloat. It is the upward pressure exerted by a fluid on a floating body. The center of gravity of the liquid displaced by the body immersed in it is called the *center of buoyancy*.

The capacity of a body or object to return to equilibrium after having been displaced is called *stability*. It is the characteristic of a

126

floating vessel (due to its shape) which gives the vessel the capacity to right itself and to assume its normal position after a roll caused by a heavy sea.

When water is placed in containers having different shapes, the intensity of the pressure in lb. per sq. in. is the same at the bottom of each container. The fact that the total liquid pressure against the bottom of a vessel may be many times greater or less than the total weight of the liquid is termed a *hydrostatic paradox.*

A body immersed in a fluid loses an amount of weight that is equivalent to the weight of the fluid displaced, according to Archimedes. When a body is immersed in a liquid, it is acted upon by two forces: (1) *gravity,* which tends to lower the body; and (2) *buoyancy,* which tends to raise the body.

The branch of physics dealing with the *motion and action* of water and other liquids is termed *hydrodynamics.* Various forces act on a liquid, causing it to be in a state of motion.

The *dynamic head* of water is an equivalent or virtual head of water in motion which represents the resultant pressure necessary to force the water from a given point to a given height and to overcome all frictional resistance. The dynamic head causing flow of a liquids is divided into three parts: (1) *velocity head;* (2) *entry head;* and (3) *friction head.*

The *dynamic lift* of water is an equivalent or virtual lift of water in motion which represents the resultant pressure necessary to lift the water from a given point to a given height and to overcome all frictional resistance. The practical limit of actual lift in pump operation ranges from 20 to 25 feet. When the water is warm, the height to which it can be lifted decreases, *due to* increased vapor pressure.

The term *total column* means *head plus lift. The static total column is the static lift plus the static head.* The height or distance from the level of supply to the level in the tank, in feet, is termed the *static total column.* The *dynamic total column is the dynamic lift plus the dynamic head,* or the equivalent total column of water in motion. It represents the pressure resulting from the static total column plus the resistance to flow caused by friction.

Friction of water in pipes results in loss of pressure and reduced volume of water per minute delivered. Also, friction in the faucets, in the fittings, and in the flow through the meter must be considered.

127

Water flow can be measured by means of the following: (1) *weir;* (2) *pitot tube;* and (3) *venturi meter.* Actual measurements of the volume and of the weight of the liquid delivered may be more accurate methods, but they can be used only when the quantity of water delivered is small.

The general equation for velocity of water flowing from an orifice or tube is: $V = \sqrt{2gh}$. The general equation for discharge of water through an orifice is: $Q = ca\sqrt{2gh}$

The path of a jet of water issuing from a horizontal orifice or a tube describes a *parabola.* The jet is drawn downward on leaving the orifice by the force of gravity.

Specific gravity is the ratio of the weight of a given substance to that of an equal volume of another substance, which is used as a standard of comparison (water for liquids and solids; air or hydrogen for gases). *One cubic inch of pure water* weighs 0.0361 lb. at 62° F. Therefore, if the specific gravity of a material is known, its weight per cu. in. can be calculated by multiplying its specific gravity by 0.0361. To calculate the weight of 1 cu. ft. of a given material, multiply its specific gravity by 62.35 (the weight of 1 cu. ft. of water at 62° F.).

A *hydrometer* is an instrument that is used to determine the specific gravity of liquids. Either a Baume scale hydrometer or an *A.P.I. (American Petroleum Institute)* hydrometer can be used to test the specific gravity of fuel oil or lubricating oil.

A specific gravity reading can be converted to a Baume reading by the formula:

$$\text{degrees Baume} = \frac{140}{\text{sp. gr.}} - 130$$

Specific gravity reading can be converted to degrees *A.P.I.* by the formula:

$$\text{degrees } A.P.I. = \frac{141.5}{\text{sp. gr.}} - 131.5$$

Degrees *A.P.I.* can be converted to specific gravity by the formula:

$$\text{sp. gr.} = \frac{141.5}{131.5 + \text{degrees } A.P.I.}$$

REVIEW QUESTIONS

1. What is hydraulics?
2. List four important principles of hydraulics.
3. What is meant by a "head" of water?
4. What is meant by "lift," hydraulically?
5. What is the difference between "static head" and "dynamic head"? "Static lift" and "dynamic lift"?
6. What is the maximum height to which atmospheric pressure can "lift" water?
7. What factor determines the maximum height to which water is lifted at standard temperature (62°F.)?
8. To what depth does an object or vessel sink in water?
9. What is buoyancy?
10. What is the practical limit of pump operation? Why?
11. What is meant by "total column" of water?
12. What is the effect of friction in pipes, fittings, etc.?
13. Name three instruments for measuring the flow of water?
14. Explain how a siphon operates.
15. What is meant by specific gravity of a substance?
16. Explain the basic principle of a hydrometer.

CHAPTER 3

Centrifugal Pumps

All types of centrifugal pumps depend on *centrifugal force* for their operation. Centrifugal force acts on a body moving in a circular path, tending to force it farther *away from* the axis or center point of the circle described by the path of the rotating body.

BASIC PRINCIPLE

The rotating member inside the casing of a centrifugal pump provides rapid rotary motion to the mass of water contained in the casing; thus the water is forced out of the housing through the discharge outlet by means of centrifugal force. The vacuum created thereby enables atmospheric pressure to force more water into the casing through the inlet opening. This process continues as long as motion is provided to the rotor, and as long as a supply of water is available. In the centrifugal pump, *vanes* or *impellers* rotating inside a close-fitting housing draw the liquid into the pump through a central inlet opening, and by means of centrifugal force the liquid is thrown outward through a discharge outlet at the periphery of the housing.

The basic principle of centrifugal pump operation is illustrated in Fig. 1 and in Fig. 2. If a cylindrical can with vanes *A* and *C* (for rotating the liquid when the can is rotated) is mounted on a shaft with a pulley for rotating the can at high speed, centrifugal force acts on the water (rotating at high speed) to press the water outward to the walls of the can. This causes the water to press outward sharply; since it cannot move beyond the walls of the can, pressure forces the water upward, causing it to overflow while the water near the center

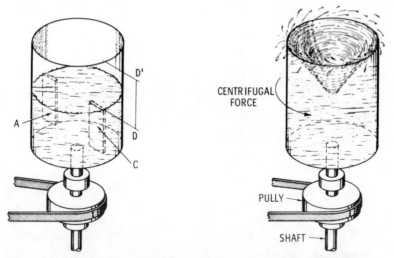

Fig. 1. Basic principle of a centrifugal pump. The radial vanes A and C cause the liquid to revolve when the cylinder is rotated (left). Centrifugal force pushes the liquid outward toward the walls of the cylinder and then upward, causing it to overflow when the cylinder is rotated at high speed (right).

of the can is drawn downward. Atmospheric pressure forces the water downward, since a vacuum is created near the center as the water moves outward toward the sides of the can. It can be noted in Fig. 1 that the water has been lifted a distance $D\ D'$.

Since the water that spills over the top has a high velocity that is equal to the rim speed, the kinetic energy that has been generated is wasted, unless an arrangement is made to catch the water and an additional supply of water is provided (see Fig. 2). In the illustration, a receiver catches the water as it spills over, and a supply tank is connected with the hollow shaft to supply water to the can. Instead of rotating the can, only the vanes can be rotated to obtain the same result.

Ques. What is the basic operating principle of the centrifugal pump?

Ans. Vanes or impellers rotating inside a close-fitting housing draw the liquid into the pump through a central inlet opening, and by means of centrifugal force the liquid is thrown outward through a discharge outlet at the periphery of the housing.

131

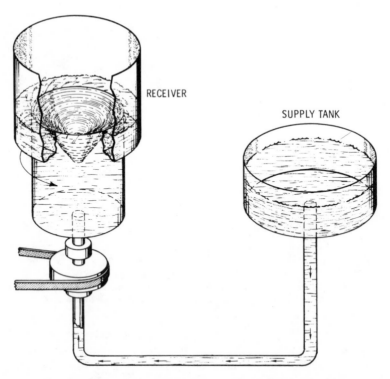

Fig. 2. Diagram of a basic centrifugal pump with supply tank and receiver.

Pump Having Straight Vanes

In the first practical centrifugal pump, the rotor was built with straight (radial) vanes (Fig. 3). The essential parts of a centrifugal pump are: (1) *impeller,* or rotating member; and (2) *case* or housing surrounding the rotating member.

In the centrifugal pump, water enters through the inlet opening in the center of the impeller, where it is set in rotation by the revolving blades of the impeller. The rotation of the water, in turn, generates centrifugal force, resulting in a pressure at the outer diameter of the impeller; when flow takes place, the water passes outward from the impeller at high velocity and pressure into the gradually expanding passageway of the housing and through the discharge connection to the point where it is used.

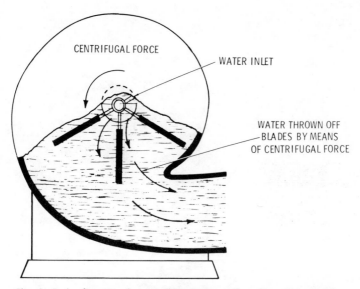

Fig. 3. Basic diagram of a centrifugal pump illustrating the principle involving centrifugal force.

Pump Having Curved Vanes

Curved vanes were first used by Appold in England in 1849. The cover and inner workings of a centrifugal pump having curved vanes and casing, commonly known as a volute pump, are illustrated in Fig. 4. An inlet pipe connection *A* to the cover directs the water to the "eye" *B* of the rotating impeller. The curved vanes *C* of the impeller direct the water from the "eye" to the discharge edge *D*, moving the water in a spiral-like path. As the impeller revolves, the water moves toward the discharge edge and then enters the volute-shaped passageway *E* where it is collected from around the impeller and directed to the discharge connection *F*.

The Volute

A *volute* is a curve that winds around and constantly recedes from a center point. It is a spiral that lies in a single plane (in contrast with a conical spiral). The volute is the shape of the periphery of the case or housing that surrounds the impeller of a volute-type centrifugal pump.

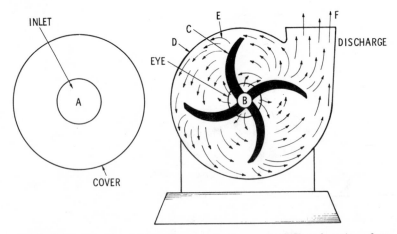

Fig. 4. Basic parts of a centrifugal pump showing cover (left) and section of a centrifugal pump, commonly termed a "volute" pump because of the shape of its housing.

The volute-type casings or housings form a progressively expanding passageway into which the impeller discharges the water. The volute-shaped passageway collects the water from the impeller and directs it to the discharge outlet.

The volute-shaped housing is proportioned to produce equal flow velocity around the circumference and to reduce gradually the velocity of the liquid as it flows from the impeller to the discharge outlet. The objective of this arrangement is to change velocity head to pressure head.

Ques. What is the advantage of the volute-type case or housing for the centrifugal pump?

Ans. It is proportioned to produce equal flow velocity around the circumference and to reduce gradually the velocity of the liquid as it flows from the impeller to the discharge outlet, thereby changing velocity head to pressure head.

Curvature of the Impeller Vanes

If the vanes could be curved to a shape that is mathematically correct, a different curve would be required for each change in working conditions; however, this is not practical because a large

134

number of patterns in stock would be required. A simple method for describing the curve of the vanes for impellers of the larger diameters and for lifts of 60 ft. or more, is shown in Fig. 5 as follows:

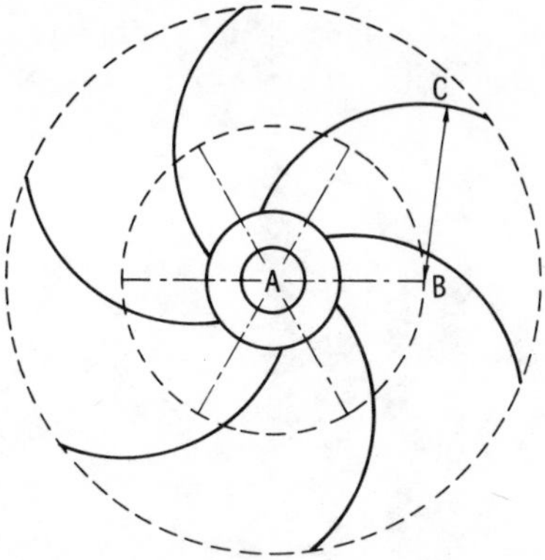

Fig. 5. Layout for the curved vanes of an impeller.

1. Divide the circle into a number of arms—six, for example.
2. Bisect each radius.
3. Using the point B as a center point and a radius BC, describe the curves which represent the working faces of the vanes.

$$BC = AB + \frac{1}{6} AB$$

BASIC CLASSIFICATION

The basic designs of centrifugal pumps correspond to the various principles of operations. Centrifugal pumps are designed chiefly with respect to:

1. Intake, as single-admission or double-admission.
2. Stage operation, as single-stage or multistage.
3. Output, as large volume (low-head), medium-volume (medium-head), and small-volume (high-head).
4. Impeller, as type of vanes, number of blades, housing, etc.

Single-Stage Pump

This type of pump is adapted to installations which pump against low to moderate heads. The head generated by a single impeller is

135

a function of its tangential speed. It is possible and, in some instances, practical to generate as much as 1000 ft. of head with a single-stage impeller, but for heads that exceed 250 to 300 ft., multistage pumps are generally used. Single-admission pumps are made in one or more stages, and the double-admission pumps may be either single-stage or multistage (Fig. 6).

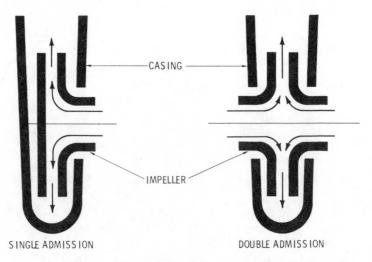

SINGLE ADMISSION   DOUBLE ADMISSION

Fig. 6. Single-admission (left) and double-admission (right) types of impeller for single-stage centrifugal pumps, illustrating flow path of the liquid.

The chief disadvantage of the single-admission pump is that the head at which it can pump effectively is limited. The double-admission single-stage pump is adapted to the elevation of large quantities of water to moderate heights. Another advantage of the double-admission type of pump is that the impeller is balanced hydraulically in an axial direction, because the thrust from one admission stream is counteracted by the thrust from the other admission stream.

Multistage Pump

The multistage centrifugal pump is essentially a high-head or high-pressure pump; it consists of two or more stages, depending on the size of head that it is to pump against. Each stage is essentially a

136

separate pump; however, they are located in the same housing and the impellers are attached to the same shaft. As many as eight stages may be found in a single housing.

The initial or first stage receives the water directly from the source through the admission pipe, builds the pressure up to the correct single-stage pressure, and passes it onward to the succeeding stage. In each succeeding stage, the pressure is increased or built up until the water is delivered from the final stage at the pressure and volume

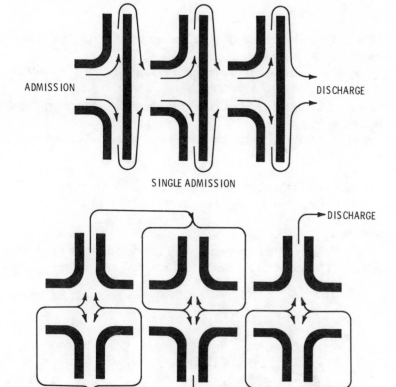

Fig. 7. Flow path of liquid from admission to discharge for single-admission (upper) and double-admission (lower) types of impellers in multi-stage pumps.

that the pump is designed to deliver. Water flow in single-admission and double-admission multistage pumps is illustrated in Fig. 7.

Ques. The single-stage pump is adapted for what type of installation?

Ans. It is adapted to installations pumping against low to moderate heads. In some instances, it may pump against as much as 1000 ft. of head, but multistage pumps are generally used for heads that exceed 250 to 300 feet.

Ques. What is the chief disadvantage of the single-admission pump?

Ans. The head at which it can pump against effectively is limited.

Ques. What is the chief advantage of the double-admission single-stage pump?

Ans. It is adapted to the elevation of large quantities of water to moderate heights.

Ques. What is the chief advantage of the multistage pump?

Ans. It is essentially a high-head or high-pressure pump.

Impellers

The efficiency of a centrifugal pump is determined by the type of impeller. The vanes and other details are designed to meet a given

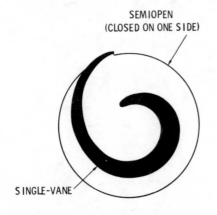

SEMIOPEN
(CLOSED ON ONE SIDE)

SINGLE-VANE

Fig. 8. A single-vane semiopen impeller.

138

set of operating conditions. The number of vanes may vary from one to eight, or more, depending on the type of service, size, etc.

A single-vane *semiopen* impeller is illustrated in Fig. 8. This type of vane is adapted to special types of industrial pumping problems which require a rugged pump for handling liquids containing fibrous materials and some solids, sediment, or other foreign materials in suspension.

The *open* type of vane is suited for liquids that contain no foreign matter or material which may lodge between the impeller and the stationary side plates. Liquids containing some solids, such as those found in sewage or drainage where there is a limited quantity of sand or grit, may be handled by the "open" type of vane.

In addition to the *open* and *semiopen* types of impellers, the *enclosed* or "shrouded" type of impeller may be used (Fig. 9), depend-

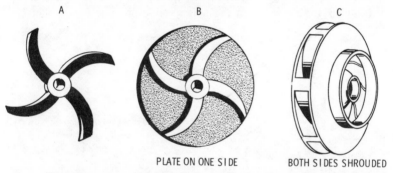

PLATE ON ONE SIDE   BOTH SIDES SHROUDED

Fig. 9. Three types of impellers (A) Open; (B) Semiopen; and (C) Enclosed.

ing on the service, desired efficiency, and cost. The enclosed type of impeller is designed for various types of applications. The shape and the number of vanes are governed by the conditions of service. It is more efficient, but its initial cost is also higher. Shrouded impellers do not require wearing plates. The enclosed impeller reduces wear to a minimum, assures full-capacity operation with initially high efficiency for a prolonged period of time, and does not clog, because it does not depend on close operating clearances.

Ques. What conditions require a single-vane "semiopen" impeller?

Ans. It is adapted to special types of industrial situations which require a rugged pump for handling liquids that contain fibrous materials and some solids, sediment, or other foreign materials in suspension.

Ques. When is the "open" type of impeller used?

Ans. For liquids that contain no foreign matter which may lodge between the impeller and the stationary side plates.

Ques. When is the "enclosed" or shrouded impeller used?

Ans. It is designed for various applications. The shape and the number of vanes are governed by the service conditions. It is more efficient, but its initial cost is higher, than either of the other two types of impellers.

Flow

The *axial-flow* type of impeller (Fig. 10) is used to obtain a flow of liquid in the direction of the axis of rotation. These propeller-type

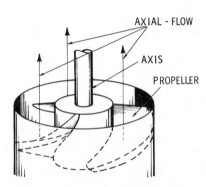

Fig. 10. Propeller-type impeller used to obtain axial flow.

impellers are designed to handle a large quantity of water at no lift and at low head in services such as drainage, irrigation, excavation, drainage, sewage, etc. The pumping element must be submerged at all times. This type of pump is not suitable for pumping that involves a lift.

The *mixed-flow* type of impeller (Fig. 11) is used to handle a large quantity of water at low head. High-capacity low-head pumps are designed on the mixed-flow principle to increase the rotative speeds, reduce the size and bulk of the pump, and to increase efficiency.

MIXED-FLOW

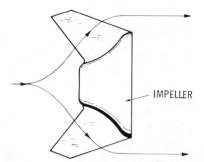

Fig. 11. Mixed-flow type of impeller.

IMPELLER

Balancing

The centrifugal pump is inherently an unbalanced machine. These pumps are subject to end thrust, which means that some method must be devised to counteract this load. In a single-admission type of impeller, an unbalanced hydraulic thrust is directed axially toward the admission side, because the vacuum in the admission side causes atmospheric pressure to produce a thrust on the impeller. Various methods of balancing have been tried as: (1) *natural balancing,* as by opposing impellers; and (2) *mechanical balancing,* as by a balancing disk, etc.

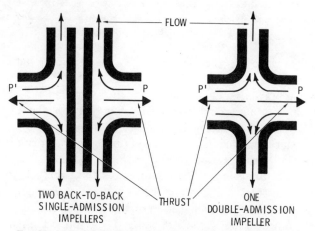

FLOW

P'   P

P'   P

TWO BACK-TO-BACK
SINGLE-ADMISSION
IMPELLERS

THRUST

ONE
DOUBLE-ADMISSION
IMPELLER

Fig. 12. Natural balancing achieved in single-stage pumps by means of two back-to-back single-admission types of impellers (left) and one double-admission type of impeller (right).

141

Natural Balancing—This method of balancing is generally used in double-admission single-stage pumps and in single- and double-admission multistage pumps. The diagrams in Fig. 12 illustrate back-to-back single-admission impellers and a double-admission impeller. In the diagrams the two thrusts P and P' act in axial directions and oppose each other.

The opposing-impellers method is applied to multistage pumps by various impeller arrangements. The three-stage pump arrangement (Fig. 13) consists of a central double-admission impeller and two

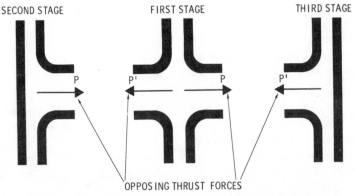

SECOND STAGE   FIRST STAGE   THIRD STAGE

OPPOSING THRUST FORCES

Fig. 13. Natural balancing achieved in a three-stage pump by means of two opposed single-admission types of impellers (left) and (right) and one double-admission type of impeller (center).

opposing single-admission end impellers. The arrows indicate the opposing thrusts.

Opposing-impellers balancing in the five-stage pump (Fig. 14) consists of a central double-admission impeller for the first stage and two pairs of opposing back-to-back impellers for the second and third stages and for the fourth and fifth stages. The method is also illustrated in the six-stage pump in Fig. 15.

Mechanical Balancing—The liquid enters through the eye of the impeller in an axial direction and leaves in a radial direction, thereby creating an end thrust which also results from the fact that the liquid in the clearance spaces is under pressure. These forces are not present in open impellers, since there are no shrouds for the forces to act upon.

142

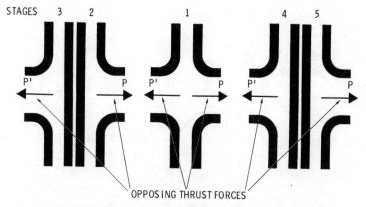

Fig. 14. Natural balancing achieved in a five-stage pump by means of an assembly of two pairs of opposed single-admission back-to-back types of impellers (left) and (right) and one double-admission type of impeller (center).

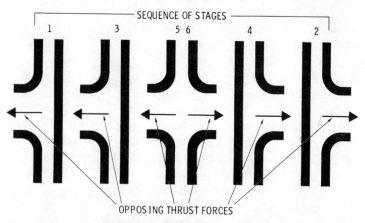

Fig. 15. Natural balancing achieved in a six-stage centrifugal pump by means of an assembly of four single-admission types of impellers (left) and (right) and one double-admission type of impeller (center).

In a single-admission enclosed-impeller pump (Fig. 16), the liquid from the housing, being under pressure, leaks backward through the clearance spaces A and D, past the sealing rings C and B, to the inlet. The impeller is usually cored in the rear shroud to permit

143

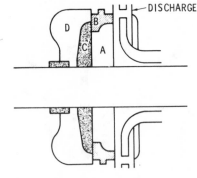

Fig. 16. Illustrating mechanical balancing in a centrifgual pump by means of a balancing disk.

the accumulating leakage to pass onward to the inlet without building up a pressure there. Therefore, forces on the two shrouds are equal to the pressure acting on the shroud areas.

Since there is a difference in pressure intensity (highest at the rim of the impeller, lowest at the sealing rings) the pressure is variable. The pressure at the holes cored through the rear shroud is not quite the same as that in the inlet chamber; therefore, the forces on the two shrouds are different. The resultant force is usually greater in clearance space D than in space A, so the resultant force is toward the inlet end of the pump.

Since normal operating wear increases the clearances in the sealing rings, the forces are changed and their proportions are changed, the end thrust increasing with wear. To balance this wear as nearly as possible, engineers have changed the diameter at which the sealing ring B (see Fig. 16) is placed, increasing the diameter to reduce the area on which the high-pressure liquid acts. Thus, if this ring were moved outward to the rim of the impeller, the force on the rear shroud could be reduced to change the resultant end thrust to the opposite direction or away from the admission.

To provide the pump with a minimum of end thrust during its useful life, the ring is placed outward at a distance far enough to reverse the thrust while the pump is new and while the clearances in the sealing rings are small. As these clearances increase with use, the thrust is reduced gradually, and finally reverses itself near the admission end. The proportions are so fixed that by the time the thrust becomes large enough to cause an undue load on the thrust bearing on the shaft, leakage through the increased clearance spaces is sufficient to affect seriously the efficiency of the pump. Then, the clearance rings can be replaced at a small cost to restore the pump to its original condition.

As previously explained, the thrust tendency is toward the admission side of the pump. The objective of the *balancing disk* method is to balance this thrust by providing a countering pressure in the opposite direction, which is maintained automatically in proper proportions against the balancing disk.

The balancing disk C (see Fig. 16) is keyed to the shaft behind the last-stage impeller and runs with a small clearance between it and the balance seat B. While in operation, the pump creates a pressure in space A that is slightly lower than the discharge pressure of the pump. This pressure acts against the balancing disk C to counterbalance the end thrust which is in the opposite direction. Since the pressure against the disk C is greater than that of the end thrust, the complete rotating element of the pump, together with disk C, is caused to move slightly, so that disk C is moved away from the seat B.

This action results in a small leakage into the balance chamber D, thereby reducing the pressure in space A, which causes the rotating element to return to a position where leakage past disk C and seat B enables the pressure in space A to balance the thrust—thrust and balance pressure are in equilibrium. The leakage between disk C and seat B is slight and not large enough to affect the efficiency or capacity of the pump for a considerable period of time.

CONSTRUCTION OF PUMPS

In its primitive form, the centrifugal pump was inefficient and was intended only for pumping large quantities of water at low heads. This type of pump is now highly developed, and many types of these pumps are available for a wide variety of service requirements.

Although the earlier pumps were adapted only to low heads, this has been overcome by connecting two or more units on a single shaft and operating them in series—passing the water through each unit in succession with the total head pumped against divided between the units (multistage pump).

The earlier multistage assemblies were bulky, because they consisted of separate units coupled together; however, several stages are now housed in a single casing or housing. The centrifugal pump usually gives best results when it is designed for specific operating conditions.

Casing or Housing

The casing is usually a two-piece casting split on a horizontal or diagonal plane with inlet and discharge openings cast integrally with the lower portion. Centrifugal pumps are either single-inlet or double-inlet types. The double-inlet type of pump is usually preferred, because the end thrusts are equalized when variations in pressure occur on either the discharge or inlet side.

The diagonally-split casing or housing (Fig. 17) permits easy removal of internal parts. The discharge and suction piping need not be disturbed.

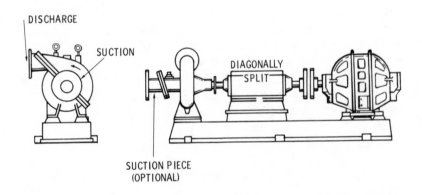

DISCHARGE

SUCTION

DIAGONALLY
SPLIT

SUCTION PIECE
(OPTIONAL)

Courtesy Buffalo Forge Company

Fig. 17. Cutaway view of a paper-stock centrifugal pump. The diagonally-split casing permits easy removal of the interior parts without disturbing the discharge or the suction piping.

The offset-volute design of casing is shown in Fig. 18. This type of casing also features top centerline discharge, self-venting and back pull-out.

Courtesy Buffalo Forge Company

Fig. 18. An offset-volute design of casing (left) and cover (right). The casing is designed for top centerline discharge, self-venting, and back pull-out.

Impeller

Impeller design varies widely to meet a wide variety of service conditions. The selection of the proper type of impeller is of prime importance in obtaining satisfactory and economical pump operation.

A high degree of efficiency can be obtained with the open-type impeller (Fig. 19) under certain conditions by carefully proportioning the curvature of the blades and by reducing the side clearances to a minimum with accurate machining of impeller edges and side plates. The open-type impeller is often used to handle large quantities of water at low heads, such as those encountered in irrigation, drainage, storage of water, and circulating of water through condensers.

The enclosed-type impeller (see Fig. 19) is generally considered to be a more efficient impeller. The vanes are cast integrally on both

147

Fig. 19. Open-type (left) and enclosed-type (right) impellers.

sides and are designed to prevent packing of fibrous materials between stationary covers and the rotating impeller.

An enclosed-type double-inlet impeller and wearing ring are shown in Fig. 20. The impeller is cast in a single piece of bronze, although

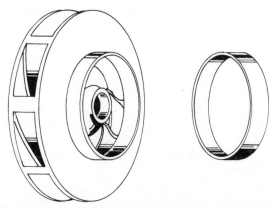

Fig. 20. Enclosed-type double-inlet impeller and wearing ring. Some liquids require that the impeller be made of special metals, such as chrome, monel, nickel, or a suitable alloy.

some liquids require that the impeller be made of chrome, monel, nickel, or a suitable alloy.

Stuffing-Box Assembly

The assembly shown in Fig. 21 is equipped with a five-ring packing and seal cage. The seal cage is split and glass-filled with *Teflon* material that is resistant to corrosion and heat. Mechanical seals can be used, and they are available in materials suitable for corrosive and noncorrosive applications.

Courtesy Buffalo Forge Company

Fig. 21. Stuffing-box assembly for a centrifugal pump.

Courtesy Buffalo Forge Company

Fig. 22. Bearings for a centrifugal pump. The outboard thrust bearing is a double-row deep-grooved ball bearing, and the inboard guide bearing is a single-row deep-grooved ball bearing.

Bearings and Housings

Most pumps are equipped with ball bearings (Fig. 22). Typical construction consists of a single-row deep-grooved ball bearing of ample size to withstand axial and radial loads. The bearing housing may be of the rotating type, so that the entire rotating element can be removed from the pump without disturbing the alignment or exposing the bearings to water or dirt. The bearing housing may be positioned by means of dowel pins in the lower portion of the casing and securely clamped by covers split on the same plane as the pump casing. Then the entire bearing can be removed from the shaft without damage by using the sleeve nut as a puller. Single ball bearings are an exception—most pumps being provided with double ball bearings.

Shaft Asembly

The shaft (Fig. 23) is machined accurately to provide a precision fit for all parts, including the impeller and bearings. The shaft in most

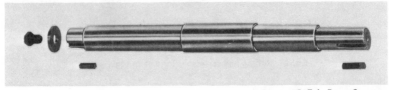

Courtesy Buffalo Forge Company

Fig. 23. A solid one-piece stainless-steel shaft for a centrifugal pump. The shaft is machined accurately to provide a precision fit for all parts.

centrifugal pumps must be protected against corrosive or abrasive action by the liquid pumped, such as cast bronze sleeves which fit against the impeller hub and are sealed by a thin gasket.

Drive

Centrifugal pumps are driven by direct drive or by a belt and pulley. A large subbase is usually provided for direct-drive connection to an engine or motor, and the two units are connected by a suitable coupling (Fig. 24). A disassembly of a dredging pump with a base or pedestal for belt-and-pulley drive is shown in Fig. 25.

Vertical pumps are generally made with a single inlet; since the weight of the impeller and shaft requires a thrust bearing, this weight

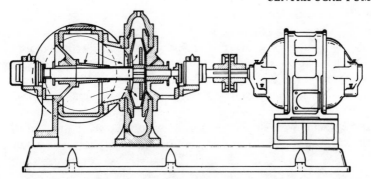

Fig. 24. Centrifugal pump and motor placed on a large subbase and connected by a suitable coupling for direct-drive.

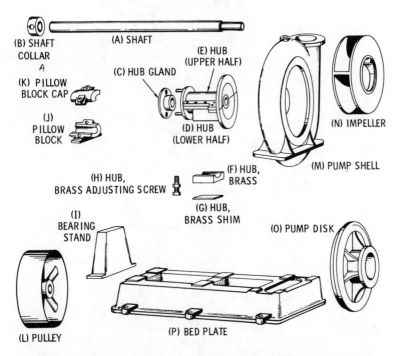

Fig. 25. Disassembly view showing parts of a belt-driven single-stage centrifugal pump. The parts shown are: (A) shaft; (B) shaft collar; (C) hub gland; (D) hub (lower half); (E) hub (upper half); (F) hub, brass; (G) hub, brass shim; (H) hub, brass adjusting screw; (I) bearing stand; (J) pillow block; (K) pillow-block cap; (L) pulley; (M) pump shell; (N) impeller; (O) pump disk; (P) bed plate.

can be proportioned to take care of the unbalanced pressure caused by the single-inlet characteristic. A vertical motor-mount dry-pit centrifugal pump is shown in Fig. 26. Gearing for vertical pumps is seldom advisable, except where bevel gears may be needed to transmit power from a horizontal shaft to a vertical shaft. A diagram showing dimensions of a horizontal angle-flow centrifugal pump is shown in Fig. 27. Prior to introduction of the angle-gear drive, most deep-well turbine pumps were driven by electric motors; however, this development has resulted in the use of more gasoline and diesel power units.

Courtesy Deming Division, Crane Co.

Fig. 26. Illustrating a vertical motor-mount type of centrifugal pump.

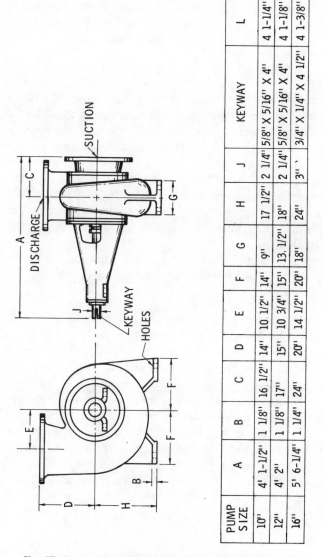

PUMP SIZE	A	B	C	D	E	F	G	H	J	KEYWAY	L
10"	4' 1-1/2"	1 1/8"	16. 1/2"	14"	10 1/2"	14"	9"	17 1/2"	2 1/4"	5/8" X 5/16" X 4"	4 1-1/4"
12"	4' 2"	1 1/8"	17"	15"	10 3/4"	15"	13. 1/2"	18"	2 1/4"	5/8" X 5/16" X 4"	4 1-1/8"
16"	5' 6-1/4"	1 1/4"	24"	20"	14 1/2"	20"	18"	24"	3"	3/4" X 1/4" X 4 1/2"	4 1-3/8"

Fig. 27. Horizontal angle-flow type of centrifugal pump with tabulated dimensions.

153

INSTALLATION

When the correct type of centrifugal pump has been selected for the service requirements, it must be installed properly to give satisfactory service and to be reasonably trouble-free. Several important factors must be considered for proper pump installation, depending on the size of the pump.

Location

The pump should be located where it is accessible and where there is adequate light for inspection of the packings and bearings. A centrifugal pump requires a relatively small degree of attention, but if it is inaccessible, it probably receives no attention until a breakdown requiring major repairs occurs.

The height of lift must also be considered. The lift is affected by temperature, height above sea level, and pipe friction, foot valve, and strainer losses. The elevation of the pump with respect to the liquid to be pumped should be at a height that is within the practical limit of the dynamic lift.

Piping also affects the location of the pump. The pump should be located so that the piping layout is as simple as possible.

Foundation

The foundation should be rugged enough to afford a permanent rigid support to the entire base area of the bed plate and to absorb normal strains and shocks that may be encountered in service. Concrete foundations are usually the most satisfactory.

Foundation bolts of the specified size should be located in the concrete according to drawings submitted prior to shipment of the unit. If the unit is mounted on steelwork or other type of structure, it should, if possible, be placed directly above the main members, beams, and walls, and it should be supported in such a way that the base plate cannot be distorted or the alignment disturbed by a yielding or springing action of the structure or the base plate. The bottom portion of the bed plate should be located approximately 3/4 in. above the top of the foundation to leave space for grouting.

Leveling

Pumps are usually shipped already mounted, and it is usually unnecessary to remove either the pump or the driving unit from the base plate for leveling. The unit should be placed above the foundation and supported by short strips of steel plate and wedges near the foundation bolts. A 3/4- to 2-in. space between the base plate and the foundation should be allowed for grouting. The *coupling bolts should be removed* before proceeding with leveling the unit and aligning the coupling halves.

When scraped clean, the projecting edges of the pads supporting the pump and motor feet can be used for leveling, employing a spirit level. If possible, the level should be placed on an exposed part of the pump shaft, sleeve, or planed surface of the casing.

The wedges underneath the base plate can be adjusted until the pump shaft is level, and the flanges of the suction and discharge nozzles are either vertical or horizontal, as required. At the same time, the pump should be placed at the specified height and location. Accurate alignment of the unbolted coupling halves between the pump and the driver shafts must be maintained while proceeding with the leveling of the pump and base.

To check the alignment of the pump and driver shafts, place a straightedge across the top and side of the coupling, checking the faces of the coupling halves for parallelism by means of a tapered thickness gauge or feeler gauges at the same time (Fig. 28).

If the coupling halves are true circles, have the same diameter, and have flat faces, true alignment exists when the distances between the faces are equal at all points and when a straightedge lies squarely

STRAIGHTEDGE

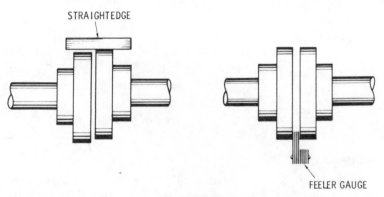

FEELER GAUGE

Fig. 28. Illustrating the use of a straightedge and feeler gauge to align the pump and driver shafts.

across the rim at all points. The test for parallelism is to place a straightedge across the top and side of the coupling, checking the faces of the coupling halves for parallelism by means of a tapered thickness gauge or feeler gauges at the same time.

Turbine Drive—If the pump is driven by a steam turbine, final alignment should be made with the driver at operating temperature. An allowance in the height of the turbine and shaft while cold should be made if this is impossible. Also, if the pump is to handle hot liquids, allowance should be made for elevation of the shaft when the pump expands. In any event, the alignment should be checked while the unit is at operating temperature and adjusted as required, before placing the pump in actual service. Application of heat to the steam and exhaust piping results in expansion; the turbine nozzles should not be subjected to piping strains in the installation.

Motor Drive—An allowance for heat is unnecessary for electric motors. The motor alone should be operated, if possible, before aligning the pump, so that the magnetic center of the rotor can be determined. If this is impossible, the rotor of the motor should be turned over and reversed to determine collar clearances, and then placed in the middle position for aligning. If the faces are not parallel, the thickness gauge, or feelers, varies at different points. If one coupling is higher than the other, the distance can be determined by means of the straightedge and feeler gauges.

Space Between Coupling Faces—The clearance between the faces of the couplings of the pin-and-buffer type and the ends of the shafts in other types of couplings should be set so that they cannot touch, rub, or exert a force on either the pump or the driver. The amount of clearance may vary with the size and type of coupling used. Sufficient clearance for the unhampered endwise movement of the shaft of the driving element to the limit of its bearing clearance should be allowed. On motor-driven units, the magnetic center of the motor determines the running position of the half-coupling of the motor. This can be checked by operating the motor while it is disconnected.

Grouting

The grouting process involves pouring a mixture of cement, sand, and water into the voids of the stone, brick, or concrete work either to provide a solid bearing or to fasten anchor bolts, dowels, etc.

The usual grouting mixture consists of one part cement, two parts sand and enough water to cause the mixture to flow freely underneath the bed plate.

A wooden form is built around the outside of the bed plate to contain the grout and to provide sufficient head for assuring a flow of the mixture beneath the entire head plate. The grout should be allowed to set for 48 hours; then the hold-down bolts should be tightened and the coupling halves rechecked.

Inlet Piping

In a new installation it is advisable to flush the inlet pipe with clear water before connecting it to the pump. Except for misalignment, most problems with individual centrifugal pump installations can be traced to faults in the inlet lines. It is extremely important to install the inlet piping correctly.

The diameter of the inlet piping should not be smaller than the inlet opening, and it should be as short and direct as possible. If a long inlet line cannot be avoided, the size of the piping should be increased. Air pockets and high spots in an inlet line invariably cause trouble. Preferably, there should be a continual rise, without high spots, from the source of supply to the pump.

When the supply liquid is at its lowest level, the end of the pipe should be submerged to a depth equal to four times its diameter (for large pipes). Smaller pipes should be submerged to a depth of 2 to 3 ft. After installation is completed, the inlet piping should be blanked off and tested hydrostatically for air leaks before the pump is operated.

A strainer should be attached to the end of the inlet pipe to prevent lodging of foreign material in the impellers. The clear and free opening of the strainer should be equal to three or four times the area of the inlet pipe. If the strainer is likely to become clogged frequently, the inlet pipe should be placed where it is accessible. A foot valve for convenience in priming may be necessary where the pump is subjected to intermittent service. The size and type of foot valve should be selected carefully to avoid friction loss through the valve.

Discharge Piping

The discharge piping (like the inlet piping) should also be as short and free of elbows as possible to reduce friction. Check valves

157

and gate valves should be placed near the pump. The check valve protects the casing of the pump from breakage caused by water hammer, and it prevents the pump operating in reverse if the driver should fail. The gate valve can be used to shut off the pump from the discharge piping when inspection or repair is necessary.

Pump Handling High-Temperature Liquids

Special types of multistage pumps are constructed for handling high-temperature liquids with a key and keyway on the feet and base of the lower one-half of the casing. One end of the pump is bolted securely, but the other end (on some units) is bolted with spring washers positioned underneath the nuts on the casing feet, permitting one end of the casing to move laterally as the casing expands. Some special types of hot-liquid multistage pumps are doweled at the inboard end, and other types are doweled at the thrust-bearing end, sometimes with the dowels placed crosswise; dowels at the opposite end, if used, are fitted parallel to the pump shaft—to allow the casing to expand at high temperatures.

When handling hot liquids, the nozzle flanges should be disconnected after the unit has been placed in service to determine whether the expansion is in the proper direction.

Jacket Piping—Multistage pumps use jacketed or separately cooled thrust bearings. If hot liquids are being handled, care must be taken to be certain that the jacket or oil-cooler water piping is connected.

Drain Piping—To determine whether the water is flowing and to regulate the amount of flow, it is good practice to pipe the discharge from the jacket or cooler into a funnel connected to a drain. All drain and drip connections should be piped to a point where leakage can be disposed of.

OPERATION

Before starting the operation of a centrifugal pump, the driver should be tested for its direction of rotation (Fig. 29), with the coupling halves disconnected. The arrow on the pump casing indicates the direction for rotation.

The ball bearings should be supplied with the grade of lubricant recommended by the pump manufacturer. Oil-lubricated bearings should be filled level with the overflow.

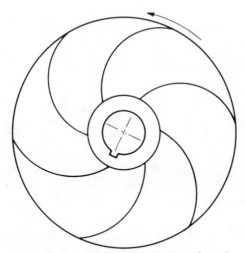

Fig. 29. Diagram indicating the direction of rotation
of the impeller.

The cooling water piping to the thrust-bearing housing also requires attention. Cooling water should not be used on bearings that
are warm to the hand only; use only sufficient water to keep the
lubricant at a safe working temperature.

Periodically, the water supply should be flushed freely to remove
particles of scale and similar particles which may stop the flow on a
throttled valve. Final inspection of all parts should be made carefully
before starting the pump; it should be possible to rotate the rotor by
hand.

Priming

A centrifugal pump should not be operated until it is filled with
water. If the pump is run without liquid, there is danger of damage
to liquid-lubricated internal parts. Some specially-constructed types
of centrifugal pumps are designed to be started dry; liquid from an
external source is used to seal the stuffing boxes and to lubricate the
impeller wearing rings and shaft sleeves in the same manner as with
a stuffing-box packing.

Ejector Method—As shown in the diagram (Fig. 30), the pump is
equipped with a discharge valve and a steam ejector. To prime, the

159

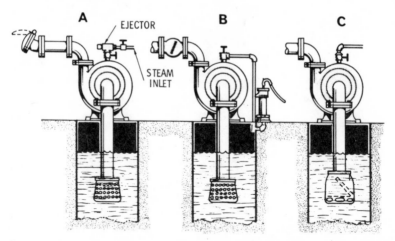

Fig. 30. Three methods of priming centrifugal pumps: (A) Ejector; (B) Lift-type pump; and (C) Foot valve with top discharge.

discharge valve is closed after the steam-inlet valve has been opened; then the valve between the ejector and the pump is opened, the air in the pump and pipes is exhausted, and the water is drawn into them. Complete priming is indicated by water issuing from the ejector.

The ejector is shut off by first closing the valve between the ejector and the pump, and then closing the steam-inlet valve. If it is inconvenient to place the ejector near the pump, the air pipe can be extended, using an air pipe that is slightly larger than when the ejector is placed near the pump.

Hand-Type Lift Pump (or Powered Air Pump) Method—A check valve can be used instead of the discharge valve, and either a hand-type old-fashioned lift pump (see Fig. 30) or a powered air pump can be used to substitute for the steam ejector. A valve should be placed in the air pipe. The valve should be closed before starting. In the older installations, the kitchen-type lift pumps were often used for priming. Sometimes the kitchen-type pumps themselves require a small quantity of water to water-seal them, making them an effective air pump.

Foot-Valve and Top-Discharge Method—When the foot valve is used (see Fig. 30), the centrifugal pump and inlet pipe are filled with water through the discharge or top portion of the pump from either a small supply tank or a hand-type pump. If the inlet pipe is long, at least 5 ft. of discharge head on the pump is required to prevent the water being thrown out before the water in the inlet line has begun to move, causing failure in starting. When check or discharge valves are used, a vacuum gauge placed on the air priming pump at the head of the well or pit indicates that the pump is primed. A steam-type air ejector may be operated with water if 30-40 lb. of water pressure is available; however, a special type of ejector is required.

For automatic priming, a pressure regulator can be connected into the discharge line. The regulator automatically starts an air pump if the main pump loses its prime; and it stops the priming pump when the priming action is completed.

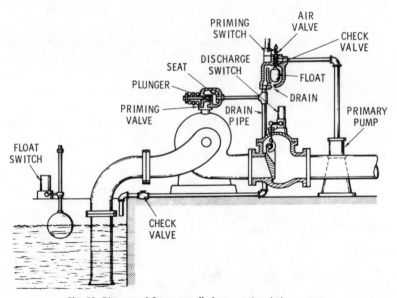

Fig. 31. Diagram of float-controlled automatic priming system.

In the float-controlled automatic priming system (Fig. 31), a priming valve is connected between the top of the casing of the pump and a float-controlled air valve. The air valve is connected to a priming switch with the contacts in series with the control circuit of the main motor starter. A check valve in the discharge line operates a switch that shunts the priming switch. In actual operation,

161

the priming valve and air valve are in the indicated positions so long as the pump is not primed. When the float switch closes, the priming pump is started; it continues in operation until the main pump is primed and until the water is high enough in the float chamber to close the priming switch. The closing of the priming switch starts the main pump, and the priming pump is stopped by a contact that is opened when the pump motor control circuit is energized. When the main pump is running, the discharge check valve is held open, and the contacts on its switch are closed to complete a holding circuit for the pump motor contactor around the priming switch. This switch permits the priming switch to open, without shutting down the pump. A number of small holes in the priming valve plunger permit air to pass freely during the priming operation. These small holes are so proportioned that the pressure developed by the pump forces the plunger to its seat, thereby cutting off communication to the priming pump when priming has been completed and the pump has started. When the priming line is sealed, the water drains from the float chamber, and the priming switch opens; but the pump motor contactor is held closed by a circuit through the discharge-valve switch. When the float switch opens, the main pump shuts down. It should be noted that the float switch starts the priming pump when it closes, and it stops the centrifugal pump when it opens.

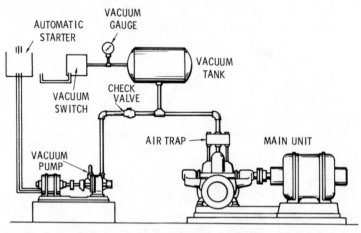

Fig. 32. Automatic priming system in which a vacuum tank is used as a reserve to keep the main pump primed.

Another type of automatic priming system in which a vacuum tank is used as a reserve to keep the main pump primed is shown in Fig. 32. This system consists of a motor-driven air pump and a vacuum tank connected between the section of the air pump and the priming connections on the centrifugal pump. The air tank serves as a reserve on the system, so that the vacuum producer needs starting only intermittently. A vacuum switch starts and stops the vacuum producer at the predetermined limits of vacuum. An air trap in the line between the pump to be primed and the vacuum tank prevents water rising into the vacuum system after the pump is primed. Air is drawn from the pump suction chamber whether the pump is idle, under vacuum, or in operation. The priming pipes and air-trap valves are under vacuum to insure that the centrifugal pump remains primed at all times. Modifications of this type of system are used for pumps that handle sewage, paper stock, sludge, or other liquids that carry solids in suspension. Other diagrams of piping for priming are shown in Fig. 33.

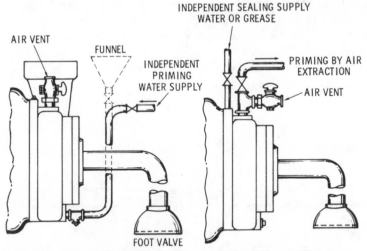

Fig. 33. Diagrams of piping for priming systems using independent priming water supply (left) and priming by extraction of air (right).

Starting the Pump

Prior to starting a pump having oil-lubricated bearings, the rotor should be turned several times, either by hand or by momentarily

163

operating the starting switch (with the pump filled with water), if the procedure does not overload the motor. This starts a flow of oil to the bearing surfaces. The pump can be operated for a few minutes with the discharge valve closed without overheating or damage to the pump.

Various items should be checked before starting the pump. On some installations an extended trial run is necessary. The vent valves should be kept open to relieve pocketed air in the pump and system during these trials. This circulation of water prevents overheating the pump.

Then, to cut the pump into the lines, close the vent valves and open the discharge valve slowly. The pump is started with the discharge valve closed, because the pump operates at only 35-50 percent of full load when the discharge valve is closed. If the liquid on the upper side of the discharge check valve is under sufficient head, the pump can be started with the discharge valve in open position.

Gland packing should not be too tight, because heat may cause it to expand, thereby burning out the packing and scoring the shaft. A slight leakage is desirable at first; then the packing can be tightened after it has been warmed and worn. A slight leakage also indicates that the water seal is effective without undue binding, keeping the gland and shaft cool.

Specific types of packings are required for high temperatures and for some liquids (Fig. 34). Soft asbestos graphite-type packing is recommended for either hot or cold water. Rapid wear of the sleeves

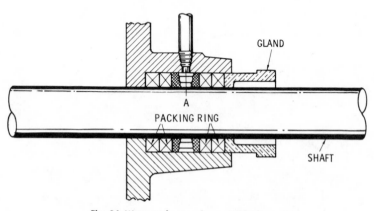

Fig. 34. Water-seal cage of a centrifugal pump.

may result if flax packing or metallic packing is used on centrifugal pumps with bronze shaft sleeves. Each ring of packing should be inserted separately and pushed into the stuffing box as far as the gland permits. The split openings of the successive packing rings should be positioned at 90° intervals.

As aforementioned, the centrifugal pump should not be operated for long periods at low capacity because of the possibility of overheating. However, a pump may be operated safely at low capacity if a permanent by-pass from the discharge to the inlet (equal to one-fifth the size of the discharge pipe) is installed.

To start a hot-condensate pump, open the inlet and discharge valves on the independent stuffing box seals before operating. Usually, the air-extraction apparatus is in service before the hot-condensate pump is started, and the main turbine is heated at the same time. This provides an accumulation of water in the hot well; if allowed to collect above the level of the hot-condensate gauge glass, the steam jets or other extracting apparatus do not entrain water, which renders them inoperative. As soon as a supply of condensate begins flowing to the hot well, the pump can be started and the air valves on top of the pump opened as the pump reaches full speed. Then the air valves should be closed.

Except for the bearings and the glands, a centrifugal pump does not require attention once it is operating properly. These pumps should operate for long periods of time without attention other than to observe that there is a drip of liquid from the glands, that the proper oil is supplied the bearings, and that the oil is changed at regular intervals.

Stopping the Pump

Normally, when there is a check valve near the pump in the discharge line, the pump is shut down by stopping the motor, securing it until needed again by closing the valves in the following order:

1. Discharge.
2. Inlet.
3. Cooling water supply.
4. At all points connecting to the system.

165

Usually, when the pump is stopped in this manner, the discharge gate valve need not be opened; however, in some installations, surges in the piping may impose heavy shocks on both the lines and the pump when the flow of water under high pressure is arrested. Then, it is good practice to first close the discharge gate valve, to eliminate shock entirely.

If a pump remains idle for some time after it is stopped, it gradually loses its priming, because the liquid drains through the glands. If it is necessary to keep the pump primed for emergency use, this should be kept in mind when the pump is stopped. It is not necessary to close the inlet and discharge valves, because the glands may leak due to sustained pressure on a stationary shaft. The gland nuts should not be tightened unless preparation is made to loosen them again when starting the pump.

Abnormal Operating Conditions

Centrifugal pumps should run smoothly and without vibration when they are operating properly. The bearings operate at a constant temperature which may be affected by the location of the units. This temperature may range as low as 100°F., but the operating temperature is usually maximum temperature at minimum flow, varying with pump capacity.

If a pump for some reason either does not contain liquid or becomes vapor bound, vibration occurs due to contact between the stationary and the rotating parts, and the pump may become overheated. Vapor may be blown from the glands and, in extreme instances, the thrust bearings may suddenly increase in temperature and damage result from the rotor being forced in a single direction.

If the pump is overheated because of a vaporized condition and the rotor has not seized, open all vents and prime or flood liquid into the pump. A low-temperature liquid should not be admitted suddenly to a heated pump, because fracture or distortion of its parts may result. An overheated pump should not be used unless an emergency exists—to save a boiler from damage, for example.

Vibration also may result from excessive wear on the pump rotor or in the pump bearings, which causes the pump and motor shafts to become misaligned. These should be corrected at the first opportunity. If a rotor has seized, it is necessary to dismantle it completely and to rectify the parts by filing, machining, etc.

TROUBLESHOOTING

Many difficulties may be experienced with centrifugal pumps. Location of these troubles and their causes are discussed here.

Reduced Capacity or Pressure and Failure to Deliver Water

When the capacity or pressure of the pump is reduced and the pump fails to deliver water, any of the following may be the cause:

1. Pump is not primed.
2. Low speed.
3. Total dynamic head is higher than the pump rating.
4. Lift is too high (normal lift is 15 ft.).
5. Foreign material is lodged in the impeller.
6. Opposite direction of rotation.
7. Excessive air in water.
8. Air leakage in inlet pipe or stuffing boxes.
9. Insufficient inlet pressure for vapor pressure of the liquid.
10. Mechanical defects, such as worn rings, damaged impeller, and defective casing gasket.
11. Foot valve is either too small or is restricted by trash.
12. Foot valve or inlet pipe is too shallow.

Loses Water After Starting

If the pump starts and then loses water, the cause may be:

1. Air leak in inlet pipe.
2. Lift too high (over 15 ft.).
3. Plugged water-seal pipe.
4. Excessive air or gases in water.

Pump Overloads Driver

If the driver is overloaded by the pump, check the following:

1. Speed too high.
2. Total dynamic head lower than pump rating—pumping too much water.
3. Specific gravity and viscosity of pumped liquid different from pump rating.
4. Mechanical defects.

Pump Vibrates

The causes of pump vibration may be:

1. Misalignment.
2. Foundation not rigid enough.
3. Foreign material causes impeller unbalance.
4. Mechanical defects, such as bent shaft, rotating element rubbing against a stationary element, and worn bearings.

Centrifugal pumps can be operated only in one direction. The arrow on the casing indicates the direction of rotation. During pump operation, the stuffing boxes and bearings should be inspected occasionally. The pump should be disassembled, cleaned, and oiled if it is to be idle for a long period of time. If the pump is to be exposed to freezing temperatures, it should be drained immediately after stopping.

Pointers on Pump Operation

Various abnormal conditions may occur during pump operations. Some suggestions are:

1. If the pump discharges a small quantity of water during the first few revolutions and then churns and fails to discharge more water, air is probably still in the pump and piping or the lift may be too great; or check for a leaky pipe, a long inlet pipe, and lack of sufficient head.
2. If the pump produces a full stream of water at first and then fails, the cause is failure of the water supply or the water level receding below the lift limit. This can be determined by placing a vacuum gauge on the inlet elbow of the pump. This problem can be remedied by lowering the pump to reduce the lift.
3. If the pump delivers a full stream of water at the surface or pump level, but fails at a higher discharge point, the pump speed is too low.
4. If the pump delivers a full stream of water at first and the discharge decreases slowly until no water is delivered, an air leak at the packing gland is the cause.

5. If a full stream of water is delivered for a few hours and then fails, the inlet pipe or the impeller is obstructed if the flow from the water supply is unchanged.

6. If heavy vibration occurs while the pump is in operation, the shaft has been sprung, the pump is out of alignment, or an obstruction has lodged in one side of the impeller.

7. If the bearings become hot, the belt is unnecessarily tight, the bearings lack oil, or there is an end thrust.

8. If hot liquids are to be pumped, the lift should be as small as possible, because the boiling point of the liquid is lowered under vacuum and the consequent loss of priming is due to presence of vapor.

9. If the water is discharged into a sump or tank near the end of the inlet pipe, there is great danger of entraining air into the inlet pipe.

10. If a pump is speeded up to increase capacity beyond its maximum rating, a waste of power results.

11. If a pump remains idle for some time, its rotor should be rotated by hand once each week—for long periods of time it should be taken apart, cleaned, and oiled.

MAINTENANCE AND REPAIR

Liberal clearances are provided between the rotating and the stationary pump parts to allow for small machining variations and for the expansion of the casing and rotor when they become heated. Stationary diaphragms, wearing rings, return channels, etc., which are located in the casing or other stationary part are slightly smaller in diameter than the bore of the casing, which is machined with a 1/32-in. gasket between the flanges. When the flange nuts are tightened, the casing must not bind on the stationary parts. Operating clearances, such as those at the wearing rings, depend on the actual location of the part, the type of material, and the span of the bearing.

Lateral End Clearances

Lateral movement between the rotor and stator parts is necessary for mechanical and hydraulic considerations and for expansion variations between the casing and rotor. End movement is limited to 1/64

169

in. in small pumps and certain other types of pumps, and it may be as much as 1/2 in. on larger units and on those handling hot liquids. On pumps handling cold liquids, the clearance is divided equally when the thrust bearing is secured in position and the impellers are centralized. The recommendations of the pump manufacturer should be consulted for the designed lateral clearances before proceeding with an important field assembly.

Parts Renewals

Since the pump casings are made from castings, it is sometimes necessary to favor variations in longitudinal dimensions on the casings by making assembly floor adjustments to the rotor, so that designed lateral clearances can be preserved and so that the impellers can be placed in their correct positions with respect to the diaphragms, diffusers, and return channels.

When a rotor with its diffusers is returned to the factory for repair, the repaired rotor can be placed in the pump with no adjustment if it is still possible to calibrate dimensions on the worn parts. When it is impossible to obtain complete details on the used parts, replacement parts are made to standard dimensions.

When the assembled rotor with stage pieces, etc., is placed in the lower portion of the casing, the total lateral clearance should be checked. With the thrust bearing assembled and the shaft in position, the total clearance should be divided properly and the impellers centered in their volutes. Final adjustments are made by manipulation of the shaft nuts.

The casing flange gaskets should be replaced with the same type and thickness of material as the original gaskets. The inner edge of the gasket must be trimmed accurately along the edge of the bore of the stuffing box. The edges must be trimmed squarely and neatly at all points where the gasket abuts on the outer diameter and sides of the stationary parts between the stages, overlapping sufficiently for the upper portion of the casing to press the edges of the gasket against the stator parts while the casing is being tightened and thereby ensuring proper sealing between the stages. In the trimming operation the gasket should first be cemented to the lower portion of the casing with shellac. Then a razor blade can be used to cut the gasket edges squarely, overlapping at the same time.

170

Pointers on Assembly

Unnecessary force should not be used in tightening the impeller and shaft sleeve nuts; bending of the shaft may result, and the concentricity of the rotor parts operating in close clearances with the stator parts may be destroyed, causing rubbing and vibration.

Locking Screws—A dial test indicator should be used to determine whether the shaft has been bent when securing the safety-type locking screws.

Design considerations require that all parts be mounted on the shaft in their original order. Opposed impellers are both right-hand and left-hand types in the same casing. Diaphragms, wearing rings, and stage bushings are individually fitted, and their sealing flanges between the stages are checked for each location. Stage bushings with stop pieces are not interchangeable with each other, because the stop pieces may locate at various positions.

All stationary parts assembled on the rotor, such as stuffing box bushings, diaphragms, etc., possess stops that consist of either individual pins or flange halves in the lower casing only, to prevent turning. These parts must be in position when lowering the rotor into the casing, so that all stops are in their respective recesses in the lower casing; otherwise, the upper casing may foul improperly positioned parts during the mounting procedure.

Deep-Well Pump Adjustments—Before operating these pumps, the impeller or impellers must be adjusted to their correct operating positions by either raising or lowering the shaft by means of the adjuster nut provided for the purpose. The shaft is raised to its uppermost position by turning the adjusting nut downward. Measure the distance the shaft has been raised above its lowest position, and then back off the adjusting nut until the shaft has been lowered one-third the total distance that it was raised. Lock the nut in position with the key, setscrew, or lock nut provided. With either a key or a setscrew, it is usually necessary to turn the adjusting nut until it is possible to insert the key or setscrew in place through both the adjusting nut and motor clutch.

Install Increaser on Discharge Line—Hydraulic losses can be reduced by installation of an increaser on the discharge line. The hookup with the check and discharge valves is shown in Fig. 35. The discharge line should be selected with reference to friction losses, and

171

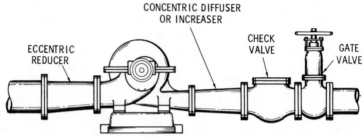

Fig. 35. Installation of a diffuser or increaser on the discharge line.

it should never be smaller than the pump discharge outlet—preferably, one to two sizes larger. The pump should not be used to support heavy inlet or discharge piping. Pipes or fittings should not be forced into position with the flange bolts, because the pump alignment may be disturbed. Independent supports should be provided for all piping. When piping is subjected to temperature changes, expansion and contraction should not exert a strain on the pump casing. In hotels, apartment building, hospitals, etc., where noise is objectionable, the discharge pipe should not be attached directly to the steel structural work, hollow walls, etc., because vibration may be transmitted to the building. Preferably, the discharge line should not be connected to the pump discharge outlet through a flexible connection.

CALCULATIONS

Experience has been an important factor in determining the design of centrifugal impellers. Fundamentally, the centrifugal pump adds energy in the form of velocity to an already flowing liquid; pressure is not added in the usual sense of the word. Kinetic energy is involved in all basic considerations of the centrifugal pump.

The design of the impeller of a centrifugal pump is based ultimately on the performance of other impellers. The general effect of altering certain dimensions is a result of modifying or changing the design of impellers that have been tested.

Calculations applicable to centrifugal pumps are based on the impeller diagram (Fig. 36) in which the following symbols are used:

V_2 is tangential velocity at outer periphery

V_1 is tangential velocity at inner periphery

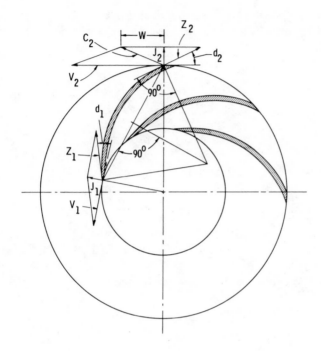

Fig. 36. Diagram of impeller, illustrating basis of calculations.

Z_2 is relative velocity of water at outlet

Z_1 is relative velocity of water at inlet

C_2 is absolute velocity of water at outlet

J_2 is radial velocity of water at outlet

J_1 is radial velocity of water at inlet

W is tangential velocity of water at outlet

a_2 is outlet angle of impeller

a_1 is inlet angle of impeller

Velocity of Impeller

In the diagram (see Fig. 36), water enters the impeller inlet with a radial velocity J_1, and it leaves the impeller at an absolute velocity C_2. The inner peripheral velocity V_1 and the outer peripheral velocity

173

V_2 are in *feet per second*. If the theoretical head *H*, in feet, represents the head against which the pump delivers water (with no losses) then:

$$H = \frac{(V_2)^2}{2g} ; \quad \text{or } V_2 = 2gH$$

in which;

g is the force of gravity = 32.2 ft. per second

If the head *H* against which the pump must work and the diameter of the impeller are known, the speed of the pump can be calculated by the above formulas.

Problem: If a pump with an impeller diameter of 10¾ in. is required to pump against a head of 100 ft., what is the required speed of the pump?

Solution: By substituting in the above formula:

$$V_2 = \sqrt{2gH}$$

$$= \sqrt{2 \times 32.2 \times 100}$$

$$= 80.4 \text{ ft. per second}$$

Since the tangential velocity V_2 at the outer periphery of the impeller is 80.4 ft. per second, this is equal to (80.4 × 60), or 4824 ft. per minute and since the circumference (πd) of a 10¾-in. diameter impeller is (3.14 × 10¾), or 33.8 in., which is equal to 2.8 ft., the impeller must rotate at a speed of 4824 ft. per minute; this is equal to (4824 ÷ 2.8), or 1722 revolutions per minute.

Total Hydraulic Load or Lift

As aforementioned, the lift is the vertical distance measured from the level of the water to be pumped to the center line of the pump inlet. If the water level is above the center line of the pump, the pump is operating under *inlet head*, or "negative" lift. Under conditions of negative lift, the inlet head must be subtracted from the sum of the remaining factors.

The *discharge head*, in contrast to the inlet head, is the vertical distance measured between the center line of the pump discharge opening and the level to which the water is elevated.

The loss of head due to friction in pipes and elbows must be considered. This loss can be obtained from Table 1. Other data for centrifugal pump calculations are given in Tables 2, 3, 4, 5, and 6.

Velocity Head

The equivalent distance, in feet, through which a liquid must fall to acquire the same velocity is called *velocity head*. The velocity head can be determined from the formula:

$$H_v = \frac{(V_2)^2}{2g} = \frac{(V_2)^2}{64.4}$$

in which;

$$V = \frac{0.408 \times \text{gal. per min.}}{D^2}$$

The following example is used to illustrate calculation of the total hydraulic head that a pump may work against, using gauge readings.

Problem: Assuming that the distance *A* (see Fig. 37) or vertical distance from the center line of the gauge connection in the inlet pipe to the center line of the pressure gauge is 2 ft.; the discharge pressure gauge reading is 40 lb,; the vacuum gauge reading is 15 in. (when discharging 1000 gal. of water minute); the discharge pipe is 6 in. in diameter (at gauge connection); and the inlet pipe is 8 in. in diameter (at gauge connection), calculate the total hydraulic load or lift.

Solution:

40-lb. pressure × 2.31 lb. per sq. in.　＝　92.40 ft.

15-in. vacuum (see Table 6)................　＝　17.01 ft.

distance *A* (see Fig. 37).....................　＝　2.00 ft.

velocity head in 6″ pipe minus velocity

head in 8″ pipe, or (1.99 − 0.63) ....　＝　1.36 ft.

total hydraulic load or lift....................　＝　112.77 ft.

Table 1. Loss of Head (in feet) Due to Friction in Pipes (Per 100 Ft. of 15-Yr.-Old Iron Pipe)

(For new and smooth iron pipe, use 0.71 of value shown in table)

Gallons per Minute	½" Pipe		¾" Pipe		1" Pipe		1¼" Pipe		1½" Pipe		2" Pipe		2½" Pipe		3" Pipe	
	Vel.	Fric.	Vel.	Fric.	Vel.	Fric.	Vel.	Fric.	Vel.	Fric.	Vel.	Fric.	Vel.	Fric.	Vel.	Fric.
1	1.05	2.1														
2	2.10	7.4	1.20	1.9												
3	3.16	15.8	1.80	4.1	1.12	1.26										
4	4.21	27.0	2.41	7.0	1.49	2.14	0.86	0.57	0.63	0.26						
5	5.26	41.0	3.01	10.5	1.86	3.25	1.07	0.84	0.79	0.39						
10	10.52	147.0	6.02	38.0	3.72	11.70	2.14	3.05	1.57	1.43	1.02	0.50	0.65	0.17	0.45	0.07
15			9.02	80.0	5.60	25.00	3.20	6.50	2.36	3.00	1.53	1.00	0.98	0.36	0.68	0.15
20			12.03	136.0	7.44	42.00	4.29	11.10	3.15	5.20	2.04	1.82	1.31	0.61	0.91	0.25
25					9.30	64.00	5.36	16.60	3.94	7.80	2.55	2.73	1.63	0.92	1.13	0.38
30					11.15	89.00	6.43	23.50	4.72	11.00	3.06	3.84	1.96	1.29	1.36	0.54
35					13.02	119.00	7.51	31.20	5.51	14.70	3.57	5.10	2.20	1.72	1.59	0.71
40					14.88	152.00	8.58	40.00	6.30	18.80	4.08	6.60	2.61	2.20	1.82	0.91
45							9.65	50.00	7.08	23.20	4.60	8.20	2.94	2.80	2.05	1.15
50							10.72	60.00	7.87	28.40	5.11	9.90	3.27	3.32	2.27	1.38
70							15.01	113.00	11.02	53.00	7.15	18.40	4.58	6.20	3.18	2.57
90									14.17	84.00	9.19	29.40	5.88	9.80	4.09	4.08
100									15.74	102.00	10.21	35.80	6.54	12.00	4.54	4.96
120									18.89	143.00	12.25	50.00	7.84	16.80	5.45	7.00
140									22.04	199.00	14.30	67.00	9.15	23.30	6.35	9.20
160											16.34	86.00	10.46	29.00	7.26	11.80
180											18.38	107.00	11.76	35.70	8.17	14.80
200											20.42	129.00	13.07	43.10	9.08	17.80
220											22.47	154.00	14.38	52.00	9.99	21.30
240											24.51	182.00	15.69	61.00	10.89	25.10
260											26.55	211.00	16.99	70.00	11.80	29.10
280													18.30	81.00	12.71	33.40
300													19.61	92.00	13.62	38.00

Table 1. Loss of Head (in feet) Due to Friction in Pipes (Per 100 Ft. of 15-Yr.-Old Iron Pipe)

(For new and smooth iron pipe, use 0.71 of value shown in table)

Gallons per Minute	4" Pipe Vel.	4" Fric.	5" Pipe Vel.	5" Fric.	6" Pipe Vel.	6" Fric.	8" Pipe Vel.	8" Fric.	10" Pipe Vel.	10" Fric.	12" Pipe Vel.	12" Fric.	14" Pipe Vel.	14" Fric.	15" Pipe Vel.	15" Fric.	16" Pipe Vel.	16" Fric.	20" Pipe Vel.	20" Fric.
40	1.02	0.22																		
45	1.17	0.28																		
50	1.28	0.34																		
70	1.79	0.63	1.14	0.21																
75	1.92	0.73	1.22	0.24																
100	2.55	1.23	1.63	0.39	1.14	0.14														
120	3.06	1.71	1.96	0.57	1.42	0.25														
125	3.19	1.86	2.04	0.64	1.48	0.28														
150	3.84	2.55	2.45	0.88	1.71	0.32														
175	4.45	3.36	2.86	1.18	2.00	0.48														
200	5.11	4.37	3.27	1.48	2.28	0.62														
225	6.32	6.61	3.67	1.86	2.57	0.74														
250	6.40	6.72	4.08	2.24	2.80	0.92	1.60	0.22												
275	7.03	7.99	4.50	2.72	3.06	1.15	1.73	0.27												
300	7.66	9.38	4.90	3.15	3.40	1.29	1.90	0.36												
350	8.90	12.32	5.72	4.19	3.98	1.69	2.20	0.41												
400	10.20	15.82	6.54	5.33	4.54	2.21	2.60	0.56												
450	11.50	19.74	7.35	6.65	5.12	2.74	2.92	0.64	1.80	0.21										
475	12.30	22.96	7.88	7.22	5.55	3.21	3.10	0.79	1.94	0.25										
500	12.77	24.08	8.17	8.12	5.60	3.26	3.20	0.81	2.04	0.28	1.42	0.11								
550			8.99	9.66	6.16	3.93	3.52	0.98	2.25	0.33	1.57	0.14								
600			9.80	11.34	6.72	4.70	3.84	1.16	2.46	0.39	1.71	0.15								
650			10.62	13.16	7.28	5.50	4.16	1.34	2.66	0.46	1.85	0.19	1.37	0.09						
700			11.44	15.12	7.84	6.38	4.46	1.54	2.86	0.52	2.00	0.22	1.47	0.10						
750			12.26	17.22	8.50	7.00	4.80	1.74	3.06	0.59	2.13	0.24	1.58	0.11						
800					9.08	7.90	5.12	1.97	3.28	0.67	2.27	0.27	1.68	0.13						
850					9.58	8.75	5.48	2.28	3.48	0.75	2.41	0.31	1.79	0.14						
900					10.30	10.11	5.75	2.46	3.68	0.83	2.56	0.34	1.89	0.16						
950					10.72	10.71	6.06	2.87	3.88	0.91	2.70	0.35	2.00	0.16	1.73	0.12				
1000					11.32	12.04	6.40	3.02	4.08	1.01	2.84	0.41	2.10	0.19	1.82	0.14				
1100					12.50	14.31	7.03	3.51	4.50	1.20	3.13	0.49	2.31	0.23	2.00	0.16				
1200					13.52	16.69	7.67	4.26	4.91	1.46	3.41	0.57	2.52	0.26	2.18	0.19				
1500							9.60	6.27	6.10	2.09	4.20	0.85	3.15	0.39	2.73	0.28	2.39	0.24		
2000							12.70	10.71	8.10	3.50	5.60	1.43	4.20	0.66	3.64	0.47	3.19	0.39		
2500									10.10	5.33	7.00	2.18	5.25	1.01	4.55	0.72	3.99	0.56		
3000									12.10	7.42	8.40	3.39	6.30	1.57	5.46	1.12	4.79	0.80	3.08	0.27

Vel.—Velocity feet per second.   Fric.—Friction head in feet.

Table 2.   Electric Current Consumption for Pumping

Percent Efficiency of Pump, Motor, and Transformer	Consumption in kilowatt-hr. per 24 hr. period (100 gal./minute; 100 ft. high)
30	149.2
34	132.0
38	118.0
42	107.0
45	100.0
50	89.0
55	81.0
60	75.0
65	69.0
70	64.0
75	59.0

Table 3.   Weight and Volume of Water (Standard Gallons)

	Imperial, or English	U.S.
cu. in./gal.	277.274	231.00
lb./gal.	10.00	8.33111
gal./cu. ft.	6.232102	7.470519
lb./cu. ft.	62.321	

Table 4.   Gallons of Water per Minute Required to Feed Boilers

(30 lb., or 3.6 gal., of water per horsepower, evaporated from 100° to 70 lb. per sq. in. of steam pressure)

H.P. Boiler	Feed Water (gallons)	H.P. Boiler	Feed Water (gallons)
20	1.2	150	9.0
25	1.5	160	9.6
30	1.8	170	10.2
35	2.1	180	10.8
40	2.4		
45	2.7	190	11.4
50	3.0	200	12.0
55	3.3	225	13.5
		250	15.0
60	3.6	275	16.5
65	3.9	300	18.0

Table 4. Gallons of Water per Minute Required to Feed Boilers (cont'd)

70	4.2	325	19.5
75	4.5	350	21.0
80	4.8		
85	5.1	400	24.0
90	5.4	450	27.0
100	6.0	500	30.0
		600	36.0
110	6.6	700	42.0
120	7.2	800	48.0
130	7.8	900	54.0
140	8.4	1000	60.0

Table 5. Capacity (in Gallons per Foot of Depth) of Round Tanks

Inside Diameter Ft.	In.	Gallons One Foot in Depth	Inside Diameter Ft.	In.	Gallons One Foot in Depth	Inside Diameter Ft.	In.	Gallons One Foot in Depth
1	0	5.87	7	6	330.38	13	9	1108.06
1	3	9.17	7	9	352.76			
1	6	13.21				14	0	1151.21
1	9	17.98	8	0	375.90	14	3	1192.69
			8	3	399.76	14	6	1234.91
2	0	23.49	8	6	424.36	14	9	1277.86
2	3	29.73	8	9	449.21			
2	6	36.70				15	0	1321.54
2	9	44.41	9	0	475.80	15	3	1365.96
			9	3	502.65	15	6	1407.51
3	0	52.86	9	6	530.18	15	9	1457.00
3	3	62.03	9	9	558.45			
3	6	73.15				16	0	1503.62
3	9	82.59	10	0	587.47	16	3	1550.97
			10	3	617.17	16	6	1599.06
4	0	93.97	10	6	653.69	16	9	1647.89
4	3	103.03	10	9	678.88			
4	6	118.93				17	0	1697.45
4	9	132.52	11	0	710.69	17	3	1747.74
			11	3	743.36	17	6	1798.76
5	0	146.83	11	6	776.77	17	9	1850.53
5	3	161.88	11	9	810.91			
5	6	177.67				18	0	1903.02
5	9	194.19	12	0	848.18	18	3	1956.25
			12	3	881.39	18	6	2010.21
6	0	211.44	12	6	917.73	18	9	2064.91
6	3	229.43	12	9	954.81			
6	6	248.15				19	0	2121.58
6	9	267.61	13	0	992.62	19	3	2176.68
			13	3	1031.17	19	6	2233.52
7	0	287.80	13	6	1070.45	20	0	2349.46
7	3	308.72						

179

Table 6. Conversion of Vacuum Gauge Reading (Inches of Mercury) To Lift In Feet

(To convert to ft., multiply by 1.13)

Inch Vac.	Feet	Inch Vac.	Feet	Inch Vac.	Feet	Inch Vac.	Feet
1/4	0.28	8 1/4	9.35	16 1/4	18.42	24 1/4	27.50
1/2	0.56	8 1/2	9.64	1/2	18.71	1/2	27.78
3/4	0.85	8 3/4	9.92	3/4	18.99	3/4	28.07
1	1.13	9	10.21	17	19.28	25	28.35
1 1/4	1.41	1/4	10.49	1/4	19.56	1/4	28.63
1 1/2	1.70	1/2	10.77	1/2	19.84	1/2	28.91
1 3/4	1.98	3/4	11.06	3/4	20.13	3/4	29.20
2	2.27	10	11.34	18	20.41	26	29.48
2 1/4	2.55	1/4	11.62	1/4	20.70	1/4	29.76
2 1/2	2.84	1/2	11.90	1/2	20.98	1/2	30.05
2 3/4	3.12	3/4	12.19	3/4	21.27	3/4	30.33
3	3.41	11	12.47	19	21.55	27	30.62
3 1/4	3.69	1/4	12.75	1/4	21.83	1/4	30.90
3 1/2	3.98	1/2	13.04	1/2	22.11	1/2	31.19
3 3/4	4.26	3/4	13.32	3/4	22.40	3/4	31.47
4	4.54	12	13.61	20	22.68	28	31.75
4 1/4	4.82	1/4	13.89	1/4	22.96	1/4	32.03
4 1/2	5.11	1/2	14.18	1/2	23.24	1/2	32.32
4 3/4	5.39	3/4	14.46	3/4	23.53	3/4	32.60
5	5.67	13	14.74	21	23.81	29	32.89
5 1/4	5.95	1/4	15.02	1/4	24.09	1/4	33.17
5 1/2	6.23	1/2	15.31	1/2	24.38	1/2	33.46
5 3/4	6.52	3/4	15.59	3/4	24.66	3/4	33.74
6	6.80	14	15.88	22	24.95	30	....
6 1/4	7.08	1/4	16.16	1/4	25.23		
6 1/2	7.37	1/2	16.45	1/2	25.51		
6 3/4	7.65	3/4	16.73	3/4	25.80		
7	7.94	15	17.01	23	26.08		
7 1/4	8.22	1/4	17.29	1/4	26.36		
7 1/2	8.50	1/2	17.57	1/2	26.65		
7 3/4	8.79	3/4	17.86	3/4	26.93		
8	9.07	16	18.14	24	27.22		

If the inlet and discharge pipes are the same diameter at the gauge connections, the velocity head is the same in both pipes, and a correction, such as was required in the above solution, is not required. Also, the friction head in the inlet and discharge pipes is included in the gauge readings.

When the discharge pipe is smaller in diameter than the inlet pipe, the difference between the velocity heads in both pipes should be added in calculating the total hydraulic load or lift; the difference

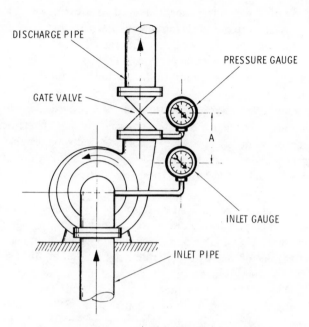

Fig. 37. Centrifugal pump showing location of gauges for taking readings to calculate total hydraulic load.

Friction of water in 90° Elbows

Size of Elbow, Inches	Friction Equivalent Feet Straight Pipe
½	5
¾	6
1	6
1¼	8
1½	8
2	8
2½	11
3	15
4	16
5	18
6	18
8	24
10	30
12	40
14	54
16	55
20	55
	70

should be subtracted if the inlet pipe is smaller than the discharge pipe.

181

SUMMARY

The rotating member (impeller) inside the casing of a centrifugal pump provides rapid rotary motion to the mass of water inside the casing, forcing the water out of the casing through the discharge outlet by means of centrifugal force. The vacuum created thereby enables atmospheric pressure to force more water into the casing through the inlet opening.

The volute-type *casing* or housing forms a progressively expanding passageway into which the impeller discharges the water. The housing is proportioned to produce equal flow velocity around the circumference and to reduce gradually the velocity of the liquid as it flows from the impeller to the discharge outlet—the object being to change velocity head to pressure head.

Single-admission centrifugal pumps are made in one or more stages, and the double-admission pumps may be either single-stage or multistage pumps. The double-admission single-stage pump can elevate large quantities of water to moderate heights. The multistage pump is essentially a high-head or high-pressure pump consisting of two or more stages, depending on the size of the head that it is to pump against. As many as eight stages may be found in a single casing.

The efficiency of a centrifugal pump is determined by the type of impeller. Three types of vanes are found on impellers as: (1) *open;* (2) *semiopen;* and (3) *enclosed,* or *shrouded,* depending on the service, desired efficiency, and cost. The enclosed-type impeller is generally considered to be a more efficient impeller. The vanes are cast integrally on both sides and are designed to prevent packing of fibrous materials between the stationary cover and the rotating impeller.

A centrifugal pump should not be operated unless it is filled with liquid. If it is run without liquid, there is danger of damage to the liquid-lubricated internal parts. Three methods of priming are: (1) *ejector* method; (2) *hand-type lift pump,* or *powered air pump;* and (3) *foot-valve* and *top-discharge* method. Automatic priming systems, such as the float-controlled and the reserve vacuum tank types, are used on some pumps.

Liberal clearances are provided between the rotating and stationary pump parts to allow for small matching variations and for the expansion of the casing and rotor when they become heated. Stationary diaphragms, wearing rings, return channels, etc., which are located in the casing are slightly smaller in diameter than the casing bore which is machined for a gasket between the flanges.

If the level of the water supply is above the center line of the pump, the pump is operating under *inlet head*. The *discharge head* is the vertical distance measured between the center line of the pump and the level to which the water is elevated.

REVIEW QUESTIONS

1. What is the basic operating principle of the centrifugal pump?
2. How is the volute-type casing proportional?
3. List three types of impeller vanes.
4. What is the chief advantage of the double-admission type of single-stage pump?
5. For what type of service is the multistage pump adapted?
6. For what types of service is the axial-flow type of impeller adapted?
7. What methods are used for balancing of impellers?
8. Why should a check valve and a gate valve be installed in the discharge piping?
9. What precautions should be taken before starting a centrifugal pump?
10. List three methods of priming centrifugal pumps.
11. Why are clearances provided between the stationary and the rotating parts in a centrifugal pump?

CHAPTER 4

Rotary Pumps

The rotary pump is used primarily as a source of fluid power in hydraulic systems. It is widely used in machine tool, aircraft, automotive, press, transmission, and mobile equipment applications.

PRINCIPLES OF OPERATION

The rotary pump continuously scoops the fluid from the pump chamber, whereas, the centrifugal pump imparts velocity to the stream of fluid. The rotary pump is a *positive-displacement* pump with a circular motion; the centrifugal pump is a *nonpositive-displacement* pump.

Ques. How does the rotary pump differ from the centrifugal pump?
Ans. The rotary pump continuously scoops the liquid from the pump chamber; the centrifugal pump imparts velocity to a stream of fluid.

Rotary pumps are classified with respect to the impelling element as: (1) *gear*-type; (2) *vane*-type; and (3) *piston*-type pumps.

Gear-Type Pumps

The gear-type pump is a power-driven unit having two or more intermeshing gears or lobed members enclosed in a suitably shaped housing (Fig. 1). The two gears fit closely inside a housing; the hydraulic oil is carried around the periphery of the two gears, and it is then forced through the outlet port by the meshing of the two

Material furnished by Commercial Shearing & Stamping Company of Youngstown, Ohio

Fig. 1. Gears for gear-type pumps and motors.

gears at their point of tangency (Fig. 2). Gear-type pumps are available in a wide range of pressure ratings. The gear-type pump is also classified as to the type of gears used as: (1) *spur-gear;* (2) *helical-gear;* and (3) *herringbone-gear* types of pumps.

Spur-Gear—Two types of spur-gear rotary pumps are used—the *external* and the *internal* types. In operation of the external type of gear pump, vacuum spaces form as each pair of meshing teeth sep-

Courtesy Roper Pump Company

Fig. 2. Movement of a liquid through a gear-type hydraulic pumps: (A) Liquid entering the pump; (B) Liquid being carried between the teeth of the gears; and (C) Liquid being forced into the discharge line.

185

arates, and atmospheric pressure forces the liquid inward to fill the spaces. The liquid filling the space between two adjacent teeth follows along with them as they revolve and is forced outward through the discharge opening, because the meshing of the teeth during rotation forms a seal which separates the admission and discharge portions of the secondary chamber (see Fig. 2).

In operation of the internal-gear type of rotary pump, power is applied to the rotor and transferred to the idler gear with which it meshes. As the teeth come out of mesh, an increase in volume creates a partial vacuum. Liquid is forced into this space by atmospheric pressure and remains between the teeth of the rotor and idler until the teeth mesh to force the liquid from these spaces and out of the pump. The internal gear type of rotary pump shown in Fig. 3

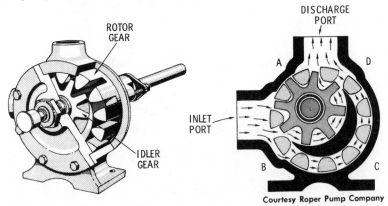

Courtesy Roper Pump Company

Fig. 3. Basic parts (left) and principle of operation (right) of the internal type of spur-gear rotary pump.

possesses only two moving parts—the precision-cut rotor and idler gears. As shown in the cross-sectional view of the pump, the teeth of the internal gear and idler gear separate at the suction port and mesh again at the discharge port. At position A, the rotor and idler gears form a barrier between the portions, and at position B, the idler withdraws from the rotor, creating a suction opening that is to be filled with liquid. At position C, the spaces between the rotor and idler gears are completely filled. As the rotor and idler gears come together again at position D, the liquid is forced outward through the discharge opening.

186

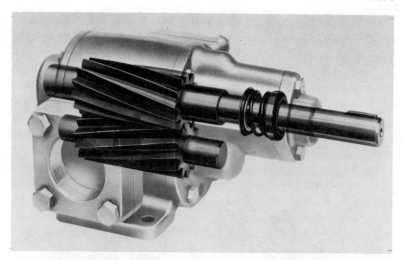

Courtesy Roper Pump Company

Fig. 4. A rotary gear-type pump with helical gears. This pump is adapted to jobs such as pressure lubrication, hydraulic service, fuel supply, or general transfer work pumping clean liquids.

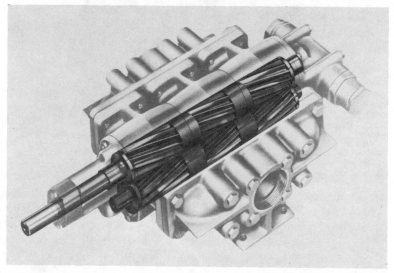

Courtesy Roper Pump Company

Fig. 5. A rotary gear-type pump with helical gears adapted to applications requiring a quiet and compact unit, such as a hydraulic lift or elevator application.

187

Helical-Gear—A Roper Series K rotary pump with helical gears is shown in Fig. 4. This pump is adaptable to jobs such as pressure lubrication, hydraulic service, fuel supply, or general transfer work pumping clean liquids. This pump is self-priming and operates in either direction. The Roper Series KE rotary pump (Fig. 5) is adapted to applications where a quiet and compact unit is required, such as a hydraulic lift or elevator application.

Herringbone-Gear—A rotary pump with herringbone gears is shown in Fig. 6. This is also a quiet and compact unit.

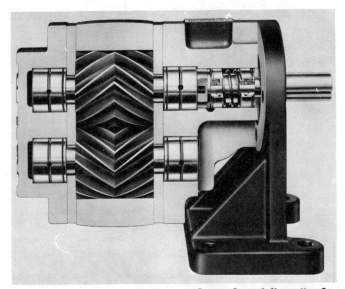

Courtesy Brown & Sharpe Mfg. Co.

Fig. 6. Sectional view of a rotary gear-type pump with herringbone gears.

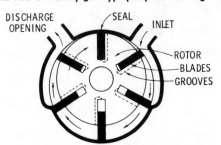

Fig. 7. Parts of a rotary vane-type pump.

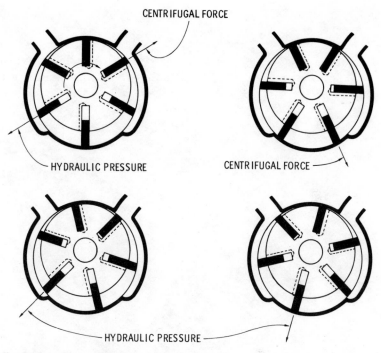

Fig. 8. Operating principle of a rotary vane-type pump. The alternate actions of centrifugal force and hydraulic pressure keep the vanes in firm contact with the walls of the casing.

Vane-Type Pumps

In the rotary vane-type pump (Fig. 7), operation is also based on the principle of increasing the size of the cavity to form a vacuum, allowing the space to fill with fluid, and then forcing the fluid out of the pump under pressure by diminishing the volume.

The sliding vanes or blades fit into slots in the rotor. Ahead of the slots and in the direction of rotation, grooves admit the liquid being pumped by the vanes, moving them outward with a force or locking pressure that varies directly with the pressure that the pump is operating against. The grooves also serve to break the vacuum on the admission side. The operating cycle and the alternate action of centrifugal force and hydraulic pressure hold the vanes in contact with the casing, as shown in Fig. 8.

189

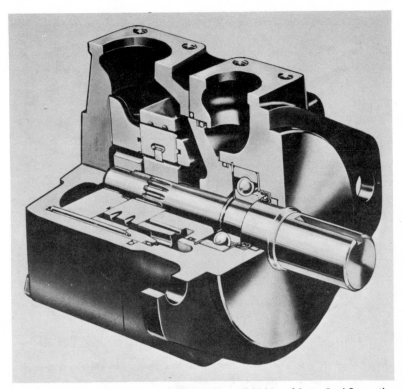

Courtesy Vickers Incorporated, Division of Sperry Rand Corporation

Fig. 9. Cutaway view of a high-speed high-pressure single-stage vane-type pump. This pump can operate at speeds to 2700 rpm and pressures to 2500 psi.

Vane-type pumps are available as *single-stage* (Fig. 9) and as *double-stage* (Fig. 10) pumps. The double-stage vane-type pump may be two single-stage pumps mounted end to end on a single shaft. A *combination* vane-type pump is also available, which may be two pumps mounted on a common shaft; the larger pump may be pumping at low pressure, and the smaller pump may be delivering at high pressure. This type of pump may be called a "hi-low" pump.

In the pumps shown in Figs. 9 and 10, the wearing parts are contained in replaceable cartridges (Fig. 11). Since the pumping cartridges within each pump series are interchangeable, the pump capacities can be modified quickly in the field.

190

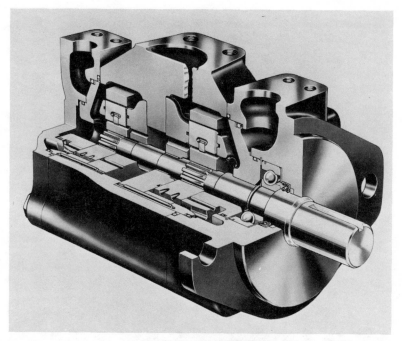

Courtesy Vickers Incorporated, Division of Sperry Rand Corporation

Fig. 10. Cutaway view of a high-speed high-pressure double-stage vane-type pump. This pump can operate at speeds to 2700 rpm and pressures to 2500 psi.

In the *variable-volume* vane-type pump (Fig. 12), a pressure compensator is used to control maximum system pressure. Pump displacement is changed automatically to supply the exact rate of flow required by the system. If the pump displacement changes, system pressure remains nearly constant at the value selected by the compensator setting.

If the hydraulic system does not require flow, the pressure ring of the pump is at a nearly neutral position, supplying only leakage losses at the set pressure. If full-capacity pump delivery is required, the pressure drops sufficiently to cause the compensator spring to stroke the pressure ring to full-flow position. Any flow rate from zero to maximum is automatically delivered to the system to match the circuit demands precisely, by the balance of reaction pressure and compensator spring force. This reduces horsepower

191

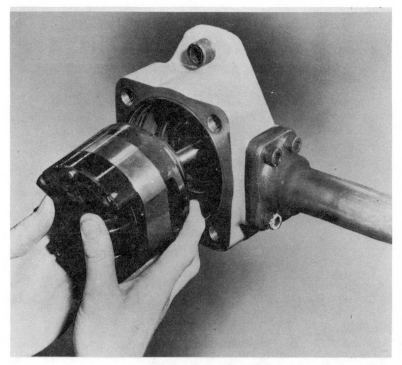

Courtesy Vickers Incorporated, Division of Sperry Rand Corporation

Fig. 11. A replaceable pump cartridge.

consumption as flow rate is reduced. By-passing of pressure oil does not occur and excess heat is not generated, which are important factors in the efficiency of the circuit.

Piston-Type Pumps

The rotary piston-type pumps are either radial or axial in design. Each of these pumps may be designed for either constant-displacement or variable-displacement.

The pistons are arranged radially around a rotor hub in the radial pump (Fig. 13). In the illustration, the slide block is at the right-hand side of the center line of the cylinder barrel. Reciprocating motion is imparted to the pistons, so that those pistons passing over the lower port of the pintle deliver oil to that port while the pistons

192

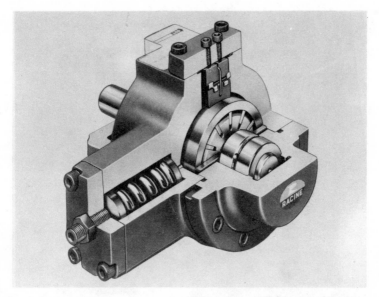

Courtesy Racine Hydraulics & Machinery, Inc.

Fig. 12. Illustrating a variable-volume vane-type pump with spring-type pressure compensator.

passing over the upper port are filling with oil. The delivery of the pump can be controlled accurately from zero to maximum capacity, because the piston and movement of the slide block can be controlled accurately.

In the axial piston-type pump, the pistons are arranged parallel to the shaft of the pump rotor. The driving means of the pump rotates the cylinder barrel. The axial reciprocation of the pumping pistons that are confined in the cylinder is caused by the shoe retainer, which is spring-loaded toward the cam plate. The piston stroke and the quantity of oil delivered are limited by the angle of the cam plate (Fig. 14).

A mechanism is used to change the angle of the cam plate in the variable-volume pump. The mechanism may be a handwheel, a pressure-compensating control, or a stem control which actuates a free-swinging hanger attached to the cam plate for changing the angle of the cam plate.

193

Courtesy Oilgear Cimpany

Fig. 13. Sectional view of a variable-delivery radial piston-type pump.

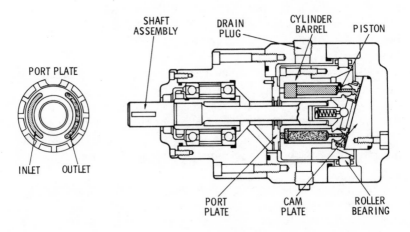

Courtesy Denison Division, Abex Corporation

Fig. 14. Cross-sectional view of a constant-displacement axial piston-type pump.

194

CONSTRUCTION

To ensure dependable, long-life operation, rotary pumps are of heavy-duty construction throughout. Fluid power components that can perform satisfactorily at higher operating pressures are needed to satisfy the ever-increasing demand for faster, more positive-acting original equipment.

Gear-Type Pumps

Heavy-duty gear-type pumps are able to withstand rugged operating conditions, are simple in construction, and are economical in cost and maintenance (Fig. 15). High volumetric efficiency of gear-

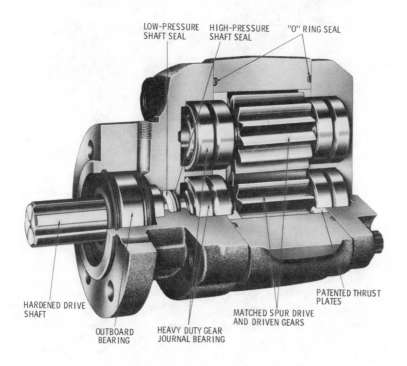

Material furnished by Commercial Shearing & Stamping Company of Youngstown, Ohio

Fig. 15. Cutaway view showing parts of a single fluid-power pump.

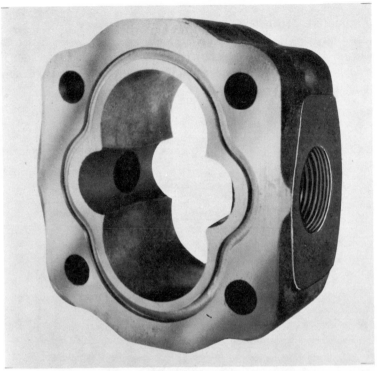

Material furnished by Commercial Shearing & Stamping Company of Youngstown, Ohio

Fig. 16. Housing for a gear-type pump.

type pumps depends on maintaining complete sealing of all gear tooth contact surfaces. All gear surfaces are precision finished, and each pair is matched carefully.

Gear-type pumps are made with fewer working parts than many other types of pumps. Castings are made of a special alloy iron, are precision machined, and are capable of resisting bursting under severe shock loading. Gear housings are available with tapered thread, *SAE* split-flange or straight-thread fittings, and with no porting or left- and/or right-hand side porting (Fig. 16).

End covers for fluid power pumps are usually specified and coded. These details are important in specifying and ordering parts. The *shaft-end* cover (Fig. 17) may be furnished in either flange or pad

196

mounting, and the *port-end* cover (Fig. 18) may be provided either with no porting or with end porting arrangements.

The *driveshafts* (Fig. 19) are also specified and ordered by code number. They may be either splined or straight-keyed shafts.

A *bearing carrier* (Fig. 20) is used on tandem pumps and motors.

Material furnished by Commercial Shearing & Stamping Company of Youngstown, Ohio

Fig. 17. A four-bolt shaft-end cover for a gear-type pump.

It is positioned between adjacent pumps or motors. The bearing carrier is also available with tapered thread, *SAE* thread and straight-thread fittings, and either with no porting or with left- and/or right-hand side porting.

Some rotary gear-type pumps for general-purpose applications use a packed box for the shaft seal (Fig. 21). The packing gland should be adjusted to permit slight seepage for best performance. A *mechani-*

Material furnished by Commercial Shearing & Stamping Company of Youngstown, Ohio

Fig. 18. A port-end cover for a gear-type pump.

Material furnished by Commercial Shearing & Stamping Company of Youngstown, Ohio

Fig. 19. Straight-splined drive shaft for a gear-type pump.

198

Material furnished by Commercial Shearing & Stamping Company of Youngstown, Ohio

Fig. 20. A bearing carrier which is placed between the two adjacent pumps in a tandem gear-type pump.

cal seal (Fig. 22) uses less power than the packed box, has longer service life under proper conditions, and does not require adjustment. Special mechanical seals, such as *Viton* (400°F.) and *Teflon* (500°F. and corrosion resistant), can be supplied for special conditions.

In the rotary pump, a *steam chest* (Fig. 23) located between the casing and the outboard bearing effectively transfers heat to both the pump and the packing. It can be used with hot water, steam, and heat transfer oil; or it can be used as a cooling chamber. The steam chest is ideal for transferring thick, viscous liquids, such as asphalt mixes, creosote, refined sugars, corn starch, etc.

An *adjustable relief valve* (Fig. 24) in the pump faceplate eliminates outside piping and protects the pump from excessive outlet line pressure; it also permits the operator to close the discharge line

199

without stopping the pump, under standard operating conditions. Various spring sizes are available to provide adjustments over the full operating range of the pump from 30 to 100 *psi*.

Many mounting styles are available for convenience in mounting rotary pumps (Fig. 25). Bedplates and mounting brackets are available to permit the coupling of pumps and motors for complete motor-

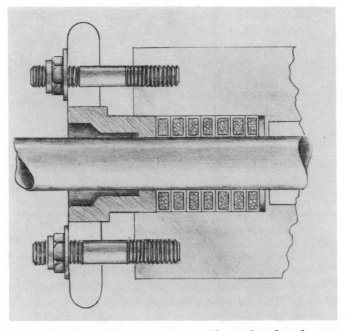

Courtesy Roper Pump Company

Fig. 21. Packing for a rotary gear-type pump.

driven units (Fig. 26). The rotary gear-type pumps also may be mounted in various other styles, including the *foot-mounted* (Fig. 27) and the *end-bell mounted* (Fig. 28) pumps.

As aforementioned, the rotary gear-type pumps are more simple in design, and they have fewer working parts than the rotary vane-type and piston-type pumps. The names of the various parts of a typical gear-type pump can be learned from the diagram and parts list in Fig. 29.

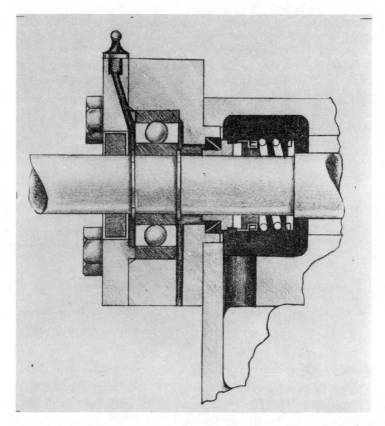

Fig. 22. Mechanical seal for a rotary gear-type pump.

Vane-Type Pumps

The design principle of hydraulic balance is illustrated in Fig. 30. Bearing loads resulting from pressure are eliminated, and the only radial loads are imposed by the drive itself. Communication holes in the rotor direct pressure from spaces behind the vanes to their lower edges. The outside edges of the vanes are machined to a bevel, holding them in continuous hydraulic balance, except for the preselected area of the intra-vane ends.

201

Courtesy Roper Pump Company

Fig. 23. Illustrating a steam chest used on a rotary pump for steam and hot-water applications.

Piston-Type Pumps

The *radial piston-type pump* (Fig. 31) is a rugged and compact high-pressure pump. The walls of the pistons are tapered to a thin-edged section capable of expanding against the cylinder wall as pressure is applied. The higher the pressure, the tighter the seal becomes to increase the efficiency of high-pressure systems. Positive-acting check valves properly port the suction and discharge oil for each piston. The suction check valves are quickly and positively seated by the action of the piston. Sectional views of a radial piston-type pump are shown in Fig. 32.

A cutaway view of a variable-volume *axial piston-type pump* is shown in Fig. 33. The pistons operate against an inclinable cam or hanger (see inset). The pump delivery is in direct proportion to the tilt of the hanger which is tilted either manually or automatically by means of various types of controls.

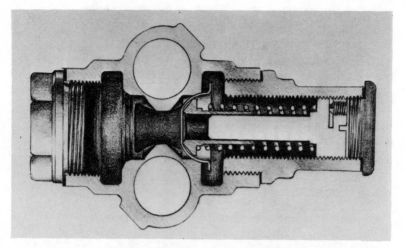

Courtesy Roper Pump Company

Fig. 24. An adjustable relief valve protects the rotary gear-type pump from excessive outlet line pressure.

INSTALLATION AND OPERATION

Many of the installation, operation, and maintenance principles that apply to centrifugal pumps can also be applied to rotary pumps. Since rotary pumps are commonly much smaller than centrifugal pumps, the foundation that is required is usually smaller, but the requirements are similar.

Alignment

Correct alignment is necessary to successful operation of the pump. A flexible coupling cannot compensate for incorrect alignment. If the rotary pumping unit is aligned accurately, the flexible coupling can then serve its purpose—to prevent the transmission of end thrust from one machine to another and to compensate for slight changes in alignment which may occur during normal operation.

Each pumping unit should be aligned accurately at the factory before it is shipped. After the unit is assembled, it is aligned accurately by placing the base plate on a surface plate and then leveling the machined pads. Shims are inserted beneath the feet of both the pump and the driver to obtain correct alignment.

203

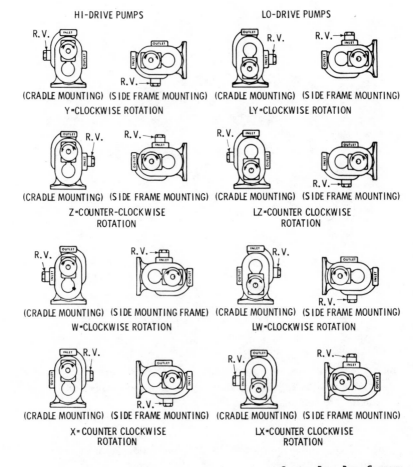

Courtesy Roper Pump Company

Fig. 25. Diagram of mounting styles available for Roper rotary pumps.

The manufacturer, in many instances, cannot assume full responsibility for proper mechanical operation, because the base plates are not rigid; this means that the unit must be aligned correctly after it is erected on its foundation. The unit is usually supported on the foundation by wedges placed near the foundation bolts. The wedges underneath the base plate are adjusted, until a spirit level placed on the pads indicates that the pump shaft is level.

204

Courtesy Roper Pump Company

Fig. 26. Bedplates and mounting brackets permit coupling of pumps and motors for complete motor-driven units.

Courtesy Roper Pump Company

Fig. 27. Foot-mounted rotary gear-type pump.

Courtesy Roper Pump Company

Fig. 28. End-bell mounted rotary gear-type pump.

The alignment should be checked and corrected to align the coupling half of the driver with the coupling half of the pump. The shafts can be aligned by means of a straightedge and thickness gauge. (Fig. 34). The clearances between the coupling halves should be set so that they cannot strike, rub, or exert end thrust on either the pump or the driver.

Before placing the unit in operation, oil should be added to the coupling. The alignment should be checked again after the piping to the pump has been installed, because the units are often sprung or moved out of position when the flange bolts are tightened, especially if the flanges were not squared before tightening.

To prevent a strain or pull on the pump, extreme care should be exercised to support the inlet and discharge piping properly. Improper support of the piping frequently causes misalignment, heated bearings, wear, and vibration.

Piping

The general requirements for installation of piping are similar to those for centrifugal pumps. Sufficient static negative lift (static head) should be provided on the inlet line, in addition to the vapor pressure, to prevent vaporization of the liquid inside the pump when highly

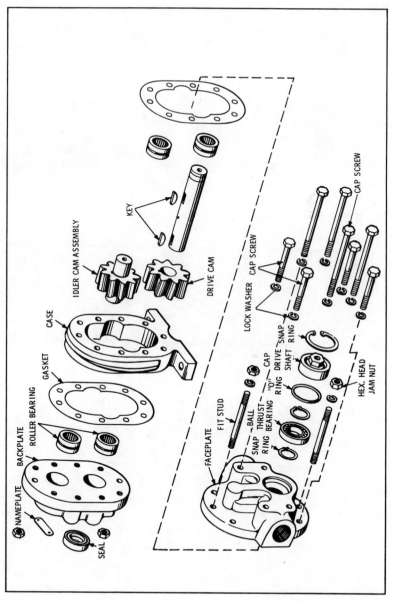

KEY

IDLER CAM ASSEMBLY

DRIVE CAM

CAP SCREW

CAP SCREW

LOCK WASHER

CASE

GASKET

SNAP RING

DRIVE SHAFT

HEX. HEAD JAM NUT

"O" RING CAP

BACKPLATE

ROLLER BEARING

FIT STUD

SNAP RING

BALL THRUST BEARING

FACEPLATE

NAMEPLATE

SEAL

Courtesy Roper Pump Company

Fig. 29. Diagram and parts list for a gear- type pump.

207

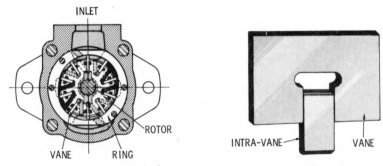

Courtesy Vickers Incorporated, Division of Sperry Rand Corporation

Fig. 30. Design principle of hydraulic balance in the rotary vane-type pump (left). The lighter-colored area is the inlet, and the darker-shaded area is the outlet—rotation is clockwise. The design of the vane is shown at right.

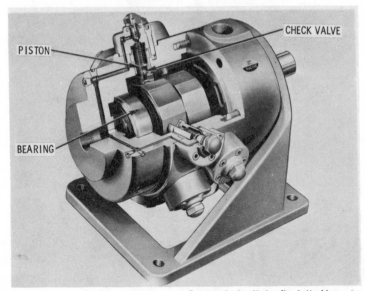

Courtesy Racine Hydraulics & Machinery, Inc.

Fig. 31. A radial piston-type pump.

volatile liquids (butane, propane, hot oils, etc.) are being pumped. The discharge piping should be extended upward through a riser that is approximately five times the pipe diameter (Fig. 35). This prevents gas or air pockets in the pump and acts as a seal in high-vacuum

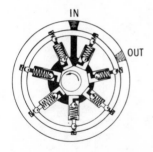 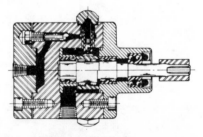

Courtesy Racine Hydraulics & Machinery, Inc.

Fig. 32. Sectional views of a radial piston-type pump.

 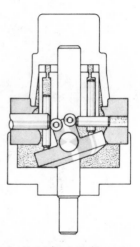

Courtesy Racine Hydraulics & Machinery, Inc.

Fig. 33. Cutaway view of a variable-volume axial piston-type pump (left) and
inclinable cam or hanger (right) which is tilted to control pump delivery.

service. A valve at the top of the riser can be used as a vent when
starting the pump. A by-pass line with a relief valve can be installed
to protect the pump from excessive pressure caused by increased pipe
friction in cold weather and from accidental closing of the valve in the
discharge line. The relief valve should be set at not more than 10
percent higher than maximum pump discharge pressure.

Ques. How is the rotary pump protected against excessive pres-

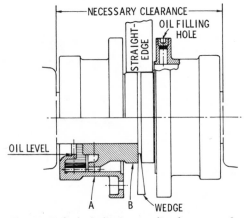

Fig. 34. Method of aligning coupling by means of a
straightedge and wedge.

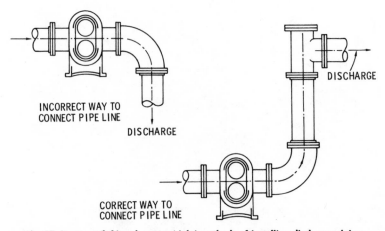

Fig. 35. Incorrect (left) and correct (right) methods of installing discharge piping.

sures caused by increased pipe friction in cold weather or by accidental closing of the valve in the discharge line?

Ans. By installation of a by-pass line with a relief valve.

Ques. How is the relief valve adjusted?

Ans. It should be set slightly higher (not more than 10 percent)
than the maximum pump discharge pressure.

210

If steam jackets are necessary, the inlet is located at the top and the outlet at the bottom. On water jackets, the inlet is at the bottom and the outlet is at the top. Valves should be installed in the inlet lines to regulate the quantity of fluid to the jackets.

Direction of Rotation

The direction of rotation of a pump is usually indicated by an arrow on the body of the pump. This varies with the type of pump. For example, in a double-helix gear-type pump, the direction of rotation is "counterclockwise when standing at and facing the shaft extension end."

Rotation of internal-gear roller bearing pumps can be reversed by removing the outside bearing cover and stuffing box; then the small plug in the side plate casting is transferred to the opposite side. These small plugs (one plug in each side plate) should be on the discharge side, to induce circulation through the bearings to the inlet and to maintain inlet pressure on the stuffing box and ends of the drive shafts.

For another example, a pump operating on the internal-gear principle gives the following directions for determining direction of rotation:

1. In determining the desired direction of rotation, the observer should stand at the shaft end of the pump.
2. Note that the balancing groove in the shoe should be located on the inlet side.
3. If a change in direction of rotation is desired, it is necessary only to remove the cover; then remove both the upper and lower shoes, turn them end for end to place the grooves on the new inlet side, and reassemble the pump.

Another model built by the same pump manufacturer is listed as an "automatic-reversing" pump. Regardless of the direction of shaft rotation and without the use of check valves, a unidirectional flow is maintained.

For a final example, the instructions for determining the direction of rotation for a helical-gear type of rotary pump are as follows: *To determine the direction of rotation, stand at the driving end, facing the pump.* If the shaft revolves in a left-hand to right-hand direction,

211

its rotation is *clockwise*; if the shaft revolves in a right-hand to left-hand direction, its rotation is *counterclockwise* (Fig. 36). As shown in the illustration, a change in direction of rotation of the pump drive shaft reverses the direction of flow of the liquid, causing the inlet and discharge openings to be reversed.

Motors usually rotate in a counterclockwise direction. The direction of rotation for a motor is determined from a position at the end of the motor that couples to the pump.

As indicated in the foregoing examples, the direction of rotation for the various types of pumps should be obtained from the manufacturers' instructions. Some types of rotary pumps are reversible and some types are nonreversible.

Starting and Operating The Pump

Before starting the pump, it should be primed; then the prime mover should be checked for proper direction of rotation. Pressure or vacuum should be checked on the inlet side, and pressure should be checked on the outlet side to determine whether they conform to specifications and whether the pump can deliver full capacity without overloading the driver.

Operation should be started at a reduced load, gradually increasing to maximum service conditions. Pumps with external bearings may require occasional lubrication or soft grease for the bearings. If grease fittings are not furnished on pumps with internal bearings, lubrication is not necessary.

TROUBLESHOOTING

Rotary pumps, like centrifugal pumps, normally require little attention while they are running; however, most troubles can be avoided if they are given only a small amount of care, rather than no attention at all. Some of the more frequent causes of trouble are indicated here.

No Liquid Delivered

The following causes and steps should be taken if no liquid is delivered:

1. Stop pump immediately.
2. If pump is not primed, prime according to instructions.

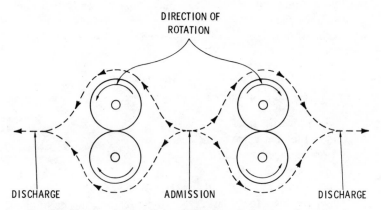

Fig. 36. Diagram showing flow of liquids and direction of rotation in rotary gear-type pumps.

3. Lift may be too high. Check this factor with a vacuum gauge on the inlet. If the lift is too high, lower the position of the pump and increase the size of the inlet pipe; check the inlet line for air leaks.
4. Incorrect direction of rotation.

Insufficient Liquid Delivered

One of the following causes may result in delivery of insufficient liquid:

1. Air leak in the inlet line or through the stuffing box. Oil and tighten the stuffing box gland. Paint the inlet pipe joints with shellac.
2. Speed too slow. The *rpm* should be checked. The driver may be overloaded; or the cause may be due to low voltage or to low steam pressure.
3. Lift may be too high. Check with vacuum gauge. Small fractions in some liquids vaporize easily and occupy a portion of the pump displacement.
4. Too much lift for hot liquids.
5. Pump may be worn.
6. Foot valve may not be deep enough.
7. Foot valve may be either too small or obstructed.

213

8. Piping is improperly installed, permitting air or gas to pocket inside the pump.
9. Mechanical defects, such as defective packing or damaged pump.

Pump Delivers for a Short Period, Then Quits

This may be a result of one of the following causes:

1. Leak in the inlet line.
2. End of the inlet valve is not deep enough.
3. Air or gas in the liquid.
4. Supply is exhausted.
5. Vaporization of the liquid in the inlet line. Check this with the vacuum gauge to be sure that the pressure in the pump is greater than the vapor pressure of the liquid.
6. Air or gas pockets in the inlet line.
7. Pump is cut by presence of sand or other abrasives in the liquid.

Rapid Wear

Some of the causes of rapid wear in a pump are:

1. Grit or dirt in the liquid that is being pumped. A fine-mesh strainer or filter can be installed in the inlet line.
2. Pipe strain on the pump casing causes the working parts to bind. The pipe connections can be released and the alignment checked to determine whether this factor is a cause of rapid wear.
3. Pump operating against excessive pressure.
4. Corrosion roughens surfaces.
5. Pump runs dry or with insufficient liquid.

Pump Requires Too Much Power

Too much power to operate the pump may be required by:

1. Speed too fast.
2. Liquid either heavier or more viscous than water.
3. Mechanical defects, such as a bent shaft, binding of the rotating element, stuffing boxes too tight, and misalignment caused by improper connections to the pipe lines or installation on the foundation in such a way that the base is sprung.
4. Misalignment of the coupling (direct-connected units).

Noisy Operation

The causes of noisy operation may be:

1. Insufficient supply, which may be due to liquid vaporizing in the pump. This may be corrected by lowering the pump and by increasing the size of the inlet pipe.
2. Air leaks in the inlet pipe can cause a crackling noise in the pump.
3. Air or gas pockets in the inlet.
4. A pump that is out of alignment may cause metallic contact between the rotors and the casing.
5. Operating against excessive pressure.
6. Coupling out of balance.

CALCULATIONS

In nearly all installations it is important to calculate size of pump, horsepower, lift, head, total load, etc. This is important in determining whether the system is operating with maximum efficiency.

Correct Size of Pump

It is always important to determine whether the pump is too large or to small for the job—either before or after it has been installed. *Problem:* In a given installation, a pump is required that can fill an 8000-gal. tank in two hours. What size of pump is required?
Solution: Since the capacity of a pump is rated in gallons per minute (*gpm*), the 8000 gal. in two hours that is required can be reduced to *gpm* as:

$$gpm = \frac{8000}{2 \times 60} = 66\text{-}2/3, \text{ or approximately 70 } gpm$$

If the rated capacity of a given pump indicates that the pump can deliver 70 *gpm* at 450 *rpm* and since the capacity of a pump is nearly proportional to its speed, the *rpm* required to deliver 66-2/3 gal. of water per minute can be determined:

$$required\ rpm = 450 \times \frac{66\text{-}2/3}{70} = 428.6\ rpm$$

215

Therefore, if the pump is rated to deliver 70 *gpm* at 450 *rpm*, it should be capable of delivering 66-2/3 *gpm* at 428.4 *rpm*, which is within the rated capacity of the pump.

Friction of Water in Pipes

The values for loss of head due to friction can be obtained from the preceding chapter. The values in the table are based on 15-yr.-old wrought-iron or cast-iron pipe when pumping clear soft water. The following coefficients can be used to determine the friction in pipes for various lengths of service:

new, smooth pipe 0.71
10-yr.-old pipe 0.84
15-yr.-old pipe 1.00
20-yr.-old pipe 1.22

Dynamic Column or Total Load

The "dynamic column" or "total load" must be calculated before the horsepower required to drive the pump can be calculated. The dynamic column, often referred to as total head consists of: The "dynamic lift" plus the "dynamic head" (Fig. 37).

Dynamic Lift

The "dynamic lift," in an installation, consists of "static lift" and frictional resistance in the entire length of inlet piping from the water level to the intake opening of the pump. To determine the static lift, measure the vertical distance from the water level in the well to the center point of the inlet opening of the pump. The frictional loss is then added to the static lift, which gives the "dynamic lift."

Example: A delivery of 70 *gpm* is required from a pump located 10 ft. (static lift) above the level of the water in the well; the horizontal distance is 40 ft., and new 2-in. pipe with two 2-in. elbows is to be used.

The friction loss for 70 *gpm* through 100 ft. of 15-yr.-old pipe is 18.4 ft. (from table). Since new pipe is to be used, multiply 18.4 ft. (loss in 15-yr.-old pipe) by the coefficient 0.71 for new, smooth pipe; thus (18.4 × 0.71), or 13.064 ft., is the friction loss. The

216

total length of the inlet line, including elbows which have been converted to equivalent feet of straight pipe is:

vertical pipe ....10 ft.
horizontal pipe ....40 ft.
elbows (equivalent to straight pipe) ....16 ft.
total.............................66 ft.

Since the values in the table for friction loss are based on 100 ft., multiply 13.06 (loss in new pipe) by 0.66 (ft. in inlet line ÷ 100); thus, (13.06 × 0.66), or 8.62 ft., is the total loss due to friction of water in the pipe.

Therefore, *dynamic lift* (static lift + frictional resistance in inlet pipe) is equal to (10.0 ft. + 8.62 ft.), or 18.62 ft. It should be noted that, in this example, the dynamic lift is less than 25 ft. If the calculated dynamic lift were more than 25 ft., either the pump may be lowered or a larger pipe is necessary to reduce the frictional resistance to flow, which may bring the dynamic lift to a value within the 25-ft. limit.

Dynamic Head

In an installation, the "dynamic head" consists of the "static head" plus the frictional resistance in the entire discharge line, including elbows, to the point of discharge. The static head is determined by measuring the vertical distance from the center point of the pump outlet to the discharge water level.

Example: The pump with a capacity of 70 *gpm* is used to force water through a vertical pipe that is 30 ft. (static head) in length and a horizontal pipe that is 108 ft. in length (2-in. new pipe with three elbows).

The friction loss at 70 *gmp* through 100 ft. of 15-yr.-old 2-in. pipe is 18.4 ft. (from table). Since the coefficient for new pipe is 0.71, the friction loss is (18.4 × 0.71), or 13.064 ft. The friction loss in the total length of the discharge line is:

total discharge line (30 + 108) ......138 ft.
equivalent for three elbows .... 24 ft.
total.............................162 ft.

217

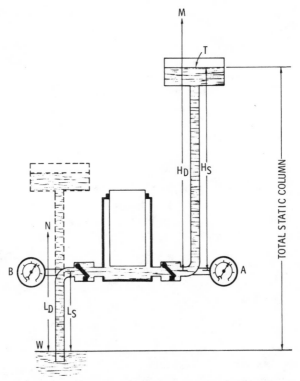

Fig. 37. Diagram illustrating the dynamic or total column for a pumping unit.

Since table values are based on 100 ft. of pipe, multiply 13.06 (loss in new pipe) by $(162 \div 100)$, or 1.62; thus (13.06×1.62), or 21.16 ft. is the total loss due to friction in the pipe.

Therefore, dynamic head (static head + friction resistance in the discharge pipe) is equal to (30 ft. + 21.16 ft.), or 51.16 ft.

After the dynamic lift (13 ft.) and the dynamic head (51 ft.) for the pump used in the two previous examples have been calculated, the dynamic column (total column) can be calculated as:

$$\text{dynamic column} = \text{dynamic lift} + \text{dynamic head}$$

substituting;

218

dynamic or total column = 13 + 51 = 64 ft.

Since the pressure, in pounds per square inch, of a column of water is equal to head (in feet) times 0.433, the pressure in lb. per sq. in. for the examples above is equivalent to the dynamic column (or total column) times 0.433; thus, (64 ft. × 0.433), or 27.7 lb. per sq. in., is the pressure of the column of water (Tables 1 and 2).

Also, the head, in feet, of a column of water is equivalent to the pressure, in lb. per sq. in., times 2.31; therefore, (64 ft. ÷ 2.31), or 27.7 lb. per sq. in., is the pressure of the column of water. This value is identical to the result in the previous paragraph.

Horsepower Required

The power required to raise a given quantity of water to a given elevation is the *actual horsepower*, rather than *theoretical horsepower*. That is, the actual horsepower is equivalent to the theoretical horsepower, plus the additional power required to overcome frictional resistance and inefficiency of the pump. Theoretical horsepower (*hp*) can be determined by the following formulas:

$$\text{theoretical hp} = \frac{gpm \times 8\text{-}1/3 \times \text{d.c.}}{33,000}$$

or;

$$\text{theoretical hp} = \frac{\text{cu. ft.} \times 62.4 \times \text{d.c.}}{33,000}$$

in which,

gpm = gallons per minute
8-1/3 = approximate wt. of one gallon of water in lb.
62.4 = wt. of 1 cu. ft. of water at room temperature
d.c. = dynamic column

To obtain the actual horsepower, the theoretical horsepower can be divided by the efficiency E of the pumping unit, expressed as a decimal. Thus, the formula can be changed to:

$$\text{actual hp} = \frac{gpm \times 8\text{-}1/3 \times \text{d.c.}}{33,000 \times E}$$

219

Problem: What is the actual horsepower required to drive a pump that is required to pump 200 *gpm* against a combined static lift and static head (static column) of 50 ft., if the pump efficiency is 57 percent and the 4-in. pipe line consisting of three 90° elbows is 200 ft. in length?

Table 1. Converting Head of Water (Feet) to Pressure
(Lb. per Sq. In.)

Feet Head	Pounds Per Square Inch	Feet Head	Pounds Per Square Inch	Feet Head	Pounds Per Square Inch
1	0.43	60	25.99	200	86.62
2	0.87	70	30.32	225	97.45
3	1.30	80	34.65	250	108.27
4	1.73	90	38.98	275	119.10
5	2.17	100	43.31	300	129.93
6	2.60	110	47.64	325	140.75
7	3.03	120	51.97	350	151.58
8	3.40	130	56.30	400	173.24
9	3.90	140	60.63	500	216.55
10	4.33	150	64.96	600	259.85
20	8.66	160	69.29	700	303.16
30	12.99	170	73.63	800	346.47
40	17.32	180	77.96	900	389.78
50	21.65	190	83.29	1000	433.09

Table 2. Converting Pressure (Lb. per Sq. In.) to Head of Water (Feet)

Pounds Per Square Inch	Feet Head	Pounds Per Square Inch	Feet Head	Pounds Per Square Inch	Feet Head
1	2.31	40	92.36	170	392.52
2	4.62	50	115.45	180	415.61
3	6.93	60	138.54	190	438.90
4	9.24	70	161.63	200	461.78
5	11.54	80	184.72	225	519.51
6	13.85	90	207.81	250	577.24
7	16.16	100	230.90	275	643.03
8	18.47	110	253.98	300	692.69
9	20.78	120	277.07	325	750.41
10	23.09	125	288.62	350	808.13
15	34.63	130	300.16	375	865.89
20	46.18	140	323.25	400	922.58
25	57.72	150	346.34	500	1154.48
30	69.27	160	369.43	1000	2308.00

Solution: The friction loss per 100 ft. of 4-in. pipe discharging 200 *gpm* is 4.4 ft.; therefore, for 200 ft. of pipe, the loss is (2 × 4.4), or 8.8 ft. The friction loss in one 90° elbow is 16 ft.; or (3 × 16 ft.) = 48 ft. for three 90° elbows. Therefore, the dynamic column is:

$$d.c. = 50 + 8.8 + 48 = 106.8 \text{ ft.}$$

Substituting in the formula for actual horsepower;

$$actual\ hp = \frac{200 \times 8\text{-}1/3 \times 106.8}{33,000 \times 0.57} = 9.46, \text{ or a } 10\text{-}hp \text{ pump}$$

SUMMARY

The rotary pump is used widely in machine tool, aircraft, automotive, press, transmission, and mobile equipment applications. It is a primary source of fluid power in hydraulic systems.

The rotary pump continuously scoops the fluid from the pump chamber. It is a positive-displacement pump with a rotary motion.

Rotary pumps are classified with respect to the impelling element as: (1) *gear*-type; (2) *vane*-type; and (3) *piston*-type pumps. The gear-type pump is classified as to the type of gears used as: (1) *spur-gear;* (2) *helical-gear;* and (3) *herringbone-gear* types of pumps. The two types of spur-gear rotary pumps are the *external* and *internal* types.

Rotary vane-type pumps are available as *single-stage* and *double-stage* pumps and as *constant-volume* and *variable-volume* pumps. In the variable-volume vane-type pump, a pressure compensator is used to control maximum system pressure.

Rotary piston-type pumps are either *radial* or *axial* in design. Each pump may be designed for either *constant-displacement* or *variable-displacement.*

Rotary pumps are of heavy-duty construction throughout. These pumps and components can perform satisfactorily at high operating pressures.

The direction of rotation for a rotary pump is usually indicated by an arrow on the body of the pump. The manufacturer's directions should be followed in determining the direction of rotation for a rotary pump.

A newly installed pump should be operated at a reduced load, gradually increasing to maximum service conditions. Rotary pumps normally require little attention while they are operating; however, most troubles can be avoided if they are given only a minimum amount of care, rather than no attention at all.

The size of pump, lift, head, total load, horsepower, etc., should be calculated for most pump installations. This is important in determining whether the pump is too large or too small—either before or after it has been installed.

The dynamic column (total column) must be calculated before the horsepower required to drive the pump can be calculated. The dynamic column is the total of the dynamic lift (static lift + frictional resistance in the inlet piping) and the dynamic head (static head + frictional resistance in the outlet piping) or:

$$\text{dynamic column} = \text{dynamic lift} + \text{dynamic head}$$

The pressure, in lb. per sq. in., of a column of water is equal to (dynamic column × 0.433). Also, the head, in feet, of a column of water is equal to pressure (in lb. per sq. in.) times 2.31.

The *theoretical horsepower,* plus the additional horsepower required to overcome frictional resistance and inefficiency, is equal to the *actual horsepower* required to raise a given quantity of water to a given elevation. The formula for theoretical horsepower is:

$$\text{theoretical hp} = \frac{gpm \times 8\text{-}1/3 \times \text{dynamic column}}{33,000}$$

or;

$$\text{theoretical hp} = \frac{gpm \times 62.4 \times \text{dynamic column}}{33,000}$$

Actual horsepower can be determined by dividing the theoretical horsepower by the efficiency E of the pumping unit as:

$$\text{actual hp} = \frac{gpm \times 8\text{-}1/3 \times \text{dynamic column}}{33,000 \times E}$$

REVIEW QUESTIONS

1. How does the basic principle of the rotary pump differ from that of the centrifugal pump?
2. What are the three types of rotary pumps?
3. List three types of gears used in gear-type rotary pumps.
4. What two designs are used for rotary piston-type pumps?
5. How is the direction of rotation indicated on a rotary pump?
6. What is meant by "dynamic column" or total load with respect to delivery capacity of a pump?

CHAPTER 5

Reciprocating Pumps

A reciprocating pump is described as: A pump having a *to-and-fro motion;* its motion is *backward and forward* or *upward and downward* —as distinguished from the circular motion of centrifugal and rotary pumps. A *piston* or *plunger* differentiates the reciprocating pump from a centrifugal or rotary pump. In the reciprocating pump, the reciprocating motion of the *wrist pin* is converted to circular motion by means of a *connecting link* or *connecting rod* (Fig. 1). Three moving elements are necessary for operation of a reciprocating pump; they are: (1) *piston* or *plunger;* (2) *inlet* or *admission valve;* and (3) *outlet* or *discharge valve.* The piston or plunger works within a watertight cylinder.

The basic difference between a piston and a plunger should be noted (Fig. 2). A piston is shorter than the stroke of the cylinder; the plunger is longer than the stroke. Also, for another distinguishing feature, the packing is inlaid on the rim of the piston for a tight seal;

the packing is placed in a stuffing box located at the end of the cylinder to provide a tight seal when a plunger is used.

PRINCIPLES OF OPERATION

In general and with respect to the way that the water is handled, reciprocating pumps may be classified as: (1) *lift pumps;* and (2) *force pumps* which, in turn, are either *single-acting* or *double-acting* pumps.

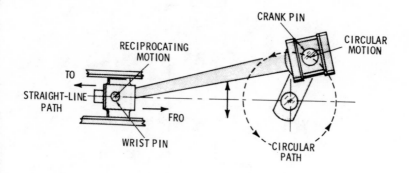

Fig. 1. Diagram illustrating the basic difference between reciprocating motion (left) and circular motion (right).

Lift Pumps

A lift pump is a single-acting pump; it consists of an open cylinder and a discharge or bucket-type valve (Fig. 3). This combination of an open cylinder and a bucket-type valve are the basic parts of the lift pump—it *lifts* the water, rather than forces it. In the lift pump, the bucket valve is built into the piston and moves upward and downward with the piston.

A four-stroke cycle is necessary to start the lift pump in operation (Fig. 4). The strokes are:

1. *Air exhaust.* The piston descends to the bottom of the cylinder, forcing out the air.
2. *Water inlet.* On this upward stroke, a vacuum is created; atmospheric pressure causes the water to flow into the cylinder.

225

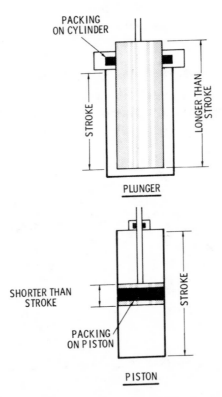

Fig. 2. Basic difference between a piston (left) and a plunger (right).

3. *Water transfer.* During this downward stroke, the water flows through the bucket valve, that is, it is "transferred" to the upper side of the piston.
4. *Water discharge.* As the piston rises, the water is "discharged," that is, it runs from the pump.

After the pump has been primed and it is in operation, the working cycle is completed in two strokes of the piston—a downward stroke and an upward stroke (Fig. 5). The downward stroke of the piston is called the *transfer* stroke, and the upward stroke is called the *intake and discharge* stroke, because water enters into the cylinder as the preceding charge of water is being discharged.

226

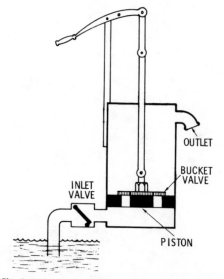

Fig. 3. Basic construction of a single-acting lift pump.

Ques. What is the usual result when the pump is out of operation for a considerable period of time?

Ans. The water leaks from the cylinder, leaving only air; therefore, in starting the pump, the first downward stroke of the piston attempts to remove the air, so that a vacuum is created for the next or upward stroke.

Ques. Why is it usually necessary to prime the pump?

Ans. In priming, a portion of the water reaches the region below the piston, reducing the clearance—some of the water seals the bucket valve. This results in a stronger vacuum for the upward stroke; therefore, more atmospheric pressure is available for causing the water to flow into the cylinder.

Force Pumps

The force pump is actually an extension of a lift pump, in that it both *lifts and forces* the water against an external pressure. The basic operating principle of the force pump is that it *forces* water above the atmospheric pressure range, as distinguished from the lift pump, which elevates the water to flow from a spout.

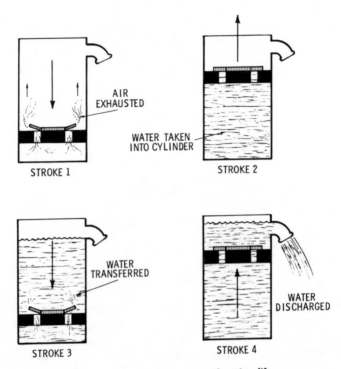

STROKE 1

AIR EXHAUSTED

WATER TAKEN INTO CYLINDER

STROKE 2

WATER TRANSFERRED

STROKE 3

WATER DISCHARGED

STROKE 4

Fig. 4. Four-stroke starting cycle for a single-acting lift pump.

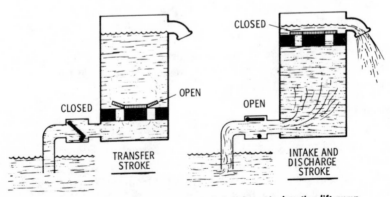

CLOSED

OPEN

CLOSED

OPEN

CLOSED

TRANSFER STROKE

INTAKE AND DISCHARGE STROKE

Fig. 5. Two-stroke working cycle (after priming) for a single-acting lift pump.

228

Single-Action—In a force pump, the water is forced out of the cylinder by means of a piston or plunger working against a pressure that corresponds to the *head* or elevation above the inlet valve to which the water is pumped. In its simplest form, the force pump consists of an inlet valve, a discharge valve, and a single-acting

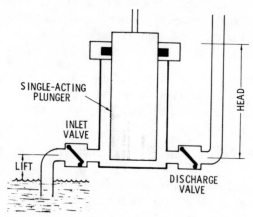

Fig. 6. Basic construction of a single-acting plunger-type force pump.

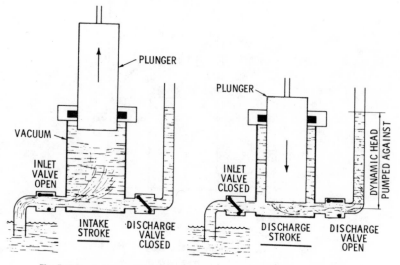

Fig. 7. Two-stroke working cycle of a single-acting plunger-type force pump.

229

plunger (Fig. 6). In a single-acting force pump, the working cycle is completed in two strokes—an upward (intake) stroke and a downward (discharge) stroke (Fig. 7). During the upward or intake stroke, the vacuum that is created enables atmospheric pressure to *force* the water into the cylinder. During this stroke the inlet valve is open and the discharge valve is closed. During the downward or discharge stroke, the plunger "displaces" or forces the discharge valve to open, and the water flows out of the cylinder against the pressure resulting from the dynamic head.

Ques. What features distinguish a *force* pump from a *lift* pump?
Ans. In place of the inlet and bucket-type valves used in the lift pump, inlet and discharge valves, along with a closed cylinder, are used in the force pump.

Ques. Describe the two-stroke working cycle in the single-acting force pump.
Ans. The vacuum created during the upward or intake stroke enables the atmospheric pressure to force water into the cylinder. The

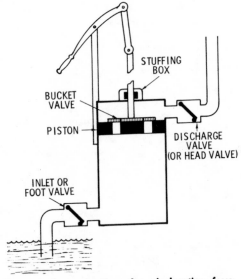

Fig. 8. Basic construction of a single-acting force pump with bucket-type valve in piston.

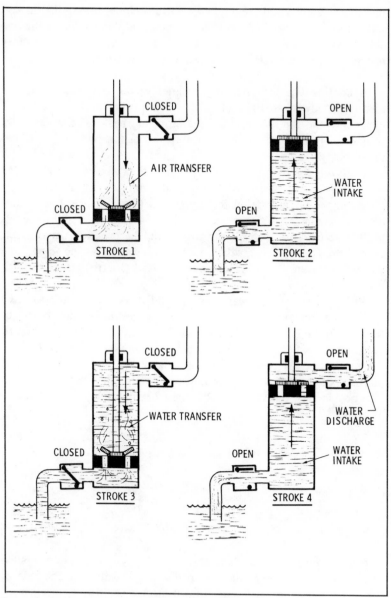

Fig. 9. Four-stroke starting cycle of a single-acting force pump with a bucket-type valve in the piston.

inlet valve is open and the discharge valve is closed during this stroke. During the downward or discharge stroke, the plunger forces the discharge valve to open, and the water is forced from the cylinder against the pressure resulting from the dynamic head.

In another type of force pump, inlet valves, bucket valves, and discharge valves are used (Fig. 8). The piston works in a closed cylinder (note the stuffing box for the piston rod). The water flows progressively through the inlet or foot valve, the bucket valve, and the discharge valve.

In *starting* the pump (Fig. 9), the air in the cylinder (assuming the system to be full of air) is transferred from the lower side of the piston to the upper side on the downward (first) stroke. On the upward (second) stroke, the vacuum that is created enables the atmospheric pressure to force the water into the cylinder. On the next downward (third) stroke, the water is transferred to the upper side of the piston, and is discharged on the upward (fourth) stroke through the discharge valve.

When the system is cleared of air and in operation, the *working cycle* is completed in two strokes of the piston—a downward or *transfer* stroke and an upward or *discharge* stroke. On the downward or transfer stroke, the water is transferred through the bucket valve. On the upward or discharge stroke, the water above the piston is discharged, and the water is admitted to the lower side of the piston. The positions of the valves during the working cycle are indicated in Table 1.

Table 1.   Valve Positions in a Single-Acting Force Pump

Stroke	Foot valve	Bucket valve	Discharge valve
Transfer (down)...............	Closed	Open	Closed
Discharge (up)...............	Open	Closed	Open

Double-Acting Force Pumps (Piston-Type)—In a double-acting piston-type force pump, the piston discharges water on one side of the piston while drawing water into the cylinder on the other side—without a transfer stroke. Thus, water is discharged on every stroke,

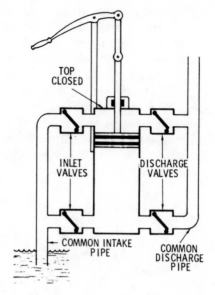

Fig. 10. Basic construction of a double-acting piston-type force pump with two sets of inlet and discharge valves.

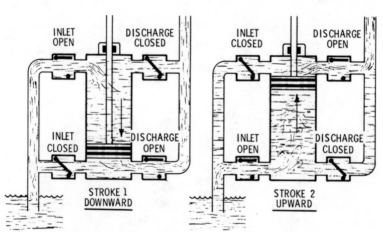

Fig. 11. Two-stroke working cycle of a double-acting piston-type force pump.

rather than on every other stroke, as in the single-acting pumps. Therefore, the capacity of a single-acting pump can be doubled in a double-acting pump having an identical cylinder displacement.

233

The basic construction of a double-acting piston-type force pump is shown in Fig. 10, and the two-stroke working cycle is illustrated in Fig. 11. The valve positions for the two strokes in the working cycle should be noted. The diagonally opposite inlet and discharge valves work in unison, that is, they are either open or closed at a given time.

Double-Acting Force Pump (Plunger-Type)—The operation of this pump is identical to the operation of the piston-type double-acting force pump, except for the replacement of the piston with a plunger. These pumps are of two different types with respect to the location of the packing, as: (1) *inside packed;* and (2) *outside packed.* The basic construction of a pump with inside packing is shown in Fig. 12.

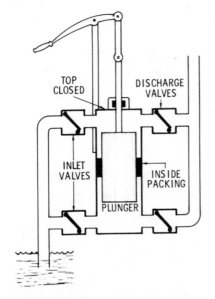

Fig. 12. Basic construction of a double-acting plunger-type force pump with inside packing.

In the pump with inside packing (see Fig. 12), the long cylinder is virtually divided into two separate chambers by the packing. The basic operation or two-stroke working cycle of this pump is illustrated in Fig. 13. In its upward and downward movements, the plunger alternately displaces water in the two chambers. A disadvantage of this type of pump is that it is necessary to remove the cylinder head to adjust or to renew the packing. Also, leakage through the packing cannot be determined while pump is in operation.

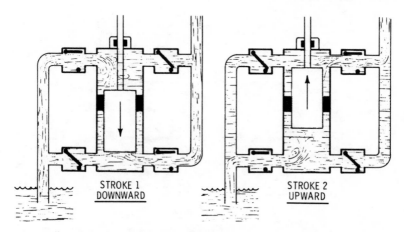

Fg. 13. Illustrating the two-stroke working cycle of a double-acting plunger-type pump with inside packing.

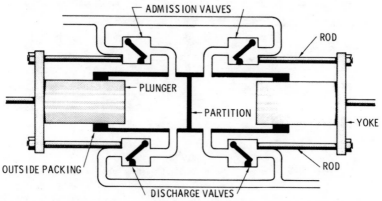

Fig. 14. Diagram showing basic construction of double-acting plunger-type force pump with outside packing.

These disadvantages are overcome in the plunger-type pump with outside packing (Fig. 14). Two plungers which are connected rigidly by yokes and rods are required in this design. The packing is on the outside; it is serviced easily and its condition can be checked easily.

The two-stroke working cycle of the outside-packed plunger-type pump is illustrated in Fig. 15. Note that the plungers move in unison

235

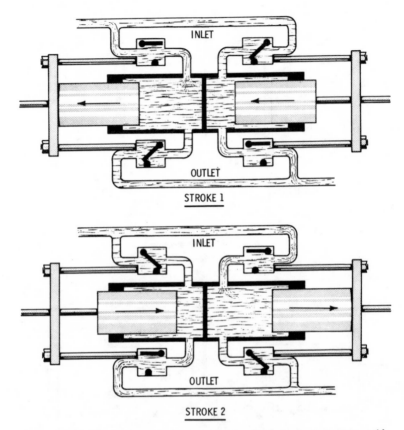

STROKE 1

STROKE 2

Fig. 15. Two-stroke working cycle of a double-acting plunger-type pump with outside packing.

—water is discharged at one end while the opposite plunger is receding to fill the other end. A disadvantage of the outside-packed pump is that its construction is more complicated and, therefore, more expensive than the inside-packed pump.

Ques. What are the disadvantages of the inside-packed plunger-type pump?

Ans. It is necessary to remove the head for adjusting or renewing the packing. Also, in operation, leakage through the packing cannot be determined.

Ques. What are the disadvantages of the outside-packed plunger-type pump?

Ans. The construction is more complicated which makes it more expensive than the inside-packed pump.

Self-Priming or Siphon Pumps

Since there is considerable clearance or enclosed space between the inlet and discharge valves, which becomes filled with air, most pumps require priming. Priming is necessary because the piston or plunger attempts to remove the air, creating a vacuum; then atmospheric pressure can force the water into the pump chamber.

Priming is an operation in which the pump chamber is filled with water to increase the vacuum; thus water is drawn in from the source. Unless the pump is provided with a vent and inlet opening, it may be necessary to remove a pump part to get water into the cylinder.

The basic construction of a self-priming or siphon pump is shown in Fig. 16. The pump casting consists of a pump barrel and a concentric outer chamber—the lower end of the barrel opening into the outer chamber. As shown in the illustration, the piston contains a bucket-type valve with a discharge valve at the top. The inlet is also at the top, so that the water is trapped in the outer chamber.

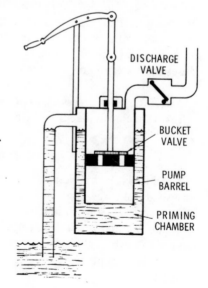

Fig. 16. Basic construction of a siphon-type or self-priming type of pump.

237

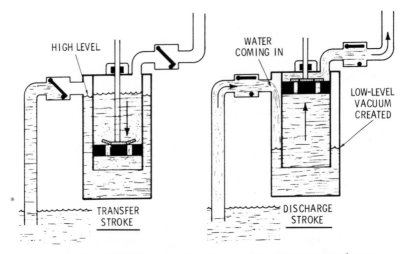

Fig. 17. Two-stroke working cycle of a siphon-type or self-priming type of pump.

The two-stroke working cycle of the self-priming pump is illustrated in Fig. 17. Initially, the outer chamber is filled with water. On the downward stroke, water is transferred through the bucket-type valve in the piston. This does not change the water level in the outer barrel. On the upward or discharge stroke, water is drawn into the barrel, which causes the water level in the outer chamber to recede to a low point. This, in turn, creates a vacuum in the outer chamber, which causes the water to flow in from the source and fill the outer chamber.

Ques. Why is it necessary to prime a pump?
Ans. To remove the air in the pump chamber.

CONSTRUCTION

In industrial hydraulic applications, the reciprocating piston pumps are usually of large capacity. These pumps are often used to supply fluid to a central hydraulic system. Water, soluble oil in water, hydraulic oil, and fire-resistant hydraulic fluid are some of the fluids that are handled by this type of pump.

Reciprocating pumps are designed with three, five, seven, or nine plungers. In the pump shown in Fig. 18, the *fluid end* of the pump

238

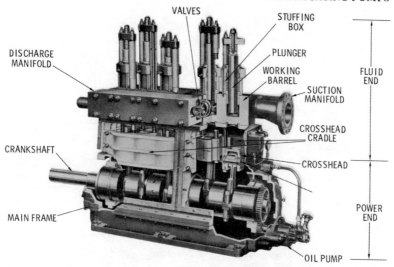

VALVES

STUFFING
BOX

DISCHARGE
MANIFOLD

PLUNGER

WORKING
BARREL

SUCTION
MANIFOLD

FLUID
END

CROSSHEAD
CRADLE

CRANKSHAFT

CROSSHEAD

POWER
END

MAIN FRAME

OIL PUMP

Courtesy The Aldrich Pump Company, Division of Ingersoll-Rand

Fig. 18. Cutaway showing the internal parts of a reciprocating piston pump.

is mounted at the top of the *power end* of the pump. This permits removal or replacement of valves without removing them from the pump entirely. In the *Aldrich* direct-flow design (Fig. 19), the liquid is passed from the suction end to the discharge end in a straight horizontal line through the valves and working barrel. The suction valve closes as the plunger moves downward, and the liquid is forced through the discharge valves which open against light spring pressure. When the plunger moves upward, the discharge valves close and liquid is drawn inward through the suction valves which open against similar spring pressure. Both valves are aided and sealed by the fluid pressure on closing.

The plunger-type pumps are widely used in industry to accomplish medium- to high-pressure chemical feeding. For example, a plunger-type pump can be used to meter chemicals and general industrial fluids, ranging from 0.2 to 1200 gallons per hour into pressures up to 1600 *psi*. This pump is available in either simplex or duplex design, with the stroke-adjustment-in-motion attachment as an optional extra. All the common water-treatment chemicals and liquids, such as acids, caustics, solvents, and many other industrial processing liquids,

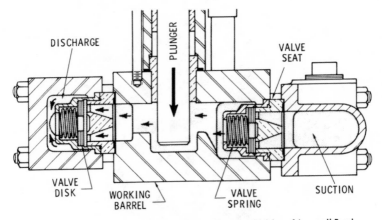

Courtesy The Aldrich Pump Company, Division of Ingersoll-Rand

Fig. 19. Direct-flow principle in the Aldrich reciprocating piston pump.

can be handled by this pump. The pump is readily adapted to applications requiring continuous, intermittent, or flow-responsive feeding.

CALCULATIONS

The numerous calculations, data, and tables relative to the various types of pumps can be useful to both operators and installation personnel. The calculations are diversified, and are intended to cover situations commonly encountered.

Lift

The theoretical lift and the actual lift are quite different; a number of factors cause the actual lift to be considerably less than the theoretical lift. Numerous installation failures have resulted from calculating the actual lift incorrectly.

Theoretical Lift—Although Torricelli demonstrated by experiment that atmospheric pressure of 14.7 lb. per sq. ft. can support a 33.83-ft. column of water at its maximum density, a pump cannot perform this feat. A barometer reading of 30 inches of mercury corresponds to the atmospheric pressure reading of 14.74 lb. per sq. in. Since a column of water approximately 2.31 ft. high exerts a pressure of 1 lb. per sq. in., the corresponding theoretical lift is:

theoretical lift = 2.31 × 14.74 = 34.049 ft.

Actual Lift—In practice, the actual lift of a pump is limited by the following factors:

1. Water temperature.
2. Air pressure decreasing at higher elevations.
3. Frictional resistance through pipes, fittings, and passages.
4. Leakage.

The practical or permissible lifts for the various temperatures and elevations are given in Table 2. Values that are preceded by a minus

Table 2. Practical Lifts at Various Temperatures and Altitudes

Alti-tude	Temperature of Water in Degrees F.															
	60	70	80	90	100	110	120	130	140	150	160	170	180	190	200	210
sea level	−22	−20	−17	−13	−13	−11	−8	−6	−4	−2	0	+ 3	+ 5	+ 7	+10	+12
2000 ft.	−19	−17	−15	−13	−11	− 8	−6	−4	−2	+1	+ 3	+ 5	+ 7	+10	+12	+15
4000 ft.	−17	−15	−13	−10	− 8	− 6	−4	−1	+1	+3	+ 5	+ 7	+10	+12	+14	
6000 ft.	−15	−13	−11	− 8	− 6	− 4	−2	+1	+3	+5	+ 7	+10	+12	+14	+16	
8000 ft.	−13	−11	− 9	− 6	− 4	− 2	0	+3	+5	+7	+ 9	+12	+14	+16		
10,000 ft.	−11	− 9	− 7	− 4	− 2	0	+2	+4	+7	+9	+11	+14	+16	+18		

(−) sign indicate *lift,* and values preceded by a plus (+) sign indicate *head*. The table does not apply for liquids other than water that are pumped; the actual lift depends on the specific gravity of the liquid being pumped. The thicker liquids, such as tar and molasses, should be moved toward the pump by means of gravity—then the inlet head is often called "negative lift."

The inlet pipe is often called the "suction pipe." To reduce frictional resistance to a minimum, elbows, or a number of closely spaced elbows, should be avoided, and the inlet pipe should be proportioned for a flow rate of 250 ft. per minute, for example. The following example may be used to determine the nominal pipe size.

Problem: Calculate the diameter of the inlet pipe (at 250 ft. per min.) required for a double-acting duplex pump with 10-in. cylinders by

241

12-in. stroke, operating at 50 *rpm*.

Solution: Since each pump makes two discharge strokes per revolution, the piston in each pump travels:

$$\frac{12 \times 2}{12} \times 50 = 100 \text{ ft.}$$

At 100 ft. per minute per pump, the total distance traveled by the two pistons, or total piston speed, is (2×100), or 200 ft. per minute. The area of the two pistons is:

$$\text{area} = 2 \times 10^2 \times 0.7854 = 157.1 \text{ sq. in.}$$

Therefore, the area of the inlet pipe is as much smaller than the cylinder area, as 200 is to 250, that is:

$$\text{area inlet pipe} = 157.1 \times \frac{200}{250} = 125.7$$

$$\text{diameter of inlet pipe} = \sqrt{\frac{125.7}{0.7854}} = 12\text{-}5/8 \text{ in. (approximately)}$$

For another example, the following problem can be used:

Problem: What diameter is required for the inlet pipe for a 1,000,000-gallon (per 24 hr.) capacity pump for a flow through the pipe of 250 ft. per minute?

Solution: For 1,000,000 gallons per 24-hr. period, the gallons per minute rating is:

$$gpm = \frac{1,000,000}{24 \times 60} = 694$$

Since one gallon of water has a volume of 231 cu. in., the volume of flow per minute is (694×231), or 160,314 cu. in. For a flow of 250 ft. per minute, the area of the inlet pipe must be:

$$\text{area inlet pipe} = \frac{160,314}{250 \times 12} = \frac{160,314}{3000} = 53.4 \text{ sq. in.}$$

$$\text{diameter of inlet pipe} = \frac{53.4}{0.7854} = 8\text{-}1/4 \text{ in. (approximately)}$$

Therefore, the next larger nominal pipe size (9 in.) is required. This is especially important for the inlet side, because increased flow with a smaller pipe adds to the frictional resistance of the pipe. Many pump manufacturers make the outlet opening one nominal pipe size smaller than the inlet opening. Nominal pipe sizes for the water end and the steam end are illustrated in Table 3.

Ques. Why is the next larger nominal pipe size used for the inlet pipe in the preceding problem?

Ans. The increased flow per minute with the smaller pipe adds to the frictional resistance of the pipe.

Ques. How is lift measured?

Ans. The vertical distance measured from the surface level of the water to the center point of the inlet opening on the pump.

Ques. What precaution is necessary in pump installation, if the surface level of the water is subject to fluctuation?

Ans. The actual lift should be calculated for the lowest water level.

Size of Discharge Pipe

The nominal size of the discharge pipe is usually smaller than the nominal size of the inlet pipe. The required size of the discharge line is dependent on its length, number of elbows in the line, and other conditions which tend to resist the flow of water. In most calculations, a flow of 400 ft. per minute can be used for building installations or tank service.

Head

As shown in Fig. 20, the static head H_s or dynamic head H_d may be determined by means of a test gauge A placed on the discharge pipe of a pump. If the pump is at rest, the gauge reading can be used to determine the static head H_s; if the pump is in operation, the dynamic head H_d can be determined.

Problem: When the gauge A indicates 35 lb., what is the static head H_s, with the pump at rest?

243

Table 3. Pipe Sizes For Pumps
(for Simplex boiler feed and general service piston-type pumps)

Size (Inches)	Boiler feed capacity		Capacities for continuous service*										Pipe Diameters (Inches)			
			Water and liquids up to 250 S.U.S. visc.		Liquids 250 to 500 S.U.S. visc.		Liquids 500 to 1000 S.U.S. visc.		Liquids 1000 to 2500 S.U.S. visc.		Liquids 2500 to 5000 S.U.S. visc.					
	Gal. per min.	Boiler horse-power	Gal. per min.	Piston speed —ft. per min.	Gal. per min.	Piston speed —ft. per min.	Gal. per min.	Piston speed —ft. per min.	Gal. per min.	Piston speed —ft. per min.	Gal. per min.	Piston speed —ft. per min.	Steam	Ex-haust	Suc-tion	Dis-charge
4½ × 2¾ × 6	8	110	13	45	11	39	10	35	8	27	6	22	¾	1	1¼	1
5¼ × 3¼ × 7	13	180	21	50	18	43	16	39	13	30	10	25	¾	1	1½	1¼
6 × 4⅛ × 8	23	325	38	55	33	48	29	43	23	33	19	27	¾	1	2½	2
7½ × 4½ × 10	31	450	52	63	45	55	40	49	31	38	25	31	1¼	1½	3	2½
8 × 5 × 12	42	600	71	70	61	60	55	54	42	42	35	35	1¼	1½	3	3
10 × 6 × 12	62	875	103	70	88	60	79	54	62	42	51	35	1¼	1½	4	3
12 × 7 × 12	84	1200	140	70	120	60	108	54	84	42	70	35	1¼	1½	5	4
14 × 8 × 12	109	1575	182	70	156	60	140	54	109	42	91	35	2½	3	5	4
16 × 10 × 18	219	3150	365	90	316	80	285	70	220	54	183	45	2½	3	8	6

*These normal operating capacities are for continuous duty. For emergency service increase about 15 per cent.

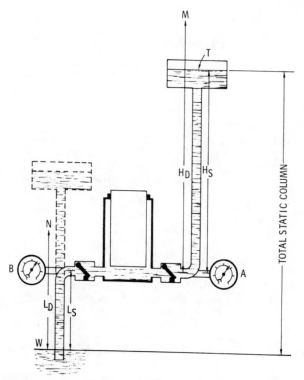

Fig. 20. Gauge method of obtaining static and dynamic head, static and dynamic lift, and static and dynamic total column.

Solution: Since a column of water 2.31 ft. in height exerts a pressure of 1 lb. per sq. in., the corresponding head H_s for a gauge reading of 35 lb. is:

$$H_s = 2.31 \times 35 = 80.9 \text{ ft.}$$

If the pump were in motion, the gauge A would indicate a higher reading because of frictional resistance to flow in the pipe, thus indicating the dynamic head H_d.

As indicated in Fig. 20, the head is not the total load on the pump, because lift must also be considered. The pump must raise the water from the level W in the well to the level T in the tank; this is referred to as total static column C_s or:

245

$$C_s = L_s + H_s$$

Also, the total dynamic column C_d is equal to:

$$C_d = L_d + H_d$$

The static lift L_s and the dynamic lift L_d can be determined by means of the vacuum gauge B (see Fig. 20); the gauge reading can be converted to the elevation in feet as shown in the following problem.

Example: What is the dynamic lift L_d if the vacuum gauge B reads 18 in.?

lift, in ft. = vacuum reading $\times$ 0.49116 $\times$ 2.31

In the equation, 0.49116 lb. per sq. in. corresponds to 1 in. of mercury, and a 2.31-ft. column of water exerts a pressure of 1 lb. per sq. in. Substituting the vacuum gauge B reading into the equation:

lift, in ft. = 18 $\times$ 0.49116 $\times$ 2.31 = 20.4 ft. (approximately)

To calculate the total column when the water flows toward the pump (from point N in Fig. 20), the inlet head should be subtracted from the discharge head. Therefore, the total column is $(H - L_n)$, in which the symbol n represents the "negative" lift. In direct-acting pumps, the allowance for velocity head is negligible if the velocities are low.

Displacement

The volume of fluid that is displaced by the piston or plunger in a single stroke is called *displacement* in a reciprocating pump. Displacement is expressed as: (1) cubic inches per stroke; (2) cubic inches per minute; and (3) gallons per minute. Displacement is more commonly stated in terms of "cubic inches per stroke." To determine piston *displacement, in cu. in. per stroke, multiply the effective area of the piston or plunger by the length of the stroke.*

246

Problem: Calculate the displacement, in cu. in. per stroke, in a dou-ble-acting simplex reciprocating pump with a water cylinder that is 5″ by 12″, with a 1-in. piston rod.

Solution: The effective piston area is:

$$\text{piston area} = (5)^2 \times 0.7854 = 19.635 \text{ sq. in.}$$

$$1/2 \text{ area piston rod} = \frac{(1)^2 \times 0.7854}{2} = -0.393$$

total effective
area of piston $= 19.242$ sq. in.

(the rod reduces displacement on only one side of piston;
therefore, one-half the rod area is an average)

$$\text{displacement} = \text{effective piston area} \times \text{stroke}$$

$$= 19.242 \times 12$$

$$= 230.9 \text{ cu. in. per stroke}$$

To determine the *displacement, in cu. in. per minute, multiply the cylinder displacement per stroke by the number of discharging strokes per minute.* Thus, in the preceding problem, each stroke is a dis-charging stroke, because the pump is a double-acting pump; there-fore, if the pump is operating at 92 strokes per minute:

$$\text{displacement} = 230.9 \times 92$$

$$= 21,242.8 \text{ cu. in. per minute}$$

To determine the *displacement, in gallons per minute, divide the displacement per minute by 231 (volume of 1 gallon of water).* There-fore, displacement is:

$$\text{displacement} = \frac{21,242.8}{231} = 91.96 \text{ gallons per minute}$$

Piston Speed

The total distance, in feet, traveled by a piston (or plunger) in one minute is referred to as the piston speed.

Example: If a piston having a 16-in. stroke operates at 60 strokes per minute, its piston speed is:

$$\text{piston speed} = \frac{16 \times 60}{12} = 80 \text{ ft. per minute}$$

In calculating displacement, piston speed can be used as a factor. Depending on the type of pump, a coefficient stated in terms of the "number of discharging strokes per revolution" must be used. For example, in the simplex *single-acting* pump (Fig. 21), only *one* dis-

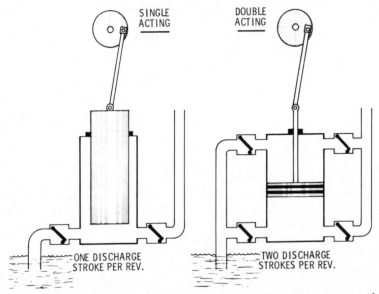

Fig. 21. Discharge strokes per revolution as a factor in determining piston speed for calculating displacement in a simplex single-acting pump (left) and double-acting pump (right).

charging stroke per revolution occurs, and in the *double-acting* pump, *two* discharging strokes per revolution occur.

Since piston speed is based on both the upward or "charging" stroke and the downward or "discharging" stroke and since only one discharging stroke occurs per revolution (two strokes) in a single-acting pump, the *coefficient* is *one-half* (0.5)—that is, the piston speed must be multiplied by 1/2, or 0.5, as in the following problem.

Problem: What is the displacement per revolution in a *single-acting* pump with a 300-cu. in. displacement, operating at 100 *rpm?*

Solution: Since, in a single-acting pump, only one discharging stroke per revolution occurs, the displacement per revolution is:

$$\text{displacement per revolution} = 300 \times 0.5$$

$$= 150 \text{ cu. in.}$$

Since two discharging strokes per revolution occur in a double-acting pump, the *coefficient* is *one-half* (0.5)—that is, the piston the preceding problem were a *double-acting* pump, the displacement per revolution would be:

$$\text{displacement per revolution} = 300 \times 1$$

$$= 300 \text{ cu. in.}$$

Since the displacement per revolution is equal to the displacement times coefficient (displacement × coefficient), the various combinations can be tabulated as follows:

	Single-Acting	Double-Acting
simplex	0.5	1.0
duplex	1.0	2.0
triplex	1.5	3.0

Therefore, a triplex single-acting pump with a displacement of 300 cu. in. per cylinder has a displacement per revolution of (300 × 1.5), or 450 cu. in.; and a duplex double-acting pump with the same displacement per cylinder has a displacement per revolution of (300 × 2.0), or 600 cu. in.

Slip

In the foregoing problems, the displacements mentioned were theoretical displacements. In actual operating conditions, a pump cannot discharge a volume of water that is equal to its theoretical displacement because of: (1) slip through the valves; and (2) leakage. The *slip* is generally expressed as a *percentage of the displacement;* it is *that amount by which the volume of water delivered per stroke falls short of the pump's displacement.*

Problem: What is the slip, in percentage of the displacement, in a pump with a displacement of 300 cu. in. per stroke, but discharges only 285 cu. in. of water per stroke?

Solution: The slip is (300−285), or 15 cu. in.; therefore, the percentage is:

$$\text{slip} = \frac{15}{300} \times 100 = 5 \text{ percent}$$

The percentage of slip varies from 2 to 10 percent, depending on the type of pump (piston or plunger), the condition of the pump, and the pressure that the pump is working against. In actual practice, a slip of 2 percent is a common value for a plunger-type pump; for light-service piston pumps, the slip is approximately 5 percent. A slip of 10 percent is common for pressure-type piston pumps. Another factor that may reduce the output of a high-speed reciprocating pump occurs when the speed is too high for the water to flow through the inlet valves fast enough to fill the cylinder completely.

In pumps with bucket valves, operating on low lift where the column of water has sufficient dynamic inertia to continue in motion during a portion, or all, of the return stroke, the discharge volume may be greater than the displacement. This condition is referred to as *negative slip.*

Capacity

The capacity of a pump is the *actual volume of water or fluid delivered;* it is usually stated in terms of *gallons per stroke* or *gallons per minute* when discharging at a given speed.

Problem: A single-acting pump with a displacement of 300 cu. in. is operating at 100 strokes per minute. What is its capacity in gallons per minute with a 5 percent slip?

Solution: For a single-acting pump, there are (100÷2), or 50 discharging strokes per minute, hence:

displacement per minute = 300 × 50 = 15,000 cu. in.

5 percent slip = 15,000 × 0.05 = 750 cu. in.

capacity per minute $= 15,000 - 750 = 14,250$ cu. in.

capacity per minute $= \dfrac{14,250}{231} = 61.59$ gallons

To calculate the *capacity of a pump: Multiply* the area of the piston (sq. in.) by the length of the stroke (in.) and by the number of delivery strokes per minute; *divide* the product by 1728 (to obtain theoretical capacity in cu. ft.) or by 231 (to obtain theoretical capacity in gallons). Multiply the result by the efficiency factor for the pump to obtain the approximate net capacity. Expressed as a formula

$$\text{approximate net capacity} = \frac{0.7854 \times D^2 \times L \times N}{1728} \times (1\text{-}f) \text{ cu. ft.}$$

or;

$$= \frac{0.7854 \times D^2 \times L \times N}{231} \times (1\text{-}f) \text{ gallons}$$

in which;

D is diameter of piston or plunger, in inches
L is length of stroke, in inches
N is number of delivery strokes per minute
f is slip, in percentage of displacement
$1728 =$ cu. in. in 1 cu. ft.
  $231 =$ cu. in. in 1 U.S. gallon

Problem: Calculate the approximate net capacity of a 3″ diameter × 5″ piston stroke double-acting pump, operating at 75 *rpm,* assuming a 5 percent slip.

Solution: Using the formula:

$$\text{approximate net capacity} = \frac{0.7854 \times (3)^2 \times 5 \times 150}{1728}$$

$$\times (1.0 - 0.05) = 2.92 \text{ cu. ft.}$$

$$= \frac{0.7854 \times (3)^2 \times 5 \times 150}{231}$$

$$\times (1.0 - 0.05) = 22.8 \text{ gal.}$$

251

Efficiency

In general, efficiency is the *ratio of the useful work performed by a prime mover to the energy expended in producing it*. In regard to pumps, there are several types of efficiency, such as hydraulic, volumetric, thermal, mechanical, and overall efficiency.

Hydraulic Efficiency—This is the *ratio of the total column (dynamic head + dynamic lift) pumped against to the total column, plus hydraulic losses,* including all losses, such as velocity head, from the source of supply through the water-end cylinders to the point of attachment of the discharge gauge.

Volumetric Efficiency—The *ratio of the capacity to the displacement* is termed *volumetric efficiency* as:

$$\text{volumetric efficiency} = \frac{\text{capacity}}{\text{displacement}}$$

Thermal Efficiency—The *ratio* of the *heat utilized* by the pump in doing useful work to the *heat supplied* is termed *thermal efficiency*. The formula is:

$$E_t = 2\,\frac{42.44 \times P \times 60}{S(H-h)}$$

in which;

P	is horsepower
S	is steam consumed, in lb. per hr.
H	is total heat in 1 lb. of steam at initial pressure
n	is total heat in 1 lb. of water supplied
42.44	is heat equivalent of 1 horsepower, in *Btu* per minute

Mechanical Efficiency—The *ratio* of the *indicated horsepower of the water end to the indicated horsepower of the steam* end is the *mechanical efficiency,* that is:

$$\text{mechanical efficiency} = \frac{\text{indicated horsepower (water end)}}{\text{indicated horsepower (steam end)}}$$

This factor can be determined only by actual test. One manufacturer states that the mechanical efficiency of direct-acting pumps

Table 4. Mechanical Efficiency of Pumps

Stroke of Pump (inches)	Piston-Type (percent)	Outside-Packed Plunger-Type (percent)
3	55	50
5	60	56
6	65	61
7	68	64
8	72	68
10	76	72
12	78	75
16	80	77
20	83	80
24	85	82

varies with the size and type of pump from 50 to 90 percent (see Table 4).

Horsepower at Water End of Pump—The horsepower required for a given pump capacity can be calculated by the following formulas:

$$thp = \frac{\text{cu. ft.} \times W(L_s + H_s)}{33,000}$$

$$ihp = \frac{\text{cu. ft.} \times W(L_d + H_d)}{33,000}$$

in which,

thp = theoretical horsepower

ihp = indicated horsepower

W = weight of one cu. ft. of water, in lb.

L_s = static lift, in ft.

L_d = dynamic lift, in ft.

H_s = static head, in ft.

H_d = dynamic head, in ft.

253

Problem: What theoretical horsepower (*thp*) is required to raise 100 cu. ft. of water to 200 ft.? The lift is 10 ft. and the water temperature is 75°F.

Solution: At 75°F., 1 cu. ft. of water weighs 62.28 lb.; substituting in the formula:

$$thp \text{ (at 75°F.)} = \frac{100 \times 62.28 \times (10 + 200)}{33,000} = 39.63$$

At 35°F. (cold weather), the weight of 1 cu. ft. of water increases to 62.42; the horsepower increases in proportion to the ratio of the two weights, as follows:

$$thp \text{ (at 35°F.)} = \frac{39.63 \times 62.42}{62.28} = 39.7$$

In comparing the preceding equations, it may be noted that temperature causes only a slight difference in the results. Thus, the temperature factor can be disregarded for most calculations, and the common weight value of 62.4 lb. per cu. ft. of water can be used. The theoretical horsepower required to raise water to various heights is shown in Table 5.

SUMMARY

A reciprocating pump has a to-and-fro motion; its motion is backward and forward—or upward and downward—as distinguished from the circular motion of centrifugal and rotary pumps. A *piston* or *plunger* differentiates the reciprocating pump from a centrifugal or rotary pump. In the reciprocating pump, the reciprocating motion of the *wrist pin* is converted to circular motion by means of a connecting link or *connecting rod.*

A lift pump is a single-acting pump; it consists of an open cylinder and a discharge or bucket-type valve. It *lifts* the water, rather than *forces* it. A *force pump* is either a *single-acting* or a *double-acting* pump.

After the lift pump has been primed, its working cycle is completed in two strokes of the piston: (1) a downward or transfer stroke; and (2) the upward stroke, which is an intake and discharge stroke, be-

Table 5. Table of Theoretical Horsepower Required to Elevate Water to Various Heights

Gallons per Minute	5 feet	10 feet	15 feet	20 feet	25 feet	30 feet	35 feet	40 feet	45 feet	50 feet	60 feet	75 feet	90 feet	100 feet	125 feet	150 feet	175 feet	200 feet	250 feet	300 feet	350 feet	400 feet	Gallons per Minute
5	.006	.012	.019	.025	.031	.037	.044	.05	.06	.06	.07	.09	.11	.12	.16	.19	.22	.25	.31	.37	.44	.50	5
10	.012	.025	.037	.050	.062	.075	.087	.10	.11	.12	.15	.19	.22	.25	.31	.37	.44	.50	.62	.75	.87	1.00	10
15	.019	.037	.056	.075	.094	.112	.131	.15	.17	.19	.22	.28	.34	.37	.47	.56	.66	.75	.94	1.12	1.31	1.50	15
20	.025	.050	.075	.100	.125	.150	.175	.20	.22	.25	.30	.37	.45	.50	.62	.75	.87	1.00	1.25	1.50	1.75	2.00	20
25	.031	.062	.093	.125	.156	.187	.219	.25	.28	.31	.37	.47	.56	.62	.78	.94	1.09	1.25	1.56	1.87	2.19	2.50	25
30	.037	.075	.112	.150	.187	.225	.262	.30	.34	.37	.45	.56	.67	.75	.94	1.12	1.31	1.50	1.87	2.25	2.62	3.00	30
35	.043	.087	.131	.175	.219	.262	.306	.35	.39	.44	.52	.66	.79	.87	1.08	1.31	1.53	1.75	2.19	2.62	3.06	3.50	35
40	.050	.100	.150	.200	.250	.300	.350	.40	.45	.50	.60	.75	.90	1.00	1.25	1.50	1.75	2.00	2.50	3.00	3.50	4.00	40
45	.056	.112	.168	.225	.281	.337	.394	.45	.51	.56	.67	.84	1.01	1.12	1.41	1.69	1.97	2.25	2.81	3.37	3.94	4.50	45
50	.062	.125	.187	.250	.312	.375	.437	.50	.56	.62	.75	.94	1.12	1.25	1.56	1.87	2.19	2.50	3.12	3.75	4.37	5.00	50
60	.075	.150	.225	.300	.375	.450	.525	.60	.67	.75	.90	1.12	1.35	1.50	1.87	2.25	2.62	3.00	3.75	4.50	5.25	6.00	60
75	.093	.187	.281	.375	.469	.562	.656	.75	.84	.94	1.12	1.40	1.69	1.87	2.34	2.81	3.28	3.75	4.69	5.62	6.56	7.50	75
90	.112	.225	.337	.450	.562	.675	.787	.90	1.01	1.12	1.35	1.68	2.02	2.25	2.81	3.37	3.94	4.50	5.62	6.75	8.87	9.00	90
100	.125	.250	.375	.500	.625	.750	.875	1.00	1.12	1.25	1.50	1.87	2.25	2.50	3.12	3.75	4.37	5.00	6.25	7.50	8.75	10.00	100
125	.156	.312	.469	.625	.781	.937	1.094	1.25	1.41	1.56	1.87	2.34	2.81	3.12	3.91	4.69	5.47	6.25	7.81	9.37	10.94	12.50	125
150	.187	.375	.562	.750	.937	1.125	1.312	1.50	1.69	1.87	2.25	2.81	3.37	3.75	4.69	5.62	6.56	7.50	9.37	11.25	13.12	15.00	150
175	.219	.437	.656	.875	1.093	1.312	1.531	1.75	1.97	2.19	2.62	3.28	3.94	4.37	5.47	6.56	7.66	8.75	10.94	13.12	15.31	17.50	175
200	.250	.500	.750	1.000	1.250	1.500	1.750	2.00	2.25	2.50	3.00	3.75	4.50	5.00	6.25	7.50	8.75	10.00	12.50	15.00	17.50	20.00	200
250	.312	.625	.937	1.250	1.562	1.875	2.187	2.50	2.81	3.12	3.75	4.69	5.62	6.25	7.81	9.37	10.94	12.50	15.72	18.75	21.87	25.00	250
300	.375	.750	1.125	1.500	1.875	2.250	2.625	3.00	3.37	3.75	4.50	5.62	6.75	7.50	9.37	11.25	13.12	15.00	18.75	22.50	26.25	30.00	300
350	.437	.875	1.312	1.750	2.187	2.625	3.062	3.50	3.94	4.37	5.25	6.56	7.87	8.75	10.94	13.12	15.31	17.50	21.87	26.25	30.62	35.00	350
400	.500	1.000	1.500	2.000	2.500	3.000	3.500	4.00	4.50	5.00	6.00	7.50	9.00	10.00	12.50	15.00	17.50	20.00	25.00	30.00	35.00	40.00	400
500	.625	1.250	1.875	2.500	3.125	3.750	4.375	5.00	5.62	6.25	7.50	9.37	11.25	12.50	15.62	18.75	21.87	25.00	31.25	37.50	43.75	50.00	500

This table gives the actual water horsepower. When selecting motors, turbines allowance must be made for pipe friction and loss in the pump, gears, belts, etc. One foot of head equals .43 pounds pressure per square inch.

cause water enters the cylinder as the preceding charge of water is being discharged.

The *force pump* is actually an extension of the lift pump—it *lifts and forces* the water against an external pressure. The basic operating principle of the force pump is that it forces water above the level attained by the atmospheric pressure range, as distinguished from the lift pump, which elevates the water to flow from a spout.

In a *single-acting force pump,* the water is forced from the cylinder by means of a piston or plunger working against a pressure that corresponds to the *head* or elevation above the inlet valve to which the water is pumped. The working cycle is completed in two strokes— an upward (intake) stroke and a downward (discharge) stroke. During the inlet stroke, the vacuum that is created enables atmospheric pressure to *force* the water into the cylinder. During the discharge stroke, the plunger "displaces" or forces the discharge valve to open, and the water flows from the cylinder against the pressure resulting from the dynamic head.

In a *double-acting force pump,* the piston discharges water from one side of the piston while drawing water into the cylinder on the other side—without a transfer stroke. Thus, water is discharged on each stroke, rather than on alternate strokes, as in the single-acting pumps. Therefore, the capacity of a double-acting pump can be twice that of a single-acting pump having an identical cylinder displacement.

Reciprocating piston pumps having a large capacity are used in many industrial applications. They are designed with three, five, seven, or nine plungers. The plunger-type pumps are widely used in industry to accomplish medium- to high-pressure chemical feeding. These pumps are readily adapted to applications requiring continuous, intermittent, or flow-responsive feeding.

Theoretical lift and actual lift are quite different. Actual lift is a lesser value than theoretical lift; it is limited by factors, such as: (1) water temperature; (2) decreased air pressure at higher elevations; (3) frictional resistance through pipes, fittings, and passages; and (4) leakage.

The nominal size of the discharge pipe is usually smaller than that of the inlet pipe. The required size of the discharge line is dependent on its length, number of elbows in the line, and other conditions that tend to resist the flow of water.

The total load on a pump is not equal to the head alone. The lift must also be considered. The pump must raise the water from the surface level in the wall to the surface level in the tank—this is termed *total static column*. The formula for total static column is: $C_s = L_s + H_s$. When all resistances to flow are considered, the total load becomes *total dynamic column,* and the formula is:

$$C_d = L_d + H_d.$$

The volume of fluid that is displaced by a piston or plunger in a single stroke is called *displacement*. Displacement is expressed as: (1) cubic inches per stroke; (2) cubic inches per minute; and (3) gallons per minute. To determine piston displacement in cubic inches per stroke, multiply the effective area of the piston or plunger by the length of the stroke.

The total distance, in feet, traveled by a piston (or plunger) in one minute is referred to as the *piston speed*. This is a factor in calculating displacement. In a simplex single-acting pump, only one stroke per revolution occurs; in the double-acting pump, two discharging strokes per revolution occur.

In a pump, *slip* is generally expressed as a percentage of the displacement. It is that amount by which the volume of water delivered per stroke falls short of the pump's displacement. The percentage of slip varies from 2 to 10 percent, depending on the type of pump (piston or plunger), the condition of the pump, and the pressure that the pump is working against. When the discharge volume is greater than the displacement, the condition is called "negative slip."

The *capacity* of a pump is the actual volume of water or fluid delivered; it is usually stated in terms of gallons per stroke or gallons per minute when discharging at a given speed. To calculate capacity, *multiply* the area of the piston (sq. in.) by the length of the stroke (in.) and by the number of delivery strokes per minute; divide the product by 1728 (to obtain theoretical capacity, in cu. ft.) or by 231 (to obtain theoretical capacity, in gallons).

Efficiency is the ratio of the useful work performed by a prime mover to the energy expended in producing it. There are several types of efficiency in regard to pumps, such as hydraulic, volumetric, thermal, mechanical, and overall efficiency.

257

REVIEW QUESTIONS

1. How does a reciprocating pump differ from a centrifugal or rotary pump?
2. How does the basic operation of a lift pump differ from that of a force pump?
3. What is the chief difference in the working cycles of the single-acting force pump and the double-acting force pump?
4. Compare the capacities of single-acting and double-acting force pumps having identical cylinder displacements.
5. What are the disadvantages of the inside-packed double-acting plunger-type force pump?
6. Describe the working cycle of the self-priming reciprocating pump.
7. What types of industrial applications use reciprocating piston pumps?
8. Compare theoretical lift and actual lift.
9. Why is the nominal size of the discharge pipe usually smaller than the nominal size of the intake line?
10 Why is the total load on a pump not equal to just the head alone?
11. What is meant by displacement, and how is it expressed?
12. What is meant by slip, and how is it expressed?
13. How is capacity of a pump calculated?

CHAPTER 6

Special Service Pumps

Pump selection should be based on a thorough understanding of the characteristics and fundamental principles of the basic types of pumps, such as centrifugal, rotary, reciprocating, etc., which have been discussed in the foregoing chapters. The basic operating principles and various design characteristics or features adapt these pumps to specialized or unusual service conditions. In some instances, pumps have been designed especially for a given type of job or service condition.

Many of the pumps that have been introduced are specifically designed for special types of service or operating conditions. Some of these special types of pumps are employed by fire departments, railroads, automobiles, diesel engines, contractors, mines, drainage, differentials, and numerous other applications throughout industry. Liquids requiring a special type of pump are pure water, sewage, paper stock, oil, milk, chemicals, magma, and various types of thick liquids.

SERVICE PUMPS

Simplex or duplex reciprocating piston-type pumps are well adapted for the service requirements found in tanneries, sugar refineries, bleacheries, etc. The duplex high-pressure reciprocating piston pump shown in Fig. 1 is adapted for high-pressure service on water supply systems in country clubs, dairies, industrial plants, etc. Two double-acting pistons actually provide four strokes per revolution, which produces a constant and even flow of liquid through the pump. This

259

Courtesy Deming Division, Crane Co.

Fig. 1. Double-acting, high-pressure, horizontal duplex reciprocating piston pump. This pump has two cylinders and is capable of capacities ranging from 5 to 9 gallons per minute at working pressures up to 350 lbs. per sq. in.

pump can handle either cold or hot water at temperatures up to 200°F. This type of pump is capable of capacities ranging from 295 to 1080 gallons per hour and working pressures ranging from 150 to 300 pounds.

The general purpose rotary gear-type pump (Fig. 2) is designed to handle either thick or thin liquids. It can operate smoothly in either direction of rotation with equal efficiency. These pumps can handle heavy, viscous materials, such as roofing materials and printing inks, as well as fuel oils, gasolines, and similar thin liquids. The pump shown is capable of capacities ranging from 40 to 600 gallons per minute and pressures to 100 pounds per sq. in.

The rotary gear-type pump shown in Fig. 3 is adaptable to a wide range of jobs, such as pressure lubrication, hydraulic service, fuel

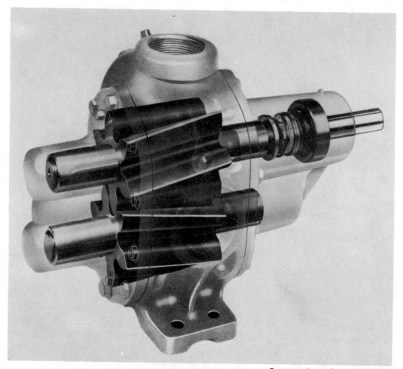

Courtesy Roper Pump Company

Fig. 2. General-purpose rotary gear-type pump designed to handle either thick or thin liquids. It is capable of capacities ranging from 40 to 600 gallons per minute and pressures up to 100 lbs. per sq. in.

supply, or general transfer work which includes pumping of clean liquids. The bearings are lubricated by the liquid being pumped. These pumps are self-priming and operate in either direction of rotation with equal efficiency. This type of pump is available in various sizes ranging from 3/4 to 110 gallons per minute at various pressure settings to 150 lb. per sq. in.

The self-priming motor-mounted centrifugal pump (Fig. 4) has several applications. It can be used on swimming pools, lawn sprinklers, booster service, recirculation, irrigation, dewatering, sump and bilge, liquid fertilizers, and chemical solutions. Its capacity is 10 to 130 gallons per minute against heads ranging to 120 ft.

261

SPECIAL SERVICE PUMPS

Courtesy Roper Pump Company

Fig. 3. Rotary gear-type pump used for a wide range of jobs, such as pressure lubrication, hydraulic service, fuel supply, or general transfer of clean liquids. Various pump sizes ranging from ¾ to 110 gallons per minute at pressure settings up to 150 lbs. per sq. in. are available.

The horizontally split casing double-suction single-stage centrifugal pump (Fig. 5) is designed for high efficiency with heavy casing walls for 175 lb. per sq. in. working pressure. This pump is used for general water supply, booster service, municipal waterworks, air washing, condenser cooling, water circulation, industrial service, building service, and chemical plants.

The dry-pit nonclog centrifugal pump (Fig. 6) is adapted to solids handling applications, such as sanitary waste, sewage lift stations, treatment plants, industrial waste, general drainage, sump service, dewatering, industrial process service, food processing, and chemical plants. The impeller is a nonclog fully enclosed type with extra-smooth passageways. The pump capacity ranges upward to 3000 gallons per minute against heads to 150 ft. This pump is available in both right- and left-hand rotation and in five styles of mechanical assemblies for ease of installation.

262

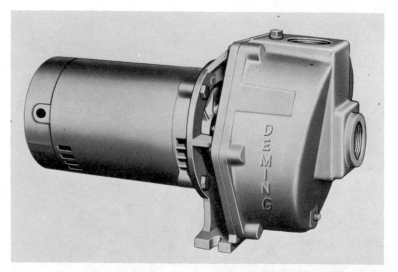

Courtesy Deming Division, Crane Co.

Fig. 4. Self-priming centrifugal pump used for applications such as swimming pools, lawn sprinkling, booster service, recirculation, irrigation, dewatering, sump and bilge, liquid fertilizer, and chemical solutions. Its capacity ranges from 10 to 130 gallons per minute against heads up to 120 ft.

The close-coupled single-suction single-stage centifugal pump (Fig. 7) is available in various sizes and designs for handling capacities to 2200 gallons per minute and heads to 500 ft. It is available in a wide variety of constructions for handling most liquids ranging from clear water to highly corrosive chemicals.

The double-suction single-stage pump shown in Fig. 8 is used extensively in nearly all types of service. The horizontally split casing provides easy access for maintenance and inspection of rotating parts without disturbing the piping. This pump is designed for capacities ranging from 10 to 20,000 gallons per minute.

For handling clear water at any temperature, the turbine-driven single-suction four-stage pump (Fig. 9) is capable of capacities ranging from 20 to 900 gallons per minute at heads up to 1500 ft. These pumps are both mechanically and hydraulically efficient.

Ques. What applications use pumps that are designed specifically for a special type of service?

Courtesy Deming Division, Crane Co.

Fig. 5. Single-stage double-suction centrifugal pump with horizontally split casing.

Courtesy Deming Division, Crane Co.

Fig. 6. Dry-pit nonclog centrifugal pump which is generally used for solids handling applications.

Courtesy Buffalo Forge Company

Fig. 7. A close-coupled single-suction single-stage centrifugal pump designed to handle most liquids ranging from clear water to highly corrosive chemicals at capacities up to 2200 gallons per minute and heads to 500 ft.

Ans. Fire departments, railroads, automobiles, diesel engines, contractors, mines, drainage, differentials, and numerous other applications throughout industry use special types of pumps.

Ques. What liquids require a special type of pump?

Ans. Pure water, sewage, paper stock, oil, milk, chemicals, magma, and various thick liquids require special types of pumps.

CHEMICAL AND PROCESS PUMPS

Centrifugal pumps are extensively used in handling the wide variety of corrosive and abrasive liquids in the chemical and paper industries. Formerly, pump life was exceedingly short, because the pump casings, impellers, shafts, and other parts were reduced rapidly by the liquid. The application of vulcanized rubber to the parts contacted by the liquid has extended the service life of these parts. Liquids handled by rubber-lined pumps are chlorinated paper stock, hypochlorous acid, chlorinated brines, sodium chloride, potassium chloride, brine slurries, hydrofluoric slurry, sulfurous water, caustic soda, and many other acids and caustics of various concentrations and temperatures.

265

Courtesy Buffalo Forge Company

Fig. 8. A double-suction single-stage pump with horizontally split casing. This pump is designed for capacities ranging from 10 to 20,000 gallons per minute.

In the operation of a paper mill, pumps are required to move the material from point to point throughout the mill—starting with the raw water and then the paper pulp—and finally to the head box on the papermaking machine. The various chemicals that are necessary in the papermaking process are handled by pumps, and the various

266

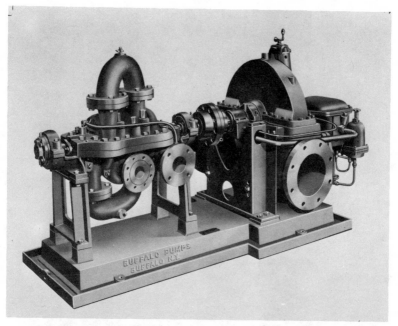

Courtesy Buffalo Forge Company

Fig. 9. A turbine-driven single-suction four-stage pump. This pump can handle clear water at capacities ranging from 20 to 900 gallons per minute and heads up to 1500 ft.

types of waste liquids are disposed of by means of pumps. The horizontal end-suction centrifugal pump shown in Fig. 10 is designed specifically for a wide range of applications in the chemical, petrochemical, and other types of material-processing industries which handle various corrosive and noncorrosive liquids, ranging from water and light hydrocarbons to heavy slurries.

Centrifugal pumps are widely used in the paper industry—the most important feature being the impeller. In general the characteristics of the impellers are few vanes, large inlets, and heavy rigid block plates and flanges. The impellers are shrouded and do not require wearing plates. The shape and number of vanes are governed by service conditions.

Centrifugal pumps made of *Pyrex* or glass are used to pump acids, milk, fruit juices, and other acid solutions. The glass is resistant to acid solutions; therefore, the liquid being pumped is not contami-

267

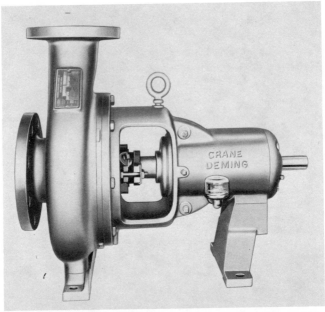

Courtesy Deming Division, Crane Co.

Fig. 10. A horizontal end-suction centrifugal pump used as a chemical and process pump.

nated by chemical reactions between the liquid and the material in the pump parts. Glass is resistant to all the acids, except hydrofluoric acid and glacial phosphoric acid. Pumps made of glass should not be used with alkaline solutions.

PUMPS FOR HANDLING OF SEWAGE

In this type of service, centrifugal pumps are required to pump either *raw sewage* or *sludge*. The *solid precipitant* which remains after the raw sewage has been treated chemically or bacterially is called "sludge."

The chief difference in centrifugal pumps used for raw sewage and those used for sludge is the design of the impeller that is used. To avoid clogging, the impeller used for raw sewage is an enclosed type, and it is usually wider with two to four vanes, depending on the size

268

Fig. 11. Vertical type of centrifugal
pump for sewage.

Courtesy Buffalo Forge Company

of the pump. The inlet portion of the vanes is usually rounded in design to offer less resistance to flow, and it is shaped to prevent its being clogged by strings, rags, and paper which tend to form a wad or ball of material.

The handling of sludge from a sewage treatment plant is more difficult than the handling of raw sewage, because larger quantities of the various solids are present. In addition to a properly designed impeller, the sludge pump is designed with a double-threaded screw in

269

Courtesy Buffalo Forge Company

Fig. 12. A horizontal type of centrifugal pump for sewage.

the inlet connection to force the sludge into the impeller; each thread of the screw connects to an impeller vane. Solids or stringy materials that extend beyond the edges of the screw are cut up as they pass between the edges of the screw and the flutes of the screw housing.

When sewage pumps are installed, they are usually relatively permanent, which means that the stationary pump parts—casing and base—should be substantial. The vertical type of sewage pump (Fig. 11) is designed with an extra-heavy cast iron base and thick casing. Hand-hole openings with quick-access covers are provided in the base and casing for convenience in inspection and cleaning. A horizontal-type sewage pump used on lift-station service is shown in Fig. 12.

OTHER SPECIAL SERVICE PUMPS

In addition to the chemical and process pumps and the sewage pumps, various other special services require pumps designed specifically for that type of service. The sugarmaking industry is an example.

Magma Pumps

The term *magma* includes any crude mixture (especially of organic matter) that is in the form of a thin paste. Therefore, a magma pump

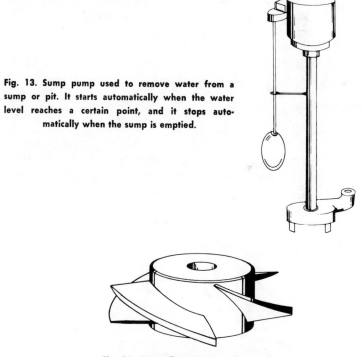

Fig. 13. Sump pump used to remove water from a sump or pit. It starts automatically when the water level reaches a certain point, and it stops automatically when the sump is emptied.

Fig. 14. "Propeller-type" impeller used on irrigation pumps.

is a reciprocating pump designed to move the various heavy confectionary mixtures and nonliquids involved in the sugarmaking process. These pumps are designed without inlet valves, which means that the

271

liquid flows by gravity to the pump (negative lift), so the function of the inlet valves is performed by the piston of the reciprocating pump.

Sump Pumps

A sump pump (Fig. 13) is not a sewage pump; the liquid that is pumped is not as thick as sewage, and it is relatively free from foreign matter. A *sump* is a cistern or reservoir constructed at a low point; the water that accumulates is drainage water, and it is pumped away by means of the sump pump.

These pumps are often used to remove excess drainage water from nonwaterproof basements which have become flooded during periods of heavy rainfall. The sump pump is entirely automatic in its action; since the pump is submerged, it does not require priming. The motor is controlled by a float which is arranged to start the motor automatically when the water level in the pit or sump reaches a given point; the motor is stopped automatically when the sump is emptied.

Irrigation Pumps

The pumps used in irrigation service are designed for large capacities and low heads. These pumps are also used for land drainage, flood control, storm water disposal, etc. Since the impeller resembles a marine type of impeller, the pumps are sometimes called "propeller" pumps (Fig. 14). Service requirements usually demand that irrigation pumps be portable self-contained pumping units that can be suspended above a flow of water or from a structure positioned above the water.

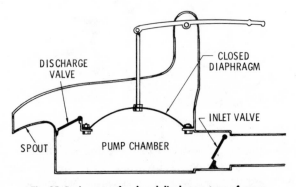

Fig. 15. Basic parts of a closed-diaphragm type of pump.

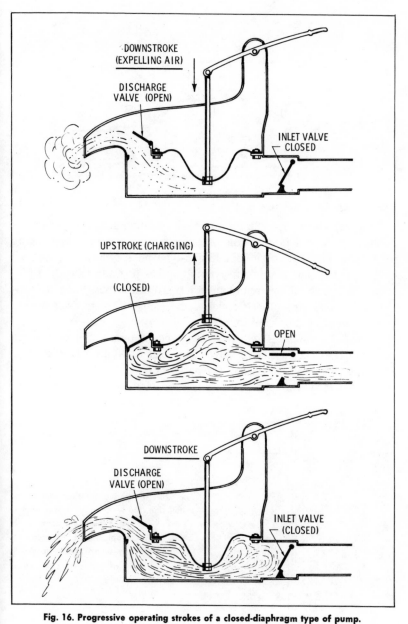

Fig. 16. Progressive operating strokes of a closed-diaphragm type of pump.

273

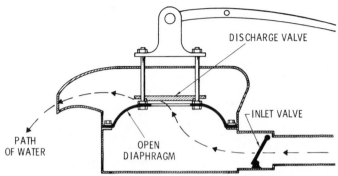

Fig. 17. Basic parts of an open-diaphragm type of pump.

Diaphragm-Type Pumps

The diaphragm-type pump employs a yielding substance (such as rubber), rather than a piston or plunger, to perform the pumping operation. The two basic diaphragm-type pumps are: (1) *closed;* and (2) *open.* The diaphragm-type pump has proved especially satisfactory for such jobs as removing water from trenches, flooded foundations, drains, and other flooded depressions where there is a high proportion of mud or sand to water.

Closed-Diaphragm Pump—In this type of pump, the diaphragm does not bear the discharge valve. The inlet valve and the discharge valve are located in the base of the pump (Fig. 15). The pump chamber is closed by a diaphragm, and is connected to the inlet. The dis-

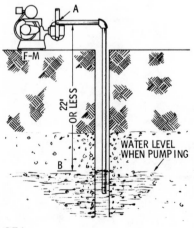

Fig. 18. Illustrating shallow-well pump installation. The working level of the water in the well cannot be more than 22 ft. below the inlet opening of the pump for satisfactory pump operation.

274

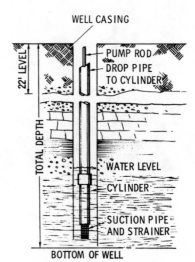

Fig. 19. Deep-well construction details.

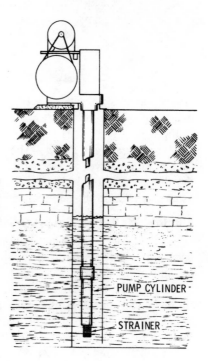

Fig. 20. The cylinder should be placed at least 5 ft. below the working level of the water in the well. A strainer should be fitted to the bottom of the cylinder.

275

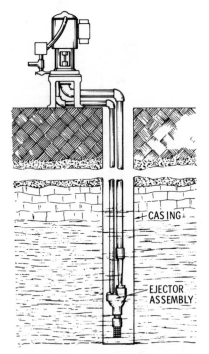

CASING

EJECTOR
ASSEMBLY

Fig. 21. A deep-well jet-type pump.

charge valve is an extension of the pump chamber. The progressive operating strokes of the closed-diaphragm type of pump are shown in Fig. 16.

Open-Diaphragm Pump—The opening in the diaphragm of this type of pump serves as a seat for the discharge valve (Fig. 17). Thus the discharge valve is borne by the diaphragm, rather than serving as an extension to the pump chamber.

Shallow-Well and Deep-Well Pumps

A *shallow-well* pump installation is shown in Fig. 18. The working level of the water in the well should be less than 22 ft. below the inlet opening of the pump.

Deep-well construction details are illustrated in Fig. 19. In successful deep-well pump installations, the cylinder is placed at least 5 ft. below the working level of the water in the well. A strainer should be fitted to the bottom of the cylinder (Fig. 20). The deep-well jet-type pump is illustrated in Fig. 21.

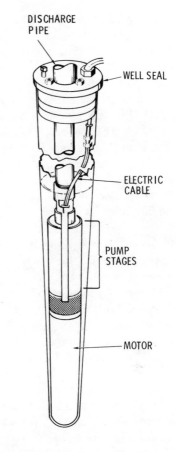

DISCHARGE
PIPE

WELL SEAL

ELECTRIC
CABLE

PUMP
STAGES

MOTOR

Fig. 22. A submersible deep-well pump. The pump-motor unit is completely submerged in the well; therefore, the pump cannot freeze or lose its prime, and it does not require a pit or well house. The entire unit can be lowered easily if the water level in the well should drop.

In the submersible deep-well pump illustrated in Fig. 22, the pump-motor unit is completely submerged in the well. The pump cannot freeze or lose its prime. This type of pump does not require a pit or well house, and it can easily be lowered if the water level in the well should drop.

Ques. Under what condition can a shallow-well pump be used?

Ans. It can be used when the working level of the water in the well is less than 22 ft. below the inlet opening of the pump.

277

SUMMARY

Pump selection should be based on a thorough understanding of the characteristics and fundamental principles of the basic types of pumps—centrifugal, rotary, reciprocating, etc. The basic operating principles and various design characteristics or features adapt these pumps to specialized or unusual service conditions.

The simplex or duplex reciprocating piston-type pumps are well adapted for the service requirements found in tanneries, sugar refineries, bleacheries, etc. They are used for high-pressure service on water supply systems in country clubs, dairies, and industrial plants.

The general purpose rotary gear-type pumps are designed to handle either thick or thin liquids, and they are designed to operate smoothly in either direction of rotation with equal efficiency. The thicker liquids, such as roofing materials and printing inks, as well as fuel oils, gasolines, and similar thin liquids can be handled by these pumps, the rotary gear-type pump is also adapted to pressure lubrication, hydraulic service, fuel supply, or general transfer work which includes pumping of clean liquids.

The self-priming motor-mounted centrifugal pump has several applications, including lawn sprinklers, swimming pools, booster service, recirculation, irrigation, dewatering, sump and bilge, liquid fertilizers, and chemical solutions. Centrifugal pumps are also adapted to solids handling applications, such as sanitary waste, sewage lift stations, treatment plants, industrial waste, general drainage, sump service, industrial process service, food processing, and chemical plants.

The chemical and processing industries employ centrifugal pumps extensively in handling a wide variety of corrosive and abrasive liquids. The service life of pumps has been extended substantially by the use of rubber-lined pump parts for handling various liquids used in the chemical and paper industries. Pyrex or glass pumps are used to pump acids, milk, fruit juices, and other acid solutions; therefore, the liquid being pumped is not contaminated by chemical reactions between the liquid and the material in the pump parts.

Centrifugal pumps are also used to pump either *raw sewage* or *sludge*. The handling of sludge from a sewage treatment plant is more difficult than handling raw sewage, because larger quantities of various solids are present. The impeller is designed differently for handling raw sewage and sludge—depending on which is to be handled.

Magma pumps are designed to handle crude mixtures (especially of organic matter) that are in the form of a thin paste. For example, in the sugarmaking process, heavy confectionary mixtures and non-liquids are involved. These pumps are designed without inlet valves. The valves are not needed, because the liquid flows by gravity to the pump, and their function is performed by the piston of the reciprocating pump.

Other special service pumps are: (1) sump pumps; (2) irrigation pumps; (3) diaphragm-type pumps, which may be either closed-diaphragm or open-diaphragm pumps; and (4) shallow-well or deep-well pumps, including the jet-type and submersible pumps.

REVIEW QUESTIONS

1. What factors determine pump selection?
2. What are the typical applications for reciprocating piston-type pumps?
3. What are the typical applications for centrifugal pumps?
4. What types of pumps are suitable for the chemical and processing industries?
5. What design feature is important in selection of pumps for raw sewage and sludge?
6. What is the chief factor in determining whether to select a shallow-well or a deep-well pump?

CHAPTER 7

Hydraulic Accumulators

An *accumulator* is a cylinder in which a liquid is stored under pressure, so that it can serve as a reservoir and regulator of power; this enables pumps operating under a uniform load to meet an intermittent or fluctuating demand for power. A *hydraulic accumulator* is designed to accumulate energy that is to be expended intermittingly.

The hydraulic accumulator can be compared to the more common storage battery in that energy is stored until it is needed. The hydraulic accumulator stores *hydraulic energy,* and the storage battery (called "accumulator" in England) stores electrical energy.

BASIC CONSTRUCTION AND OPERATION

The essential parts (Fig. 1) of an accumulator are: (1) *plunger* or *ram;* (2) *cylinder;* and (3) *weights.* In the accumulator, a plunger is placed within a vertical cylinder which is closed at the lower end and provided with a stuffing box at the upper end. Weights are secured in position at the upper end of the plunger to produce the desired pressure. An outlet and an inlet for the liquid are located at the lower end of the cylinder.

As shown in Fig. 1, water is forced into the cylinder by means of the force pump, which causes the weighted plunger to rise. The force or pressure from the weighted plunger on the water is transmitted to the machines operated by the system, as long as the plunger has not reached the lower end of its stroke.

During periods when there is no demand for power, the plunger is prevented from rising too high and leaving the cylinder by means of stops which arrest the motion of the plunger when it arrives at the

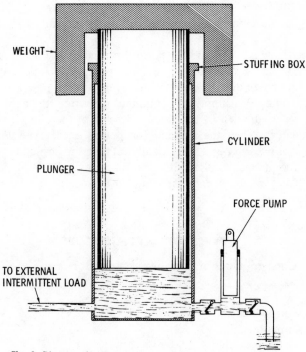

Fig. 1. Diagram showing the essential parts of a weight-loaded hydraulic accumulator.

upper end of its stroke. If there is a demand for power and the load is small, the force pump can supply the required quantity of water by continuing to operate. However, if the load is large and more power is demanded than the pump can supply, a portion of the power is supplied by the slow descent of the plunger inside the accumulator. When the load is removed or power is no longer demanded, the force pump continues to operate, gradually filling the cylinder and causing the plunger to rise to the upper end of its stroke; thus a quantity of energy equal to the quantity of energy expended in the descent of the plunger is "accumulated" or stored in the cylinder.

Ques. How does the accumulator operate?

Ans. As shown in Fig. 1, water is forced into the cylinder by the force pump, causing the weighted plunger to rise. The force or pressure of the water is transmitted to machines operated by the system, as long as the plunger has not reached the lower end of its stroke.

Ques. How is a demand for power satisfied by the accumulator?

Ans. If the load is small, the force pump can supply the water needed by continuing to operate; however, if more power is required than the pump can supply by continuous operation, the extra demand for power is supplied by the gradual descent of the plunger inside the accumulator. When the demand for power is met (no load), the pump continues to operate, gradually refilling the accumulator, which causes the plunger to rise to the top of the cylinder until the energy accumulated in the cylinder is equal to the energy expended during the descent of the plunger.

TYPES OF ACCUMULATORS

Three general types of hydraulic accumulators are in use. They are as follows:

1. Weight-loaded.
2. Spring-loaded.
3. Air- or gas-type.

Weight-Loaded

In the weight-loaded accumulator (Fig. 2) the dead weight on the plunger or ram may be cast iron, steel, concrete, water, or other heavy material. The weight-loaded accumulator may be either a direct or an inverted type (Fig. 3). In the direct type of accumulator, the plunger is movable; the cylinder is movable in the inverted type.

In the larger direct-type accumulators, the plunger may be provided with a yoke at its upper end. Two rods are suspended in the ends of the yoke, and the required number of weights (ring-type weights) are threaded onto the rods (Fig. 4). This type of accumulator may be provided with a 24-in plunger, and it may be weighted to develop 600 lb. of pressure per sq. in. The accumulator is self-contained; therefore, it requires no frame or guide posts. A desirable feature is that the packing is readily accessible at the top of the cylinder. An undesirable feature of the inverted type of accumulator is that it is dif-

Courtesy The Aldrich Pump Company, Division of Ingersoll-Rand

Fig. 2. Weight-loaded accumulators. The weighted-tank type of accumulator (left) and the cast-iron weighted type of accumulator (right) store hydraulic fluid under constant pressure during periods of off-peak demand and return it to the system to meet peak demands with minimum pump capacity.

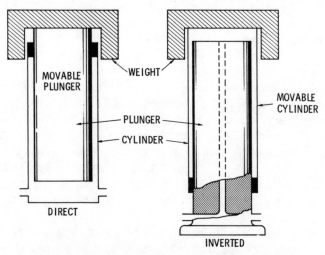

Fig. 3. The direct type (left) and the inverted type (right) of weight-loaded accumulator. The plunger is movable in the direct type, and the cylinder is movable in the inverted type.

283

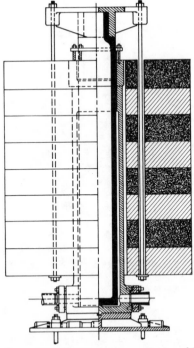

Fig. 4. Diagram showing construction details of a weight-loaded
direct-type accumulator. Ringed
weights are threaded onto the two
rods suspended at the ends of the
yoke at the upper end of the
hydraulic cylinder.

ficult to adjust or renew the packing in the stuffing box at the lower
end of the cylinder.

Stops or lugs are provided to prevent the plunger overtraveling its
stroke (Fig. 5). As shown in the illustration, four stops or lugs are
provided on the lower end of the cylinder, and similar lugs are provided on the inner portion of the upper end of the cylinder to prevent
plunger overtravel. Since both the plunger and the cylinder are provided with lugs or stops, when the plunger is inserted into the cylinder, it is necessary to turn the plunger until the lugs are in position to
pass. Then the plunger is turned (one-eighth turn) and fastened in
position. Therefore, the ends of the lugs register, to prevent overtravel of the plunger. Suitable provision is made to prevent turning
of the yoke.

Weight Required—A number of cast iron rings can be used as
weights to develop the required hydraulic pressure (see Fig. 4). Calculations for determining the weight required to develop a given hydraulic pressure are illustrated in the following problem.

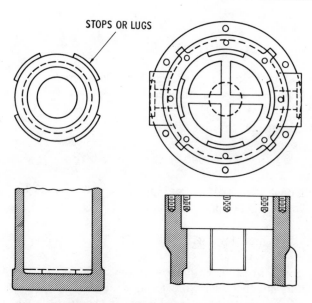

STOPS OR LUGS

Fig. 5. Diagram of construction details of the direct type of
accumulator, showing lugs on the lower end of the plunger
(left) and on the upper end of the cylinder (right), which
prevent overtravel of the plunger.

Problem: In a direct-type accumulator, the 14-in. diameter plunger
weighs 10,000 lb. What additional weight is required to develop a
hydraulic pressure of 600 lb. per sq. in.?

Solution: The cross-sectional area of the plunger can be found by the
formula:

$$a = d^2 \times 0.7854$$

For a 14-in. diameter plunger, the area is:

$$a = (14)^2 \times 0.7854 = 153.94 \text{ sq. in.},$$

$$\text{or } 154 \text{ sq. in.}$$

Then the total weight W required to balance the hydraulic pressure
can be determined by the formula:

$$W = Pa$$

in which;

W is wt. of plunger + additional wt. required
a is area, in sq. in., of plunger

Substituting in the formula:

$$W = 600 \times 154 = 92,400 \text{ lb.}$$

Additional weight, or wt. of rings required, is equal to total load W minus weight of plunger (10,000 lb):

$$\text{additional wt.} = 92,400 - 10,000 = 82,400 \text{ lb.}$$

Plunger Dimensions Required—In the design of weight-loaded accumulators, it is necessary to determine the dimensions of the plunger or ram for a given set of conditions. It should be noted that less weight is required to balance the hydraulic pressure as the diameter of the plunger decreases; also, if adequate vertical space is available, less weight is required as the length of the plunger stroke increases.

If one of the dimensions of the plunger is fixed, the other dimension can be determined for a given displacement (volume displaced by the plunger per stroke), as shown in the following problem.

Problem: If the diameter of the plunger is 14 inches, what length of stroke is required for the plunger in an accumulator having a displacement of 250 gallons?

Solution: Since one gallon of water displaces a volume of 231 cu. in., the total displacement is:

$$\text{displacement} = 250 \times 231 = 57,750 \text{ cu. in.}$$

The plunger area is:

$$(14)^2 \times 0.7854 = 154 \text{ sq. in. (approximately)}$$

The formula for determining length of stroke is:

286

$$\text{length of stroke} = \frac{\text{displacement}}{\text{area of plunger} \times 12} \text{ (for length of stroke, in ft.)}$$

Substituting in the formula:

$$\text{length of stroke} = \frac{57{,}750}{154 \times 12} = 31.25 \text{ ft.}$$

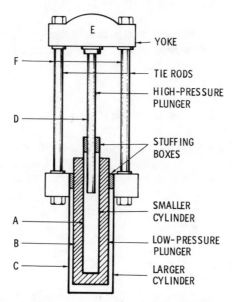

Fig. 6. Diagram showing basic construction of a pressure booster or intensifier which is a differential type of accumulator. The intensifier is a hydraulic device that is used to convert a liquid under low pressure to a liquid under high pressure.

A *pressure booster* or *intensifier* (Fig. 6), or differential type of accumulator, is a hydraulic device that is used to convert low pressure to high pressure. Its function is similiar to that of an electrical transformer which converts low-voltage current to high-voltage current.

To operate an intensifier, water is supplied at low pressure to a piston in a large cylinder which, in turn, operates a ram in a smaller

287

cylinder. As shown in Fig. 6, the basic construction of the intensifier consists of a smaller cylinder and a larger cylinder. The smaller cylinder *A* is part of the plunger *B* which fits inside the larger cylinder *C*. The smaller high-pressure plunger *D* fits inside the smaller cylinder *A*. The low-pressure plunger *B* acts as a movable ram for the larger cylinder *C,* and the high-pressure plunger *D* acts a stationary ram for the smaller cylinder *A;* the latter plunger is attached to the yoke *E* which is, in turn, attached to the larger cylinder *C* by means of the tie rods *F*.

In actual operation, the force pump (not shown in Fig. 6) forces the low-pressure plunger *B* upward, thereby exerting pressure on the water in the smaller cylinder *A* which is acted upon by the smaller plunger *D*. This pressure is intensified in the smaller cylinder *A* in proportion to the ratio of the cross-sectional areas of the two plungers, as shown in the following calculations.

Problem: If the diameter of the smaller plunger is 3 in. and the diameter of the larger plunger is 10 in., what is the pressure in the smaller cylinder if the pressure in the larger cylinder is 600 lb. per sq. in.?

Solution: The areas of the smaller and the larger cylinders are:

$$\text{area smaller cylinder} = (3)^2 \times 0.7854 = 7.07 \text{ sq. in.}$$

$$\text{area larger cylinder} = (10)^2 \times 0.7854 = 78.54 \text{ sq. in.}$$

Then the plunger ratio is 78.54:7.07, and the pressure in the smaller cylinder can be found by the equation:

$$\text{pressure in smaller cylinder} = 600 \times \frac{78.54}{707} = 6665 \text{ lb. per sq. in.}$$

Spring-Loaded Accumulators

In the spring-loaded type of accumulator (Fig. 7), a spring (or springs), rather than a weight, provides the means of exerting pressure on the liquid. As the hydraulic liquid is pumped into the accumulator, the plunger or piston is compressed; thus energy is stored in the spring, and it is released as required by the demands of the system. Since the force of the spring depends on its movement, the pres-

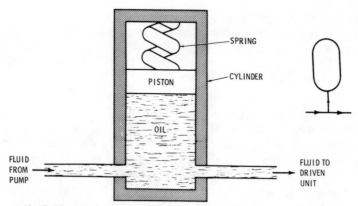

Fig. 7. Diagram showing basic parts of a spring-loaded type of accumulator.

sure on the liquid is not constant for all different positions of the plunger or piston. This type of accumulator is usually used to deliver small quantities of oil at low pressure.

Ques. What materials are used for weight on the plunger of a weight-loaded accumulator?

Ans. The dead weight on the plunger or ram may be cast iron, steel, concrete, water, or other heavy material.

Ques. How does the spring-loaded accumulator differ from the weight-loaded accumulator?

Ans. A spring (or springs), rather than a weight, is used to exert force against the plunger.

Ques. How is overtravel of the plunger stroke prevented in the accumulator?

Ans. Stops or lugs may be provided on both the plunger and the cylinder (see Fig. 5). When in correct position, the lugs register properly to prevent overtravel.

Ques. What is the chief disadvantage of the inverted type of accumulator?

Ans. Since the stuffing box is located at the lower end of the cylinder, access is a problem which makes adjustment and packing renewal more difficult.

Ques. What is a pressure booster or intensifier?

Ans. It is a hydraulic device that can be used to convert low pressure to high pressure.

Air- or Gas-Type Accumulators

Water and the other liquids that are used in hydraulic systems are nearly incompressible. This fact means that a large increase in hydraulic pressure decreases the volume of the liquid only slightly. On the other hand, a large increase in air or gas pressure results in a large decrease in the volume of the air or gas. Relatively speaking, the hydraulic liquids are less elastic or spring-like than air or gas, which indicates that the liquids cannot be used effectively to store energy; whereas, air or gas can be compressed to store energy. Therefore, this type of accumulator uses air or gas, instead of a weight or a mechanical spring, to provide the spring-like action. Air or gas accumulators can be divided into two types: (1) *nonseparator;* and (2) *separator*.

Nonseparator Type—In this type of accumulator (Fig. 8), a so-called "free surface" exists between the liquid and the air or gas. As an increased quantity of liquid is pumped into the accumulator, the

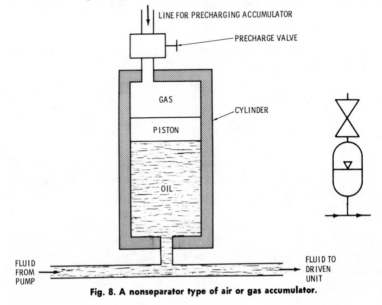

Fig. 8. A nonseparator type of air or gas accumulator.

air or gas above the liquid is compressed still further. The energy stored in the compressed air or gas is released as it is needed to meet the requirements of the system.

As shown in the illustration (see Fig. 8), the accumulator consists of a fully enclosed cylinder, ports, and a charging valve. Before this type of accumulator can be placed in operation, a portion of the liquid must be trapped in the lower portion of the cylinder. Then, air, nitrogen, or an inert gas is forced into the cylinder, which

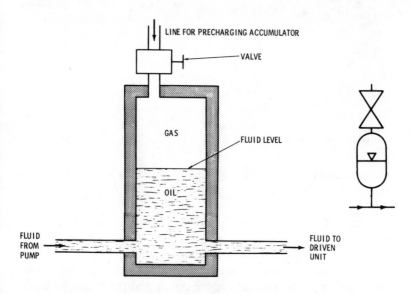

Fig. 9. A separator type of accumulator in which a floating piston separates the air or gas and the working hydraulic fluid.

precharges the accumulator to the minimum pressure requirements of the system. The accumulator is mounted in a vertical position, because the gas must be retained in the upper portion of the cylinder. The air or gas volume can occupy only about two-thirds of the accumulator volume; the remaining accumulator volume (or approximately one-third) should be reserved for the hydraulic liquid, which prevents the air or gas being exhausted into the hydraulic system. The nonseparator type of accumulator requires a compressor for the precharging operation. The precharge of the accumulator may be di-

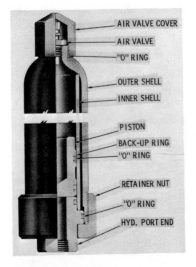

AIR VALVE COVER
AIR VALVE
"O" RING
OUTER SHELL
INNER SHELL
PISTON
BACK-UP RING
"O" RING
RETAINER NUT
"O" RING
HYD. PORT END

Fig. 10. Cutaway view of a piston-type hydraulic accumulator.

Courtesy Superior Hydraulics,
Division of Superior Pipe Specialties

minished if aeration, or mixing, of the liquid and the air or gas occurs. If the liquid absorbs the air or gas, the accumulator does not function properly.

Separator Type—A free or floating piston serves as a barrier between the liquid and the air or gas in the separator type of accumulator (Fig. 9). The piston and packing separate the liquid and the air or gas in the cylinder. The accumulator is precharged with high-pressure air or gas on one side of the piston and the hydraulic liquid or fluid on the opposite side.

In the double-shell construction of the cylindrical accumulator shown in Fig. 10, the pressure-balanced inner shell contains a floating piston and serves as a separator between the precharge air or gas and the hydraulic fluid; the outer shell serves as a gas container. A coolant for the working area of the inner shell is provided by rapid decompression of the precharged air or gas, resulting from rapid discharge of the working hydraulic fluid.

The *bladder or bag type* of accumulator (Fig. 11) should be installed with the end that contains the air or gas at the top, so that the hydraulic fluid is not trapped when discharging. A gas valve that opens into the shell is located at one end of the shell. A plug assem-

292

bly containing an oil port and a poppet valve is mounted on the opposite end of the shell.

As shown in the diagram (Fig. 12), the bladder or bag is pear-shaped and is made of synthetic rubber. The bladder including the molded air stem, is fastened by means of a lock nut to the upper end of a seamless steel shell which is cylindrical in shape and spherical at both ends.

In the *diaphragm-type* accumulator (Fig. 13), two steel hemispheres are locked together, and a flexible rubber diaphragm is

Fig. 11. Illustrating a bladder-type hydraulic accumulator.

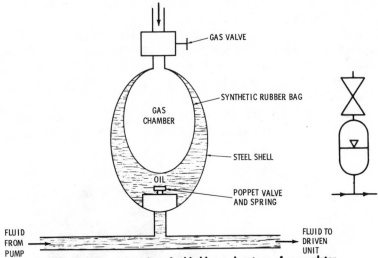

Fig. 12. Basic construction of a bladder- or bag-type of accumulator.

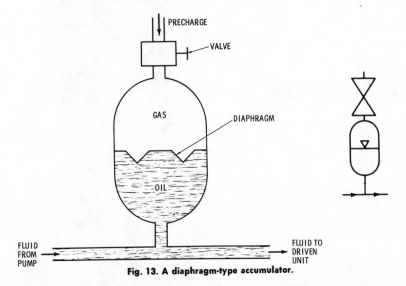

Fig. 13. A diaphragm-type accumulator.

clamped around the periphery. The gas and hydraulic oil pressures are equal, because the separating member is flexible. The air or gas acts as a spring which is compressed as the pressure increases.

294

Shock Absorbers or Alleviators

A hydraulic shock absorber or alleviator (Fig. 14) is used in conjunction with hydraulic systems and pipe lines to absorb shocks caused by the sudden halting of the flow of a liquid. If sudden shocks

Fig. 14. A shock-absorbing alleviator. Hydraulic system shocks are absorbed safely and smoothly by means of a packed spring-loaded plunger which rises and relieves sudden pressure surges.

Courtesy The Aldrich Pump Company,
Division of Ingersoll-Rand

occur in the hydraulic line, they are absorbed safely and smoothly by means of a packed spring-loaded plunger which rises and relieves sudden pressure surges.

The basic construction of a shock absorber or alleviator is shown in Fig. 15. A spring-loaded plunger moves inside a cylinder that is long enough to provide sufficient travel for it to function properly. If a sudden shock occurs in the hydraulic line, the piston moves upward in the cylinder to another position A (dotted lines in the diagram). The movement of the piston does not permit the liquid to escape.

Shock absorbers or alleviators are installed in the hydraulic system at the pump, accumulator, and hydraulic press (Fig. 16). They absorb the shock caused by the sudden closing of a valve or the sudden halting of the weight in a weight-loaded accumulator. A violent ham-

295

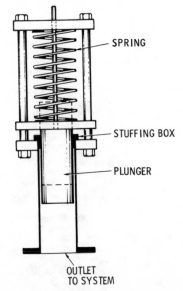

Fig. 15. Diagram showing basic construction of a shock absorber or alleviator.

mering action may damage the fittings and piping. The entire hydraulic system can be fully protected against shock to increase its effectiveness.

Ques. What property adapts air or gas for use in the accumulators of hydraulic systems?

Ans. Air or gas is compressible—a large increase in air or gas pressure results in a large decrease in the volume of the air or gas. In con-

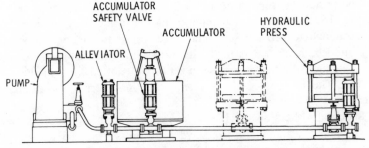

Fig. 16. Installation of shock absorbers or alleviators on the pump, accumulator, and hydraulic press in a hydraulic system.

296

trast, water and other liquids are nearly noncompressible, which means that they decrease in volume only slightly as the hydraulic pressure increases.

Ques. How does the nonseparator type of accumulator differ in construction from the separator type?

Ans. In the nonseparator type of accumulator, a so-called "free surface" exists between the liquid and the air or gas. A free or floating piston serves as a barrier between the liquid and the air or gas in the separator type.

Ques. Why should the bladder type of accumulator be installed with the end that contains the air or gas at the top?

Ans. So that the hydraulic fluid is not trapped when the accumulator is discharging.

Ques. What is the basic operating principle of the diaphragm-type accumulator?

Ans. The gas and hydraulic pressures on each side of the diaphragm are equal because the diaphragm is flexible. The air or gas acts as a spring which is compressed as the pressure increases.

Ques. What is the basic operating principle of a shock absorber or alleviator in the hydraulic system?

Ans. If a sudden shock occurs in a hydraulic line, it is absorbed safely and smoothly by the alleviator in which a packed spring-loaded plunger rises and relieves the sudden surge of fluid.

AIR AND VACUUM CHAMBERS

As aforementioned, water is nearly incompressible; therefore, pumps—especially high-speed reciprocating types—are constructed of rugged material for withstanding hydraulic shocks, and they can be provided with cushioning chambers for softening these shocks. These hydraulic shocks are usually called "water hammer." An air chamber is usually provided to eliminate water "hammer"; in addition, a vacuum chamber is sometimes provided in the system to eliminate this problem.

Air Chambers

The air chamber is usually installed on the discharge side of the discharge valve. It is a cone-shaped member that is connected vertically with the neck or small end (the end with the opening) placed downward to reduce the surface area of the water that is in contact with the air in the chamber. A minimum amount of absorption of the air by the water occurs if the contact surface area is reduced. If absorption occurs, the air chamber fills with water gradually, until it is rendered ineffective for cushioning of the shocks.

A diagram showing location of the air chamber in relation to the pump is shown in Fig. 17. Since the water is under pressure in the

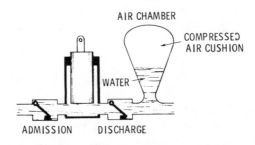

Fig. 17. Location of the air chamber in relation to the pump in a water system.

discharge chamber, the air in the air chamber is compressed during each discharge stroke of the pump piston. When the piston stops its movement, momentarily, at the end of the discharge stroke and during the return stroke, the air in the chamber expands slightly to produce a gradual halting of the flow of water; thus the valves are permitted to seat easily and without shock (Fig. 18).

Air chambers are useless unless they are provided with a device for keeping them supplied with air. At pressures above 300 lb. per sq. in., water absorbs air so rapidly that an air charging device is necessary. A small petcock can be installed near the pump in the admission line. By opening the petcock slightly, a small volume of air and the water are admitted to the pump; thus the air chamber is supplied with enough additional air to redeem the loss of air absorbed by the water. During the admission stroke, the additional air is drawn into the line through the petcock. Subsequently, during the

298

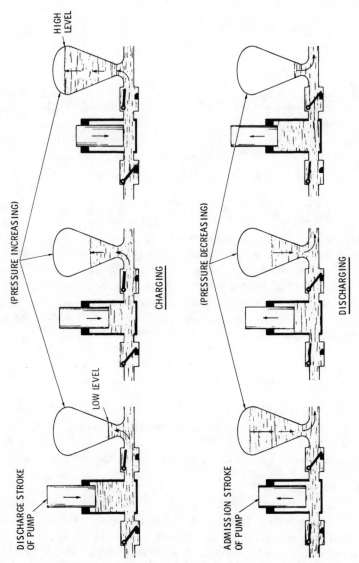

Fig. 18. Progressive steps in charging the air chamber during the discharge stroke of the pump (top) and discharging the air in the air chamber during the intake stroke of the pump (bottom).

299

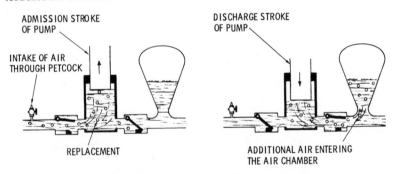

AIR INTAKE CYCLE

Fig. 19. Method of supplying additional air to replace air that is absorbed by the water.

discharge stroke, the air is discharged from the cylinder and enters the air chamber (Fig. 19).

The size of air chambers may vary considerably, depending on the type of service. For boiler feed and many types of service pumps, the volume of the air chamber should be two to three times the piston displacement of a simplex pump and one to two times the displacement of a duplex pump. If the piston speed is unusually high—fire pumps, for example,—the volume of the air chamber should be approximately six times the piston displacement.

Ques. Why is an air chamber used in a water system?

Ans. It is used to soften hydraulic shocks or prevent "water hammer."

Ques. Where is the air chamber usually located in a hydraulic system?

Ans. It is installed on the discharge side of the discharge valve.

Vacuum Chambers

A vacuum chamber (Fig. 20) is sometimes installed in the admission line to a pump, especially if the line is lengthy and the resistance to water flow is high. Once the column of water in the admission line is in motion, it is quite important—especially at high speeds and with long intake—to keep the water at full flow and to stop its flow gradually when its flow is halted. This is accomplished by means of a vacuum chamber placed in the inlet line to the pump.

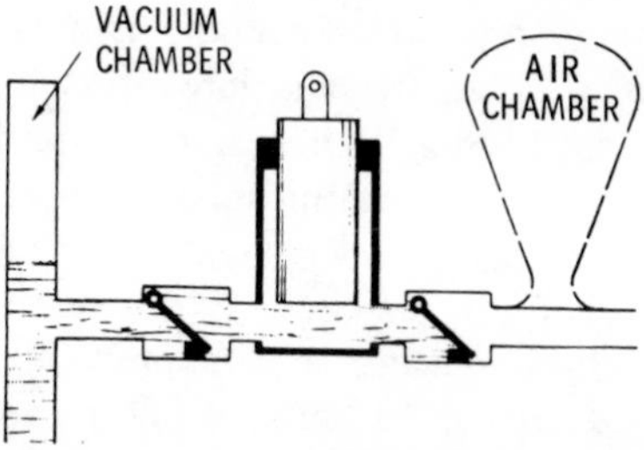

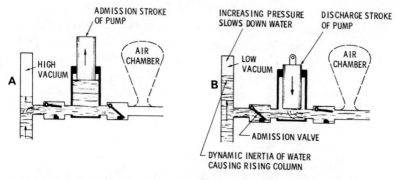

VACUUM CHAMBER

AIR CHAMBER

Fig. 20. Location of the vacuum chamber in the inlet line to the pump.

The operating principle of the vacuum chamber is nearly opposite that of the air chamber—it facilitates the changing of a continuous flow to intermittent flow. The flowing column of water compresses the air in the vacuum chamber at the end of the pump stroke; when the piston starts to move, the air expands (thereby creating a partial vacuum), which aids the piston in returning the column of water to full flow.

ADMISSION STROKE OF PUMP

AIR CHAMBER

HIGH VACUUM

A

INCREASING PRESSURE SLOWS DOWN WATER

DISCHARGE STROKE OF PUMP

LOW VACUUM

AIR CHAMBER

B

ADMISSION VALVE

DYNAMIC INERTIA OF WATER CAUSING RISING COLUMN

Fig. 21. Basic operation of the vacuum chamber at the end of the admission stroke of the pump (top) and at the end of the discharge stroke (bottom).

The basic operation of the vacuum chamber is shown in Fig. 21. As the water is drawn into the cylinder on the upward stroke of the cylinder, the least volume of water (or highest vacuum) is present in the vacuum chamber; the receding column of water reaches the low point A. When the piston begins its downward stroke, the inlet valve closes. Since it is impossible to halt instantly the flow of a column of water, the water in the inlet pipe continues its motion into the vacuum chamber until it reaches its highest point B. The highest volume of water (or lowest vacuum) is present in the vacuum chamber at this point. Also, the absolute pressure in the vacuum chamber has increased from its lowest pressure at point A to its highest pressure (perhaps above atmospheric pressure) when the column of water is brought to rest at its highest point B.

Ques. When is a vacuum chamber used in a pumping system?

Ans. If the admission line to a pump is lengthy and the resistance to water flow is high, the vacuum chamber is often used in the admission line.

Ques. What is the function of the vacuum chamber in the system?

Ans. It is used to keep water at full flow and to stop its flow gradually when its flow is halted. It facilitates changing a continuous flow of water to intermittent flow.

SUMMARY

An *accumulator* is a cylinder in which a liquid is stored under pressure, so that it can serve as a reservoir and regulator of power; this enables pumps operating under a uniform load to meet an intermittent or fluctuating demand for power. A *hydraulic accumulator* is designed to accumulate hydraulic energy that is to be expended intermittently.

The three general types of accumulators are: (1) weight-loaded; (2) spring-loaded; and (3) air- or gas-type. A pressure booster or *intensifier* is a type of accumulator that is used to convert low pressure to high pressure. A shock absorber or *alleviator* is also used in conjunction with hydraulic systems and pipe lines to absorb sudden shocks caused by the sudden halting of the flow of a liquid.

The *air chamber* is provided in a hydraulic system to cushion or soften hydraulic shocks or "water hammer." When an air chamber is used in the system, it is usually installed on the discharge side of the discharge valve.

In addition to the air chamber, a *vacuum chamber* is sometimes installed in the admission line to a pump, especially if the line is lengthy and the resistance to water flow is high. The purpose of the vacuum chamber is to keep the water at full flow and to stop it gradually when its flow is halted. This facilitates changing a continuous flow of water to an intermittent flow.

REVIEW QUESTIONS

1. What is the purpose of the hydraulic accumulator?
2. What is the purpose of a pressure booster or intensifier in the hydraulic system?
3. What is the purpose of an alleviator or shock absorber in the hydraulic system?
4. Describe the basic operation of an air chamber in a hydraulic system.
5. Describe the basic operation of a vacuum chamber in a hydraulic system.

CHAPTER 8

Power Transmission

The early internal-combustion engines were lacking in power and torque flexibility, in comparison with the steam engines of the period. With a mechanically connected driving means, it was impossible for the internal-combustion engine to attain the smoothness and flexibility of the steam engine, because the internal-combustion engine depends on a series of quick successive explosions in the cylinder to produce power and torque and on the momentum stored in a heavy flywheel to keep it operating between explosions. Also, the steam engine was capable of delivering rapid, smooth acceleration of the load to maximum speed within its power range, without pauses or slow-downs for shifting gears, as was required with the internal-combustion engine. All these factors contributed to the development of hydraulic drives for internal-combustion engines.

Ques. What characteristic of the steam engine has been an important factor in the development of hydraulic drives?

Ans. The smoothness and flexibility of power and torque possessed by the steam engine were lacking in the early internal-combustion engine.

HYDRAULIC DRIVES

A *hydraulic drive* (also called fluid drive or liquid drive) is a flexible hydraulic coupling. It is a means of delivering power from a prime mover to a driven member through a liquid medium—with no mechanical connection. A pioneer type of hydraulic drive (Fig. 1) was invented and built by H. E. Raabe in 1900. In construction, a

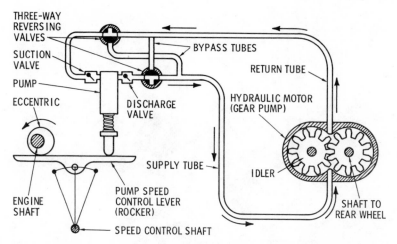

Fig. 1. Diagram of a pioneer type of hydraulic drive invented and built by H. E. Raabe in 1900.

separate hydraulic motor (similar to a common gear-type pump) was attached to each rear wheel, thereby permitting differential rotation on curves. In the illustration, one of the motors, the connecting piping, the reversing valves, the pump, and the pump drive are shown. In the actual operation of the system, an eccentric on the engine shaft provides an oscillating motion to the rocker which operates the pump, forcing oil through the system as indicated by the arrows in the diagram. If the two reversing valves are turned 90 degrees in unison, the flow of the oil and the motion of the car are reversed. Variable speed is obtained by shifting the position of the fulcrum of the rocker, which varies the stroke of the pump. A multicylinder pump is used to avoid pulsations and a jerky movement of the car.

Basic Operating Principles

The hydraulic drive mechanism consists of three essential parts. They are: (1) *driver;* (2) *follower,* sometimes called *runner;* and (3) *casing* or *housing.* The power from the engine is delivered to the driver; it is then transmitted (flexibly) to the follower through the hydraulic medium.

In actual operation of the hydraulic drive, the power is transmitted from the driver to the follower as a result or effect of circulation of

305

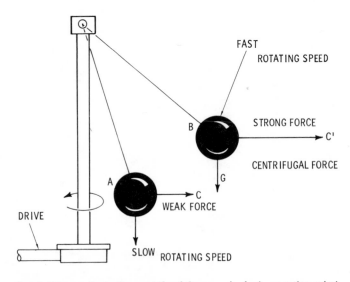

Fig. 2. Diagram illustrating centrifugal force as the basic operating principle of the common "fly-ball" type of engine governor. At slow speed, the ball is forced outward to position "A" in its circular path. If the engine load decreases, the engine speed increases, and the increased centrifugal force moves the ball outward to position "B" in its circular path. The increased centrifugal force is indicated by the lengths of the vectors "C" and "C'". In each instance, the downward pull of gravity "G" is constant and is overcome by centrifugal force. Similiarly, in the hydraulic drive, centrifugal force is greater in the high-speed driver than in the follower rotating at a slower speed. This difference in the centrifugal forces causes the hydraulic oil to circulate.

the hydraulic medium or oil. The circulation of the hydraulic oil is caused by the difference in the centrifugal force set up in the driver and the centrifugal force set up in the follower.

It should be remembered that centrifugal force (Fig. 2) is the force which acts on a body moving in a circular path, tending to force it farther from its axis of rotation. Hydraulic oil *does not circulate* if both the driver and the follower rotate at the *same speed,* because the centrifugal force in the driver is equal to the centrifugal force set up in the follower. Hence, the oil does not tend to circulate, because neither force is excessive. This also indicates that the hydraulic oil *does circulate* only when the centrifugal force set up in the driver is *greater than* the centrifugal force set up in the follower (Fig. 3). To obtain this condition, it is necessary for the driver to rotate at a higher speed than the follower, because the intensity of the centrifugal force depends on the speed of rotation.

Essentially, the driver in the hydraulic drive is a centrifugal pump, and the hydraulic oil circulates in circular paths (Fig. 4). In travers-

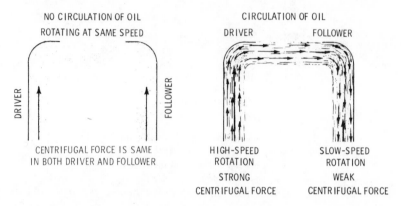

Fig. 3. Diagram illustrating the basic cause of oil circulation in a hydraulic drive. The centrifugal forces in the driver and follower are opposed, and hydraulic oil does not circulate unless the force in one of the members is greater as a result of increased rotation speed.

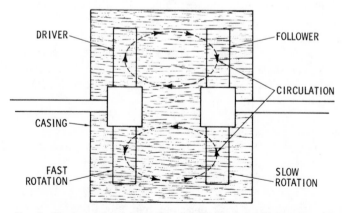

Fig. 4. Circular path of hydraulic oil particles in circulating from the driver to the follower. Centrifugal force forces the oil particles outward from the hub to the rim, and they return at the hub.

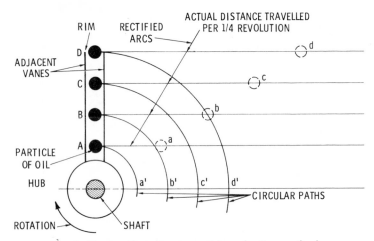

Fig. 5. Diagram illustrating tangential acceleration as the hydraulic oil particles move outward from the hub to the rims of the adjacent vanes of the driver.

ing the circular paths during circulation of the oil, the hydraulic oil particles are forced outward by centrifugal force; the length of the circular path increases for each revolution, which means that the oil particles are accelerated tangentially (tangential acceleration) as shown in Fig. 5. This is illustrated by the successive positions *A, B, C,* and *D* of an oil particle as it is forced outward from the hub to the rims of the adjacent vanes of the driver. As shown in the diagram, the distance traveled by an oil particle in one revolution increases as the oil particle moves outward to positions *C* and *D*. Similarly, the *tangential velocity* increases; this means that there is *tangential acceleration,* which is indicated by the increasing distances *Aa, Bb, Cc,* and *Dd* from the axis of rotation.

Ques. What is the basic definition of a hydraulic drive?

Ans. Power is delivered from a driving member through a liquid medium (no mechanical connection) to a driven member. A hydraulic drive is essentially a flexible hydraulic coupling.

Ques. What are the basic parts of a hydraulic drive?

Ans. The basic parts are: / 1) *driver;* (2) *follower;* and (3) *casing* or *housing.*

Ques. What is the basic operating principle of hydraulic drives?

Ans. Centrifugal force resulting from rotation of the driver causes the hydraulic oil to circulate; circulation of the oil causes the follower to rotate, thereby rotating the output shaft.

Ques. What is dynamic inertia?

Ans. It is that property of a moving body that causes the body to remain in a state of uniform motion, until it is acted upon by a force that compels it to change that state of motion.

Tangential Acceleration

Both tangential acceleration and tangential deceleration require an expenditure of energy (supplied by the engine). Most of the tangentially accelerated oil in the driver is converted at the follower into torque during deceleration. An expenditure of energy is required to tangentially accelerate the oil, because the oil particles press against the vanes of the driver as they move outward. Strictly speaking, the vane presses against the oil particles to overcome the dynamic inertia resulting from acceleration of its tangential velocity as the oil moves outward from the hub to the rim of the vane. Dynamic inertia causes a moving body to remain in a state of uniform motion, unless acted upon by a force that compels it to change that state (Fig. 6).

Dynamic inertia enables the hydraulic oil to drive the follower. The hydraulic oil entering the passages formed by the follower vanes possesses both a *forward* (axial) motion and a *lateral* (tangential) motion. The lateral or tangential movement of the oil causes the

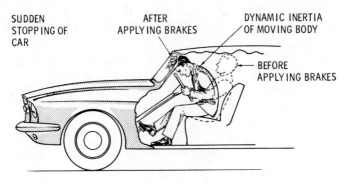

SUDDEN STOPPING OF CAR

AFTER APPLYING BRAKES

DYNAMIC INERTIA OF MOVING BODY

BEFORE APPLYING BRAKES

Fig. 6. Dynamic inertia.

309

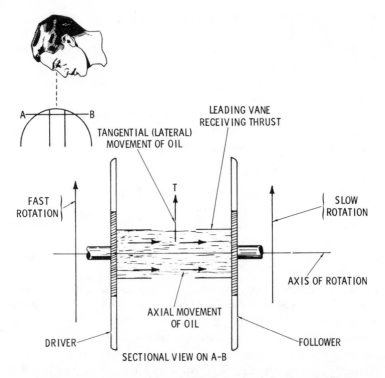

Fig. 7. Sectional diagram (bottom) with a portion of the rims of adjacent
vanes cut away (on line "AB" in upper left), showing the axial movement
"A" and the tangential movement "T" of hydraulic oil.

hydraulic oil to press against the leading vane, thereby driving the
follower in the tangential direction in which the oil tends to continue
to move because of its dynamic inertia.

A diagram of two adjacent vanes illustrating oil flow from the
driver to the follower is shown in Fig. 7. The axial movement A of
the oil flow and the tangential movement T are shown in the diagram.
The sidewise movement (from driver to follower) is the result of the
driver rotating faster than the follower.

The flow of hydraulic oil resulting from both axial movement and
tangential movement is illustrated in the diagram in Fig. 8. In the
diagram, the direction and velocity of axial movement OA and the
direction and velocity of tangential movement OB represent the sides

310

of the parallelogram $OABR$. Then the diagonal OR represents the direction and velocity of the actual oil flow resulting from the two component movements. Since the diagonal OR of the parallelogram represents the actual direction of oil flow, the oil strikes the leading vane of the follower at an angle AOR. The normal thrust AR on the

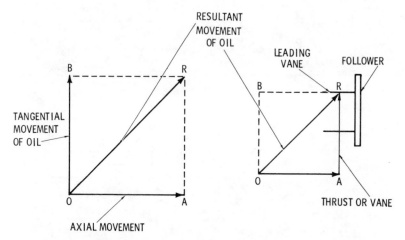

Fig. 8. Diagrams illustrating the flow of hydraulic oil resulting from tangential and axial movements (left); tangential acceleration produces torque which tends to rotate the vane of the follower (right).

leading vane of the follower produces torque which tends to rotate the vane. Since the tangential direction and velocity of the oil OB is equal to the thrust AR on the vane of the follower, tangential acceleration produces torque which tends to rotate the follower.

Tangential Deceleration

As aforementioned, an expenditure of energy is required either to increase the velocity of a moving body or to slow it down (Fig. 9). For example, work is required by a locomotive in increasing the speed of a train to its top speed; the kinetic energy (stored capacity resulting from the momentum of the moving body) acquired thereby is expended by applying the brakes to slow the speed of the train. In this instance, the energy is converted to heating of the brake shoes.

Tangential deceleration also produces torque which tends to rotate the follower. On entering the follower, the hydraulic oil is forced (by

311

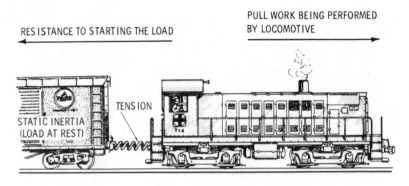

RESISTANCE TO STARTING THE LOAD

PULL WORK BEING PERFORMED BY LOCOMOTIVE

TENSION

STATIC INERTIA (LOAD AT REST)

STARTING THE LOAD

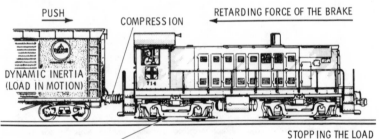

PUSH

COMPRESSION

RETARDING FORCE OF THE BRAKE

DYNAMIC INERTIA (LOAD IN MOTION)

STOPPING THE LOAD

KINETIC ENERGY OF MOVING CARS BEING CONVERTED INTO HEAT (HEATING OF THE BRAKE SHOES)

Fig. 9. Kinetic energy. Work is required by the locomotive to start the load (top), and work is required for the moving cars to stop the load which tends to remain in motion (bottom). Note that the work required to stop the load is converted to heating of the brake shoes.

excessive forward centrifugal force) to flow from the rim to the hub, which decelerates its tangential velocity. In the meantime, the tangential component (AR in Fig. 8) of the kinetic energy originally possessed by the hydraulic oil on entering the follower is expended against the leading vane to produce torque which tends to rotate the follower. The kinetic energy, in this instance, represents the work necessary to change the body from its actual velocity or state of motion to a state of rest.

The effect of tangential deceleration is illustrated in Fig. 10. Note that in positions A, B, C, and D in the follower, the oil particle is

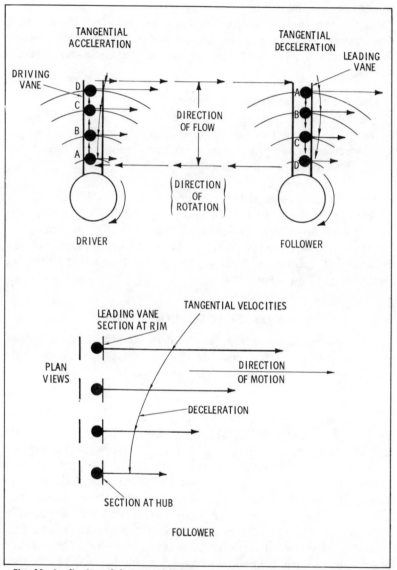

Fig. 10. Application of force to the driver to obtain tangential acceleration of the hydraulic oil (upper left); and why tangential deceleration produces torque or a tendency to rotate the follower (upper right). The effect of tangential decleration is illustrated further in the lower diagram.

moving toward the hub and that these positions are the same distance from the axis in tangential deceleration as they were in tangential acceleration. This indicates that tangential deceleration of the hydraulic oil produces a driving force or thrust on the leading vane of the follower.

Ques. What is tangential acceleration?

Ans. As the oil particles are thrown outward by tangential acceleration from the hub to the rim of the rotating member, the length of its circular path increases during each revolution. This lateral motion is termed "tangential acceleration."

Ques. What is tangential deceleration?

Ans. On entering the follower, the oil particles are forced by excessive centrifugal force to flow from the rim to the hub which decelerates the tangential velocity of the oil; therefore, the kinetic energy is expended against the leading vane of the follower, resulting in production of torque and rotation.

TYPES OF HYDRAULIC DRIVES

The basic operating principle of the hydraulic drive is used in many different types of transmissions. In all these drives, the two rotating members are the *driver* and the *follower* or runner.

Fluid Drive

A sectional diagram showing details of construction of a typical fluid drive is shown in Fig. 11. Stamped, pressed, and forged parts are used in construction of the fluid drive. The hubs for the impeller housing and the follower (runner) are forged; the outer housing and the follower disk are made of pressed cold-rolled steel, and the vanes (22 in the impeller and 24 in the follower) are made of stamped cold-rolled steel (Fig. 12). The vanes are assembled permanently onto the impeller and follower disks by spot welds on each vane. The follower disk is welded permanently to the follower hub. The follower is mounted in the impeller on a ball bearing, and is located in the forward portion of the assembly. The follower is supported in the assembly by the transmission drive pinion shaft. A low-viscosity mineral oil is used in the fluid coupling; it provides the lubrication required

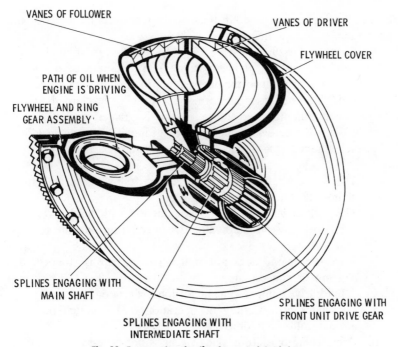

VANES OF FOLLOWER

VANES OF DRIVER

FLYWHEEL COVER

PATH OF OIL WHEN
ENGINE IS DRIVING

FLYWHEEL AND RING
GEAR ASSEMBLY

SPLINES ENGAGING WITH
MAIN SHAFT

SPLINES ENGAGING WITH
FRONT UNIT DRIVE GEAR

SPLINES ENGAGING WITH
INTERMEDIATE SHAFT

Fig. 11. Construction details of a typical fluid drive.

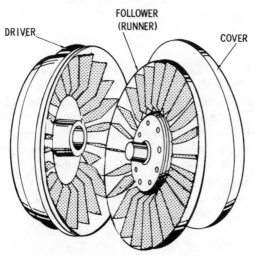

DRIVER

FOLLOWER
(RUNNER)

COVER

Fig. 12. Appearance of members of a fluid drive.

315

by the bearing enclosed within the coupling, and the oil pours at the lowest temperature anticipated.

As shown in the diagram (see Fig. 11), the two rotating elements are the *driver* and the *follower* (runner). The difference or *slip* in rotating speeds of the two members is approximately one percent in average driving conditions at normal speeds over level roads. On a long difficult pull, the percentage of slip is greater, and it is 100 percent when the car is stopped and in gear with the engine idling.

The chief advantages claimed for fluid drive are:

1. The car can be placed in high gear in following normal traffic without declutching or shifting gears.
2. The kick-down overdrive in conjunction with fluid drive provides virtually an automatic two-speed transmission in high gear.
3. Since the engine does not stall when the car is stopped, declutching is unnecessary.
4. A fluid drive dampens engine tortional vibrations.
5. Eliminates gear shifting or operation of the clutch pedal in normal traffic conditions.
6. Declutching or shifting out of gear is not necessary in starting the engine.
7. The engine can be used as a brake.

Hydraulic Drive

A type of hydraulic drive (called *Hydramatic* by the manufacturer) combined with a fully automatic four-speed transmission eliminates the conventional clutch and clutch pedal. The automobile is set in motion by merely depressing the accelerator pedal, and the hydraulic drive unit transmits power smoothly and firmly. Motion starts in low gear, shifting successively to second, third, and fourth gears in order; shifting is dependent on the throttle opening.

The two rotating members are the *driver* and the *follower* (Fig. 13). In construction, both members are made of pressed steel and each contains 48 half-circular divisions called *torus passages*. Hydraulic oil circulation around these passages is shown in Fig. 14. When the driver and the follower are turning at the same speed, the hydraulic oil does not circulate; therefore, there is no torque produced. The oil

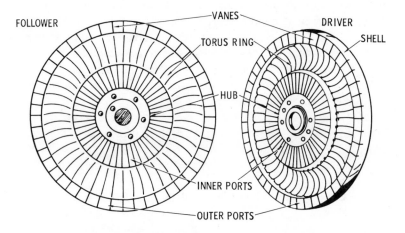

Fig. 13. The driver and follower in a "Hydramatic" drive.

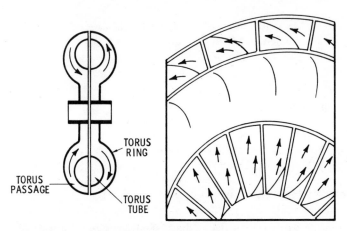

Fig. 14. Cross-sectional diagram showing circulation of hydraulic oil in the driver and follower (left); circulation of oil in the rotor is illustrated further (right).

circulates only when one member rotates at a faster speed. The member that rotates faster becomes the *driver,* and the other is the *driven* member. Thus, the automobile can "drive" the engine—in the same manner that the engine can "drive" the car. If more power is required, the operator depresses the accelerator to provide the en-

317

gine with more gasoline, which, in turn, increases the speed of the driver; this circulates more hydraulic oil to meet the increased load—the speed of the driver relative to the speed of the driven member is increased—which, in effect, delivers more power to the rear wheels. The automobile cannot begin motion while the engine is idling, because the "driver" is not rotating at a speed that is fast enough to overcome the static inertia of the car.

Ques. What are the two rotating members of the *Hydramatic* drive called?

Ans. They are the *driver* and the *follower* or runner.

Ques. Why is the automobile not in motion when the engine is idling?

Ans. The speed of the driver is not fast enough to overcome the static inertia of the car.

Ques. When is torque produced?

Ans. Only when one member rotates faster than the other member to circulate the hydraulic oil. The member that is rotating faster becomes the "driver" and the other member becomes the "driven" member; therefore, the automobile can "drive" the engine in the same manner that the engine "drives" the car.

Ques. How can increased power be obtained?

Ans. By increasing the speed of the driver relative to the speed of the driven member.

Twin-Disk Hydraulic Drive

In the twin-disk hydraulic drive (Fig. 15), two parallel units deliver power to the same drive shaft. The basic parts are: (1) *front driver;* (2) *twin follower* (two followers); and (3) *rear driver.* This drive is sometimes called a hydraulic clutch and hydraulic power takeoff.

Hydraulic Torque Converter

The torque converter operates on the same basic principle—circulation of the fluid for the transmission of power—as the twin-disk hydraulic drive; however, in the torque converter, a stationary member

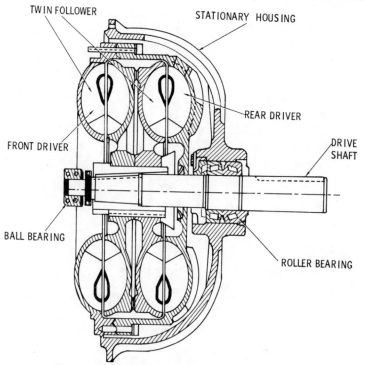

Fig. 15. Cross-sectional view of a twin-disk hydraulic drive.

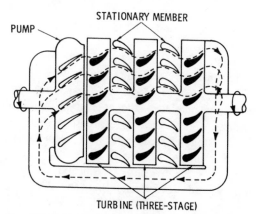

Fig. 16. Basic operating principle of a hydraulic torque converter.

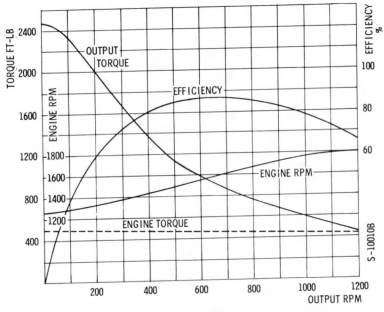

Fig. 17. Performance characteristics of a typical hydraulic torque converter.

is placed between the pump and the turbine to change the direction of the fluid. The pump is coupled to the engine and circulates the fluid. The centrifugal pump imparts velocity to the fluid which becomes the transmission medium for the power delivered by the engine.

As the fluid is forced against the turbine blades and the blades mounted on the stationary housing, its energy is reached in the form of torque and speed. As a result of the action of the fluid on the turbine and stationary blades, the engine or input torque is multiplied increasingly as the speed of the output shaft is reduced. The engine cannot be stalled, because there is no mechanical connection between the engine and the turbine.

In construction of the hydraulic torque converter (Fig. 16), two sets of stationary blades are located between the three stages of the turbine. When the stationary blades that redirect the flow of fluid are mounted in the stationary housing and when the housing is fastened either to the engine or to a solid base, the blades cannot move when the fluid is forced against them; therefore, the fluid flow is redirected and the resistance of the fluid to this change (resistance of a fluid in motion to a change in direction and speed fits flow) results in torque multiplication or in an increase in torque at each turbine stage with a corresponding decrease in speed of the output shaft.

As shown in Fig. 17, the curve indicates the output torque obtained with an engine delivering 500 ft-lb of torque at 1800 *rpm* which is the full-throttle speed of the engine. Top efficiency is indicated by the broad, nearly flat curve, peaking at approximately 85 percent. As the output shaft speed approaches nearly two-thirds the speed of the engine (depending on losses in the system), the engine torque and the converter torque become equal.

Ques. How does construction of the torque converter differ in construction from other hydraulic drives?

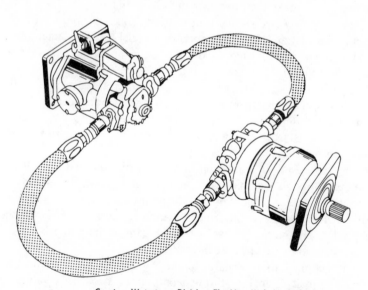

Courtesy Watertown Division, The New York Air Brake Company

Fig. 18. "Dynapower" hydrostatic transmission system. "Dynapower" is the registered trademark of the New York Air Brake Company for its hydrostatic transmission and related components. The transmission system consists of a closed hydraulic system.

Ans. Two sets of stationary blades are located between the three stages of the turbine.

Ques. What is the function of these stationary blades?

Ans. Since the blades cannot move when the fluid is forced against them, the fluid flow is redirected; the resistance of the fluid to this change in direction and speed of its flow results in an increase in torque at each turbine stage and a corresponding decrease in speed of the output shaft.

Hydrostatic Transmission System

The *Dynapower* transmission system (Fig. 18), with proper controls, manufactured by The New York Air Brake Company is designed to produce constant horsepower, constant torque, and constant speed within close tolerances. Reversibility, instantaneous response, stepless speed variation, dynamic braking, and built-in overload protection make the drive extremely versatile.

The *Dynapower* hydrostatic transmission utilizes a closed hydraulic system. The inlet and discharge ports of a variable-displacement axial piston pump are connected to the discharge and inlet ports of an axial piston motor (fixed or variable) by hose or tubing.

The filter, reservoir, charge pump, and valves are also part of the transmission. The charge pump and check valves are located in the cover of the pump, and the other valves are built into the cover of the motor. This feature minimizes the plumbing and hardware required in the system.

In operation, the hydraulic oil flows from the pump (Fig. 19) to the motor through the main system lines and causes the motor to rotate, when the variable cam in the pump is moved from neutral position. The discharge oil from the motor returns directly to the pump inlet. The motor reverses when the cam in the pump is moved through neutral to the opposite direction.

Oil is supplied to the charge pump by a line directly from the reservoir, and it discharges through one of the two check valves to the low-pressure side of the system. This provides makeup oil and inlet pressurization to the closed system. Pressurization is maintained by the low-pressure relief valve which also relieves excess oil from the charge pump back to the reservoir.

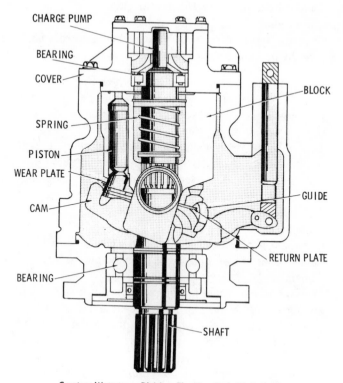

Courtesy Watertown Division, The New York Air Brake Company

Fig. 19. Cutaway view showing the basic parts of the pump in a "Dynapower" hydrostatic transmission system.

The system is protected from oversurges or extremely high starting pressures by the pilot-operated high-pressure relief valve. The valve discharges to the low-pressure side of the system, to prevent depletion of oil in the closed system.

A pressure-actuated shuttle valve directs both high pressure and low pressure to the respective relief valves. The shuttle valve moves toward the low-pressure side when one line is high pressure; this, in turn, ports the high pressure to the high-pressure relief valve and the low-pressure side to its relief valve. The shuttle valve is also used to direct high-pressure relief valve discharge to the low-pressure side of the system.

323

The output of standard production machines can be made suitable to specific needs by selecting the correct control. A wide variety of interchangeable types of controls is available. Controls used on the *Dynapower* hydrostatic transmission system are:

1. *Manual.* The cam angle is determined by the position of a simple control rod linked directly to the pump or motor cam. A handwheel on a threaded rod is attached for fine positioning of the pump or motor cam.

2. *Low-pressure hydraulic control.* Charge pump pressure (approximately 100 *psi*) is utilized by the control to position the cam and to provide overcenter travel. The actuating arm of the control requires 2 to 4 pounds of effort for its operation.

3. *Input torque limiting control.* Stalling of the engine is prevented under all conditions.

4. *Constant-speed control.* Input speeds can be varied while maintaining constant output speed. The output torque varies with demand.

5. *Pressure-compensated motor control.* Motor speed is increased automatically by decreasing the cam angle in the motor, as pressure decreases. Conversely, by increasing the cam angle in the motor as the pressure increases, lower speed and higher torque output are obtained.

6. *Pressure-compensator pump control.* This control has been made necessary by the hydrostatic transmission, although it is not normally a component of the system itself. Full flow (maximum cam angle) is maintained until a predetermined system pressure is attained. The flow is then halted while the pressure is maintained. Flow resumes to compensate for system leakage —or at system demand. A manual cutoff of flow and pressure can be used to reduce wear and horsepower demand on the system.

Hydrostatic hydraulic drives have been developed for many mobile and industrial applications. These drives are used on machine tools, centrifugal pumps, production machines, winches, paper and textile rolls, surface and center winders, conveyors, reels, calenders, printing presses, fans and blowers, agitators, mixers, disintegrators, materials handling machines, plastic extruders, and dynamometers.

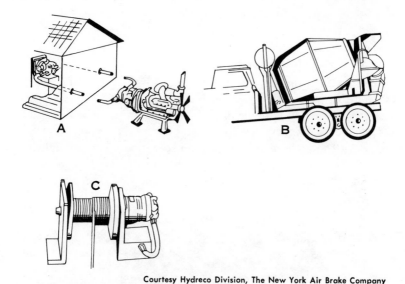

Courtesy Hydreco Division, The New York Air Brake Company

Fig. 20. Applications of the hydrostatic transmission: (A) Remote drive; (B) Mixing-drum drive; and (C) Winch drive.

The hydrostatic transmission has several advantages. Some of these advantages are utilized in the drives in the applications shown in Fig. 20, as follows:

1. *Remote drives.* The transmission can be located at a distance from the power source. Since the output unit is inherently explosion-proof, it can be used in atmospheres where there is danger of explosion if a combustion-type engine or electric motor is used as a power source (see Fig. 20A).

2. *Automatic torque control at output shaft.* This is important in many types of production machinery and machine tools.

3. *Output shaft can be reversed quickly and without shock.* In the mixing-drum drive (see Fig. 20B), the need for a second engine is eliminated. The drum speed is variable in either direction of rotation, and it can be controlled either from outside the cab or from within the cab. Shock loads are eliminated.

4. *Full output torque obtained at minimum input speeds.* In the winch drive (see Fig. 20C), variable drum speeds can be ob-

325

tained without use of clutches or gear changers from a constant-speed motor. Indefinite stalling can occur without damage.

Hydraulic Adjustable-Speed Drive

The Vickers hydraulic adjustable-speed drives (Fig. 21) are also based on the hydrostatic principle. Power is transmitted by means of an electrically-driven variable-displacement pump providing pressure and a flow that is converted to usable power by a hydraulic motor (Fig. 22). The hydraulic fluid is returned to the pump, completing the cycle without entering a tank or sump. In the diagram, both the pump and the motor are fitted with stroke controls. The pump con-

Courtesy Vickers Incorporated, Division of Sperry Rand Corporation

Fig. 21. Vickers hydraulic adjustable-speed drives are based on the hydrostatic principle.

trol can be adjusted to obtain an output-speed range from minimum to intermediate speed, with constant torque throughout the range. The fluid motor can be adjusted to obtain speeds above this range—with a decrease in torque.

Hydraulic adjustable-speed drives provide either a direct or indirect drive for many industrial applications, including hoists and winches, food machinery, and processing equipment. The Vickers adjustable-speed transmission shown in Fig. 23 is used on many fractional-horsepower machinery drives. With constant output torque characteristics, it can be started under full-load torque from zero *rpm* in either direction of rotation. Overload protection permits stalling of the unit without damage, and the output speed is smooth and stepless over its entire range.

326

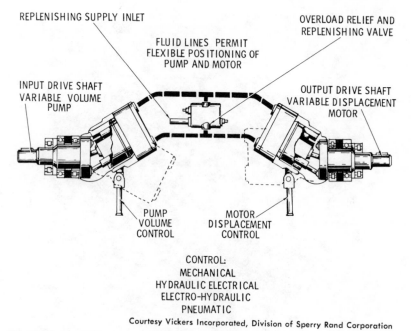

Courtesy Vickers Incorporated, Division of Sperry Rand Corporation

Fig. 22. Diagram of hydraulic adjustable-speed drive. Both the pump and the motor are fitted with stroke controls.

Farm Tractor Applications

The hydraulic transmission is used extensively on farm tractors. A large-capacity variable-displacement pump is used to provide remote control of equipment (Fig. 24). The pump is also used to provide -power steering and power braking which have become standard equipment on many farm tractors. In addition, remote cylinders, a three-point hitch, and a power differential lock are all parts of the hydraulic system.

On tillage operations, instant shifting (without stopping) permits ground-travel speeds to be maintained; a constant load on the engine is retained, and the engine *rpm* stays within the operating range— for greater economy and efficiency. Power takeoff equipment can be kept working at full capacity when harvesting heavy crops by merely moving the shifter lever to maintain the proper ground speed (including neutral position).

Courtesy Vickers Incorporated, Division of Sperry Rand Corporation

Fig. 23. An adjustable-speed transmission used on many fractional-horsepower machinery drives. With constant-output torque characteristics, it can be started under full-load torque from zero rpm in either direction of rotation.

Action that requires direction reversal can be provided without clutching—and without stopping. This is ideal for operations that require constant changing in direction, such as stacking and loading.

SUMMARY

A *hydraulic drive* (also called fluid drive or liquid drive) is a flexible hydraulic coupling. It is a means of delivering power from a prime mover to a driven member through a liquid medium—with no mechanical connection.

The hydraulic drive mechanism consists of three essential parts. They are: (1) *driver;* (2) *follower;* and (3) *casing* or *housing.*

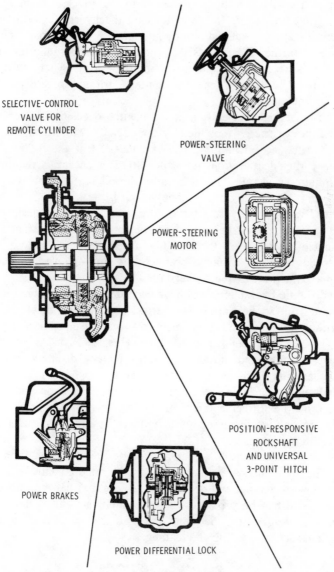

SELECTIVE-CONTROL
VALVE FOR
REMOTE CYLINDER

POWER-STEERING
VALVE

POWER-STEERING
MOTOR

POSITION-RESPONSIVE
ROCKSHAFT
AND UNIVERSAL
3-POINT HITCH

POWER BRAKES

POWER DIFFERENTIAL LOCK

Fig. 24. A single-pump hydraulic system can be used on a farm tractor to provide
power for steering, braking, position control for a three-point hitch, and a power
differential lock.

The power from the engine is delivered to the driver; it is then transmitted (flexibly) to the follower through the hydraulic medium.

Centrifugal force acts on a body moving in a circular path, tending to force it farther from its axis of rotation. For hydraulic oil to circulate, it is necessary for the driver to rotate at a higher speed than the follower, because the intensity of the centrifugal force depends on the speed of rotation.

Both tangential acceleration and tangential deceleration require an expenditure of energy (supplied by the engine). Most of the tangentially accelerated oil in the driver is converted at the follower into torque during deceleration. An expenditure of energy is required to tangentially accelerate the oil, because the oil particles press against the vanes of the driver as they move outward.

The *Dynapower* hydrostatic transmission system is designed to produce constant horsepower, constant torque, and constant speed within close tolerances. Reversibility, instantaneous response, stepless speed variation, dynamic braking, and built-in overload protection make the drive extremely versatile.

Hydrostatic hydraulic drives have been developed for many mobile and industrial applications. These drives are used on machine tools, centrifugal pumps, production machines, winches, paper and textile rolls, surface and center winders, conveyors, reels, calenders, printing presses, fans and blowers, agitators, mixers, disintegrators, materials handling machines, plastic extruders and dynamometers.

Hydraulic adjustable-speed drives are also based on the hydrostatic principle. Either a direct or an indirect drive is provided for many applications, including hoists and winches, food machinery, and processing equipment.

The hydraulic transmission is also used extensively on farm tractors. The hydraulic system is used to provide remote control of equipment, power steering, and power braking. Action that requires direction reversal can be provided without clutching—and without stopping. This is ideal for operations that require constant changing in direction, such as stacking and loading.

REVIEW QUESTIONS

1. What is the basic operating principle of a hydraulic drive?
2. What are the essential parts of a hydraulic drive mechanism?

3. What conditions are necessary for hydraulic oil to circulate in a hydraulic drive?
4. Why is torque a result of both tangential acceleration and tangential deceleration of the hydraulic oil?
5. List the advantages of a fluid drive.
6. How does construction of the "torque converter" differ in construction from the other hydraulic drives?
7. List the advantages of the hydrostatic transmsision.
8. List six typical applications of the hydrostatic transmission.
9. List the advantages of the hydraulic transmission for farm tractor applications.

CHAPTER 9

Hydraulic Power Tools

The development of hydraulic power transmission methods has contributed to the replacement of pulleys and belts and of electric motor drive units, in many instances, with hydraulically controlled circuits and systems for operation and control of machine tools in industry. The hydraulic circuit includes a hydraulic motor pumping unit and the necessary control valves.

HYDRAULIC CIRCUITS

The hydraulic motor in a hydraulic circuit is operated by hydraulic oil under pressure. The function of the hydraulic motor is similar to that of a prime mover, such as an electric motor or a steam engine. In the same manner that steam under pressure is piped to the steam engine, the hydraulic pump is used to supply hydraulic oil under pressure to the hydraulic motor. The hydraulic pump can be positioned near the motor, combined with the motor in a single unit, or installed at a location remote from the motor.

Ques. What is the basic operating principle of the hydraulic motor?
Ans. It is operated by hydraulic oil under pressure in the same manner that steam under pressure is used to operate the steam engine.

Ques. How is the hydraulic oil for the hydraulic motor supplied under pressure?
Ans. It is supplied by a hydraulic pump.

332

Hydraulic Motors

In the hydraulic pump, mechanical energy is converted to liquid pressure energy. In the hydraulic motor, liquid pressure energy is converted to mechanical energy.

Hydraulic motors may be classified as either *constant-displacement* or *variable-displacement* motors. In the constant-displacement motor, speed changes are accomplished by varying the volume of oil that flows through the motor. Speed changes in the variable-displacement motor are accomplished by varying displacement of the motor, in addition to controlling the supply of hydraulic oil from the pump. A wider range of speed can be obtained from the variable-displacement type of motor.

Ques. How are hydraulic motors classified?

Ans. They are either constant-displacement or variable-displacement motors.

Ques. How are speed changes accomplished in these two types of motors?

Ans. In the constant-displacement motor, speed changes are accomplished by varying the volume of oil that flows through the motor. In the variable-displacement motor, speed changes are accomplished by varying the displacement of the motor, in addition to controlling the supply of hydraulic oil from the pump.

Ques. Which type of hydraulic motor can provide a wider range of speed?

Ans. The variable-displacement motor.

Constant-Displacement Motors—A sectional diagram showing the basic construction of a typical constant-displacement motor can be seen in Fig. 1. Hydraulic oil under pressure enters the cap-end section, and is forced into the cylinders through suitable openings in a port plate. A single circular valve mounted on an eccentric stud formed on the end of the shaft controls the passage of oil through the ports. The valve does not rotate, but it does receive a gyrating motion as the shaft turns.

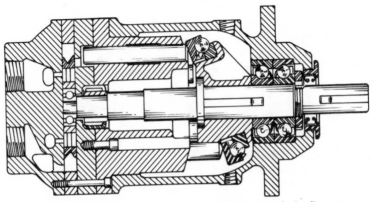

Fig. 1. Basic construction of a typical constant-displacement hydraulic motor.

Hydraulic oil pressure forces the pistons (Fig. 2) against the non-rotating "wobbler." The thrust of the pistons is both perpendicular and tangential, because the wobbler is inclined at an angle. The resultant force is transmitted through ball bearings to the wobbler plate on the shaft, thereby imparting a rotating action to the plate. On the return stroke, the cylinders are emptied through the same ports in the port plate.

Variable-Displacement Motors—The piston stroke can be varied in the variable-displacement type of hydraulic motors by changing the angle at which the "wobbler" is inclined. The axial piston-type motor can be either a constant-displacement or a variable-displacement motor, depending on the angle between the cylinder axis and the output shaft. If this angle can be varied (either manually or automatically), the motor is a variable-displacement motor.

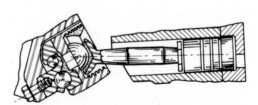

Fig. 2. Construction details of piston and connecting
rod used in a hydraulic motor.

Ques. How is the displacement varied in the variable-displacement hydraulic motors?

Ans. The piston stroke can be varied by changing the angle at which the "wobbler" is inclined. The axial piston-type motor can be either a constant-displacement or a variable-displacement motor, depending on the angle between the cylinder axis and the output shaft. If this angle can be varied (either manually or automatically), the motor is a variable-displacement motor.

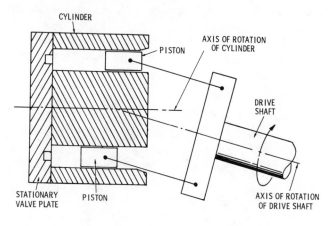

Fig. 3. Basic operating principle of an axial piston-type motor.

The basic operation of an axial piston-type motor is shown in Fig. 3. Hydraulic oil under high pressure enters the stationary valve plate. This oil forces the pistons outward, thus rotating the output shaft.

Types of Hydraulic Motors

The rotary hydraulic motor is used in many applications. The hydraulic motor may be a gear-type, vane-type, or piston-type motor. These motors are similar in construction to the gear-type, vane-type, and piston-type pumps.

Gear-Type—The basic principle of operation of the gear-type motor (Fig. 4) is nearly the same as the reverse action of a gear-type pump. The hydraulic oil under high pressure enters at the inlet, pushes each of the gears, and then flows outward. The load is usually connected to only one of the gears. In most instances, the gears are

335

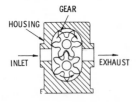

Fig. 4. Basic operating principle of a gear-type hydraulic motor.

of the spur type; however, they may be the helical or herringbone type in some motors. A gear-type motor is a constant-displacement motor.

Vane-Type—The basic operating action of a rotary vane-type motor is illustrated in Fig. 5. Oil under high pressure enters at the inlet,

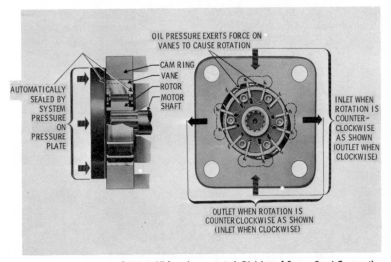

Courtesy Vickers Incorporated, Division of Sperry Rand Corporation

Fig. 5. Basic operating principle of a rotary vane-type hydraulic motor.

exerts pressure on the vanes to turn the rotor, and passes through to the outlet. Either fluid pressure or springs are required as a means of holding the vanes against the contour of the housing at the start of rotation. Centrifugal force holds the vanes against the housing. The vane-type motor is a constant-displacement motor.

Piston-Type—Piston-type motors are available in both radial and axial designs. A *radial piston-type constant-displacement hydraulic*

336

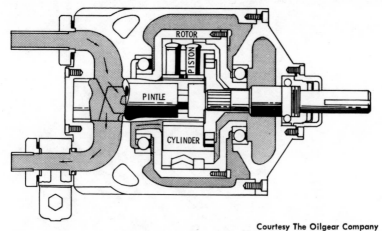

Fig. 6. Construction of a radial piston-type constant-displacement hydraulic motor.

motor is illustrated in Fig. 6. The cylinder rotates around a fixed pintle. Hydraulic oil under high pressure enters the upper ports of the pintle; this forces the pistons to move outward, causing the cylinder and the output shaft to rotate in a clockwise direction.

An *axial piston-type constant-displacement hydraulic motor* is illustrated in Fig. 7. These motors are used in hydraulic circuits to convert hydraulic pressure to rotary mechanical motion. The direction of rotation is determined by the path of the oil flow. Speed control and rotation reversals are accomplished easily and simply. Stalling caused by overloading does not damage this type of motor, and it can be used for dynamic braking. If proper overload relief valve settings are used in the system, the operation can be continuous, intermittent, continuously reversing, or stalled without damage to the motor. The mounting position is not restricted, except that the drain line must be connected to the reservoir, so that the motor case is filled with hydraulic fluid during all operations. The internal parts of the motor depend on the hydraulic oil for lubrication.

In the Vickers *fixed-displacement* hydraulic motors (Fig. 8), a continuous flow of hydraulic oil under pressure is converted to rotary mechanical motion. The cylinder block is offset relative to the drive shaft, which causes the pistons to traverse their respective cylinder

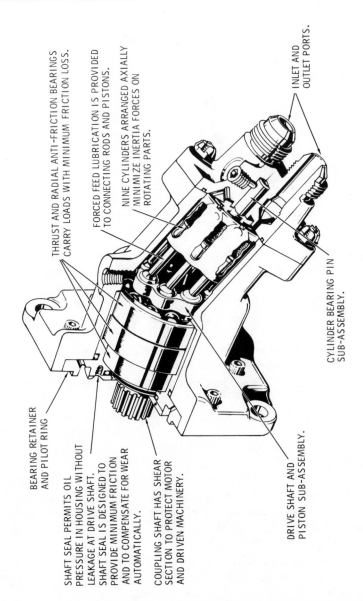

THRUST AND RADIAL ANTI-FRICTION BEARINGS CARRY LOADS WITH MINIMUM FRICTION LOSS.

FORCED FEED LUBRICATION IS PROVIDED TO CONNECTING RODS AND PISTONS.

NINE CYLINDERS ARRANGED AXIALLY MINIMIZE INERTIA FORCES ON ROTATING PARTS.

INLET AND OUTLET PORTS.

CYLINDER BEARING PIN SUB-ASSEMBLY.

BEARING RETAINER AND PILOT RING

SHAFT SEAL PERMITS OIL PRESSURE IN HOUSING WITHOUT LEAKAGE AT DRIVE SHAFT. SHAFT SEAL IS DESIGNED TO PROVIDE MINIMUM FRICTION AND TO COMPENSATE FOR WEAR AUTOMATICALLY.

COUPLING SHAFT HAS SHEAR SECTION TO PROTECT MOTOR AND DRIVEN MACHINERY.

DRIVE SHAFT AND PISTON SUB-ASSEMBLY.

Courtesy Vickers Incorporated, Division of Sperry Rand Corporation

Fig. 7. Cutaway view of an axial piston-type constant-displacement hydraulic motor.

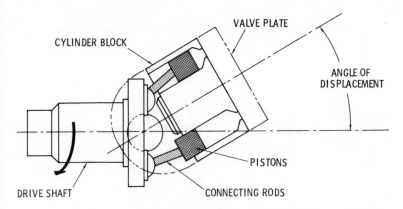

Fig. 8. Basic principle of operation of fixed-displacement piston-type hydraulic motor.

Fig. 9. Cutaway view of a variable-displacement axial piston-type hydraulic motor.

339

bores. As each piston moves away from the valve plate under pressure, the opposite bottomed piston moves toward the valve plate, exhausting the spent hydraulic oil. Since the nine pistons perform the same operation in succession, the acceptance of hydraulic oil under pressure is continuous, and the conversion of the rotary motion is very smooth.

In the Vicker's *variable-displacement* axial piston-type motors (Fig. 9), hydraulic oil under high pressure enters at the inlet port, passes through the pintle, yoke, valve block, and inlet of the valve plate, and then passes into the cylinder. The oil under high pressure pushes the pistons away from the valve plate, causing the cylinder and the output shaft to rotate. The hydraulic oil leaves through the outlet port of the valve plate, passing through the yoke, outlet pintle, and outward through the discharge flange. The angle between the cylinder axis and the output shaft can be varied from 7-1/2 to 30 degrees; therefore, the displacement can be varied from a minimum quantity to four times the minimum quantity.

The piston-type motors are available commercially for oil pressures as high as 5000 pounds, and more, per square inch. Horsepower outputs range to 150 horsepower, and more.

Ques. What are the three basic types of hydraulic motors?

Ans. They are gear-type, vane-type, and piston-type motors. The piston-type motors are either radial or axial in design.

HYDRAULICALLY CONTROLLED CIRCUITS

The hydraulic circuit consists of the combination of a pumping unit and the necessary control valves properly connected to deliver oil at the pressure and volume required. Numerous types of pumps are used to supply power to the hydraulic drive motors. These pumps can be classified as: (1) *single-acting;* (2) *double-acting;* (3) *internal gear;* (4) *rotating;* and (5) *nonrotating.*

In some designs, the pumping unit consists of the pump only, and a separate control unit is necessary. A variable-displacement pump for feeding action and a constant-displacement pump for rapid-traverse action may be mounted on a common shaft and assembled in a compact housing.

Combination Pump and Control Valve Unit

In the sectional diagram (Fig. 10), a hydraulic motor with the control valves in the same casing is illustrated. A single shaft is mounted in two large antifriction-type bearings. The constant-displacement

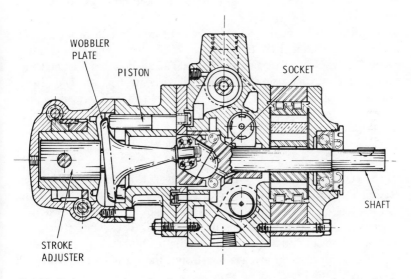

WOBBLER PLATE

PISTON

SOCKET

SHAFT

STROKE ADJUSTER

Fig. 10. Basic construction of a hydraulic motor having main control valves in the same housing.

pump is mounted on the end of the shaft. A hardened and ground roller that is keyed to the shaft rotates in positive contact with a rotor or ring. The ring turns in its housing or roller bearings.

The shaft extends through the main control valve section; a socket bearing—with its axis placed at an angle to the axis of the shaft—is provided at the end of the shaft. The ball-bearing end of the shank of a wobbler plate is borne in the socket. The pistons contact the wobbler plate near its outer edge.

As the shaft rotates, a wobbling action (without rotation) is imparted to the wobbler plate. The stroke of the piston is varied by the forward movement of the stroke adjuster, which more nearly aligns the axis of the wobbler plate shank and the shaft, to reduce the "wobble." The stroke of the piston can be changed either manually or automatically.

341

Remote Directional Control Valves

As mentioned previously, the hydraulic circuit consists of the pumping unit and the necessary control valves. The pumping unit and the main control valves can be actuated by a remote pilot-operated directional control valve; or by a remote solenoid-operated directional control valve.

A typical hydraulically controlled circuit may consist of a pumping unit and a directional control valve to produce a complete operating cycle. The cycle can be controlled by placing dogs on the machine slide to actuate the arm of the directional control valve. The circuit can be designed to provide two rates of feed in only one direction. Skip feeds, and other actions such as rapid-traverse, fast or slow feed, or both—then rapid-traverse action repeated, followed by either fast or slow feed, or both, as many times as desired; and, finally, quick-return action can be obtained.

For starting the cycle by remote control, a solenoid-operated directional control valve can be added to the circuit; then the starting of the cycle can be accomplished by means of an electrical switch or push button. After the unit has been actuated, it can be returned to its starting position at any time during the reading action (except during "rapid-approach") by again pressing the push button. Reversal is effected at the rapid-traverse rate.

Ques. What are the basic elements of a typical hydraulic circuit?

Ans. The hydraulic circuit consists of the pumping unit and the necessary control valves. The pumping unit and the main control valves can be actuated by a remote pilot-operated directional control valve or by a remote solenoid-operated directional control valve.

A "dwell" period at the end of the feed stroke can be obtained by addition of a preset time-delay relay to the electrical circuit. A dog located on the machine slide contacts a limit switch to operate the relay. Following a preset time interval, which can be adjusted for machining conditions, the solenoid valve is energized momentarily to produce the quick-return action. In this installation, the dog is not necessary for tripping the pilot-operated valve to the "return" position, but the traveling machine member must register against a positive stop at the end of the feed stroke and during the "dwell" period.

A triple solenoid-operated directional control valve can be used to actuate the main control valves in the pumping unit; the solenoids are, in turn, actuated by means of limit switches contacted by dogs on the machine slide. One solenoid-operated valve is used to start the cycle when it is energized; "neutral" is produced when the valve is de-energized. A second solenoid valve produces "rapid-traverse" while it is energized and "feed" when it is de-energized. When energized momentarily, a third solenoid-operated valve causes reversal. If the circuit provides "rapid-approach," a single rate of feed, and "quick-return," a fourth solenoid-operated valve can be added to provide a second rate of feed; the addition of a fifth solenoid valve provides a third rate of feed when the proper pumping unit is used.

The addition of a preset time-delay can provide "dwell" against a positive stop. Since the relay operates in conjunction with the reversing solenoid-operated valve, further control valves are not needed.

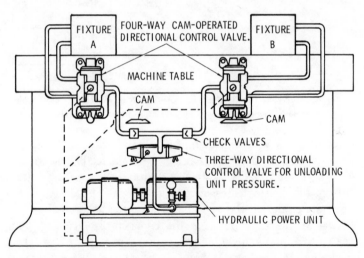

Fig. 11. Diagram illustrating a hydraulic circuit with a cam-operated four-way directional control valve.

A hydraulic circuit with a cam-operated four-way directional control valve is diagrammed in Fig. 11. An accumulator-type power unit used with a hand-operated four-way hydraulic directional control valve is shown in Fig. 12.

343

Operation of a Cylinder on a Machine Tool

A typical hydraulic circuit for operating a cylinder on a machine tool is diagrammed in Fig. 13. This circuit is controlled by varying the oil pressure from the constant-displacement pump to obtain "neu-

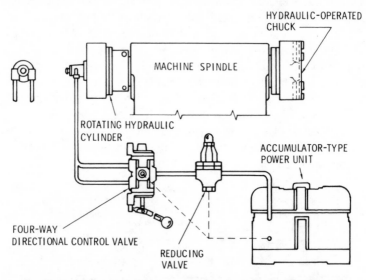

Fig. 12. Hydraulic circuit with an accumulator-type power unit used with a hand-operated four-way hydraulic directional-control valve.

tral" or stop, as well as feeding and "rapid traverse" actions. The variable-displacement pump is used to obtain feeding actions.

Neutral or Stop Position—In this position, there is very little pressure from the constant-displacement pump. The piston-type pump is not operating, and all the hydraulic oil returns to the tank.

Feed—As the pressure from the constant-displacement pump is increased to approximately 50 or 60 pounds per square inch, the variable-displacement pump is charged, the excess oil returning to the tank. The length of stroke of the piston can be adjusted to provide the desired rate of feed.

Rapid-Traverse—This action is controlled by the constant-displacement pump. The hydraulic oil is directed through the chambers of the piston and onward to the main cylinder to provide the rapid-traverse action.

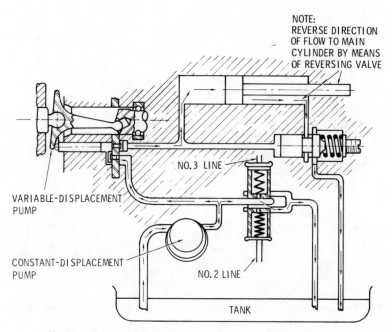

NOTE:
REVERSE DIRECTION
OF FLOW TO MAIN
CYLINDER BY MEANS
OF REVERSING VALVE

NO.3 LINE

VARIABLE-DISPLACEMENT
PUMP

CONSTANT-DISPLACEMENT
PUMP

NO.2 LINE

TANK

Fig. 13. Hydraulic circuit used to operate a cylinder on a machine tool.

Circuit Elements—Other valves and pipe lines can be added to the hydraulic circuit to provide various desirable features (Fig. 14). In this circuit, the main control valves are located in the pump housing. They are, in turn, controlled by pilot-operated or solenoid-operated directional control valves.

In the circuit (see Fig. 14), the feed-control pump or *variable-displacement pump* consists of five pistons, each with an intake and outlet check valve. When the piston chamber is filled with oil, the piston forces the oil outward through the outlet check valve to feed the main cylinder. The intake valve closes automatically. As a result, all the trapped hydraulic oil is used to feed the main cylinder. Two rates of feed (both adjustable from zero to maximum) can be provided; some pumps can provide three rates of feed.

A *feed adjustment* for the two rates of feed is provided on the outside of the pump housing by two knobs (one for "fast" feed and the other for "slow" feed). The two knobs turn the worms which rotate

345

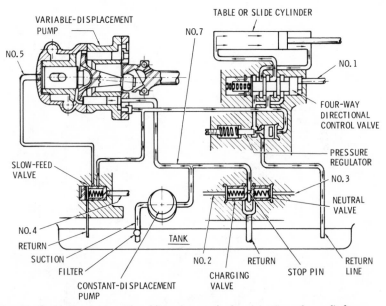

Fig. 14. Hydraulic circuit with additional controls for operation of a cylinder on a machine tool.

the cams. One of the cams provides the setting for "fast" feed, and the other cam provides a "slow" feed. On the "wobbler" support plunger, a pin registers against one of the cams to provide either a fast or slow rate of feed.

The *constant-displacement pump* in Fig. 14 produces the rapid-traverse action. It is a self-priming rotary pump consisting of an external rotor, an internal rotor, and a crescent. This pump also provides oil for charging the variable-displacement pump.

The *main control valves* located in the pump housing are controlled by pilot-operated directional control valves, such as the 14X and 16X valves, or electrical solenoid-operated directional control valves. These auxiliary valves are connected to the main control valves by pipe lines, and they are actuated by dogs located on a moving member of the machine. The dogs trip the pilot-operated directional control valves or open and close limit switches to operate the electrical solenoid-operated directional control valves. The main control valves are as follows:

346

1. *Pressure-regulating valve.* This valve is used on the return side of the main cylinder. A slight back pressure is produced—enough to provide a steady feed under no load. This valve also blocks the return of the hydraulic oil to the tank when in a climb cut or when a drill breaks through the work.

   The valve is opened by the working pressure, and is closed by a spring. The spring determines the minimum (but not maximum) working pressure; therefore, there is a fixed minimum working pressure at all times. The spring also controls the opening required in the valve during a climb cut to keep the piston in the main cylinder from traveling at a faster rate than the preset rate of the variable-displacement pump. The pump is not required to build up pressure during a climb cut (as on a milling machine), because the milling cutter pulls the work, which forces the oil out of the main cylinder.

2. *Four-way directional control valve.* The spring-return four-way directional control valve is positioned in the circuit between the main cylinder and the pressure-regulating valve. The valve is positioned at one end of the valve bore by means of a spring, thereby creating forward cylinder movement by directing oil to an outlet port. Reversing movement occurs when hydraulic oil pressure is exerted against the plunger end opposite the spring end, directing the oil to the other outlet port.

3. *Neutral control valve.* When this valve is open, the entire output of the constant-displacement pump returns to the tank. When the circuit is in "feed" and "rapid-traverse" positions, the neutral control valve is closed and remains closed during the entire cycle. A small hole in the valve pump permits oil to return to the tank through a pilot line to the pilot-operated valve. When the pilot-operated valve closes the escape of oil through this hole, the neutral control valve closes.

4. *Charging valve.* When it is open, this valve creates the pressure required to charge the variable-displacement piston-type pump with oil from the constant-displacement pump, and permits the surplus oil to return to the tank at charging pressure. When the valve is closed, the entire output of the constant-displacement pump is forced through the check valves in the variable-displacement pump to the actuated unit, producing the rapid-

traverse action. A small hole in the valve plunger permits oil to return to the tank through a pilot line to the pilot valve. The pilot-operated directional control valve closes the escape of oil through the small hole to close the charging valve.

5. *Slow-feed valve.* With this valve, two preset rates of feed can be obtained. When the valve is open, a fast feed results; a slower rate of feed is obtained when the valve is closed. An intermediate feed can be obtained while the valve is open for a third rate of feed.

6. *Pressure relief valve.* When an actuated machine member feeds against a positive stop or during overload, this relief valve serves as a safety valve. A preset pressure setting is used for the valve.

The pipe lines (see Fig. 14) serve various purposes. The pipe line from the pilot-operated directional control valve to the tank is not numbered in the illustration; it returns the excess oil to the tank.

A pipe line (see No. 1 in Fig. 14) is connected to each end of the spring-return four-way directional control valve to control the position of the valve spool. Actuation of the pilot- or solenoid-operated directional control valve admits pressure to one of the lines, and opens, simultaneously, the other line to the tank. This moves the four-way valve spool to the desired position.

In some four-way directional control valves, the spool is held in position by a spring for forward travel; then only the pipe line (No. 1) is necessary. Oil pressure in the pipe line (No. 1) overcomes the resistance of the spring and shifts the valve spool to "rapid-return" position. When the line (No. 1) is opened to the tank, the spring returns the valve spool to its former position.

The spring end of the charging valve chamber is connected with the pilot-operated directional control valve by the pipe line (No. 2). When the pilot-operated directional control valve closes the line, the valve plunger in the charging valve is seated. This is accomplished by preventing passage of the oil through the line (No. 2) and returning to the tank. When the pipe line (No. 2) is open, the charging valve is open and feeding action occurs. Rapid-traverse action occurs when the pipe line (No. 2) is closed and the charging valve is closed.

The spring end of the neutral control valve chamber is connected to the pilot-operated directional control valve by a pipe line (No. 3).

HYDRAULIC POWER TOOLS

When the control valve closes the pipe line, the valve plunger in the neutral valve is seated. This is accomplished by preventing the escape of oil to the control valve and back to the tank. When the pipe line (No. 3) is closed, the neutral valve closes and either a feeding action or a rapid-traverse action occurs. When the pipe line (No. 3) is open, the neutral valve is open and the circuit is neutral.

The pipe line (No. 4) connects slow-feed valve to the charging valve, and the pipe line (No. 5) connects the chamber of the slow-feed control valve with the feed-adjustment housing.

The pipe line (No. 6) is used only in conjunction with solenoid-operated directional control valves for remote push-button starting and for emergency-return action. Charging pressure from the constant-displacement pump is conducted through the pipe line (No. 7) to the remote directional control valve which, in turn, distributes the pressure to accomplish various functions.

OPERATION OF HYDRAULIC CIRCUIT

In the hydraulic circuit (see Fig. 14), opening and closing of the neutral valve and the charging valve controls both the constant-displacement pump and the variable-displacement pump. The constant-displacement pump, which is self-priming, pumps hydraulic oil to a chamber that is open to the valve side of both the neutral valve and the charging valve.

In *rapid-traverse action,* all the oil from the constant-displacement pump is required, forcing it through the piston chambers in the variable-replacement pump and onward to the main cylinder. This is accomplished by actuating the pilot-operated control valve which closes the pipe lines (No. 2 and No. 3), thereby closing both the neutral valve and the charging valve. The direction of rapid-traverse is determined by the position of the four-way directional control valve spool. On some models, the four-way directional control valve is constructed in such a manner that the pipe line (No. 2) is blocked automatically, to eliminate a reverse feed, when the valve spool is in the reverse rapid-traverse position.

The *feeding action* (either fast or slow) is obtained by opening the charging valve. This establishes sufficient pressure to keep the pistons in the variable-displacement pump against the "wobble" plate, there-

349

by charging the piston-type pump which is not self-priming. The excess oil is returned to the tank through the charging valve. In "fast-feed" position, the pipe lines (No. 2 and No. 4) are open to the tank, and the pipe line (No. 3) is closed. In "slow-feed" position, the pipe line (No. 2) to the tank is open, the pipe line (No. 3) is closed, and the pipe line (No. 4) is open to the charging pressure. The charging pressure shifts the "slow-feed" valve plunger to direct the pressure in the pipe line (No. 5) to the wobbler support plunger in the variable-displacement pump, which forces the plunger forward to provide the slow rate of feed by decreasing the piston travel.

The third or intermediate rate of feed can be obtained by means of a special feed-adjustment housing which contains an auxiliary wobbler plunger, feed-adjusting screw, and feed-adjusting cam used in conjunction with a solenoid-operated directional control valve. The additional directional control valve is connected to a high-pressure port in the pump housing and to a port in the feed-adjustment housing. When the solenoid-operated directional control valve is energized, pressure from the high-pressure port in the pump is admitted to the feed-adjusting housing and acts on the auxiliary wobbler plunger. De-energizing the solenoid-operated directional control valve blocks the high-pressure port and opens the port in the feed-adjustment housing to the tank. Then the feed-adjusting mechanism is free to be shifted to another rate of feed.

SUMMARY

The hydraulic circuit, including a hydraulic pumping unit and the necessary controls, can be used to operate and control machine tools in industry. Electric motors, along with the pulleys and belts, have been replaced, in many instances, by hydraulic power transmission units.

In the hydraulic pump, mechanical energy is converted to liquid pressure energy. In the hydraulic motor, liquid pressure energy is converted to mechanical energy.

Hydraulic motors are classified as either *constant-displacement* or *variable-displacement* motors. To change the speed of the constant-displacement motor, the volume of oil flowing through the motor must be changed. Change of speed in the variable-displacement motor is accomplished by varying the displacement of the motor, in addition to controlling the supply of hydraulic oil from the pump. A wider range of speed can be obtained from a variable-displacement motor. The rotary hydraulic motors are classified as: (1) *gear-type;* (2) *vane-type;* and (3) *piston-type.* These motors are similar in construction to their respective types of hydraulic pumps.

In a typical hydraulic circuit that is used to control a machine tool, the pumping unit and a directional control valve are necessary to produce a complete operating cycle. The cycle can be controlled by placing dogs on the machine slide to actuate the arm of the directional control valve. The main control valves can be actuated by remote pilot-operated or solenoid-operated directional control valves. Additional rates of feed, etc., can be accomplished by the addition of the necessary directional control valves for performing the various machine functions.

REVIEW QUESTIONS

1. Explain the basic operating principle of the hydraulic motor in the hydraulic circuit.
2. What are the basic operating units in a typical hydraulic circuit for operating a cylinder on a machine tool?
3. Explain the basic difference between a constant-displacement motor and a variable-displacement motor.
4. List the various types of hydraulic motors.

CHAPTER 10

Hydraulic Cylinders

The hydraulic cylinder is the component of the hydraulic system that receives the fluid, under pressure, from a supply line. The hydraulic oil in the cylinder acts on a piston to do work in a linear direction. The work that is performed is the product of the fluid

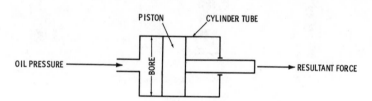

Fig. 1. Schematic diagram of a hydraulic cylinder.

pressure and the area of the cylinder bore (Fig. 1). The quantity of fluid delivered into the cylinder determines the speed or rate of doing work. The chief types of hydraulic cylinders are: (1) *nonrotating;* and (2) *rotating.*

NONROTATING CYLINDERS

The applications for the nonrotating cylinders are more common (Fig. 2) than for the rotating cylinders. There are three types of non-rotating cylinders (Fig. 3): (1) *double-acting;* (2) *single-acting;* and (3) *plunger* or *ram-type.*

353

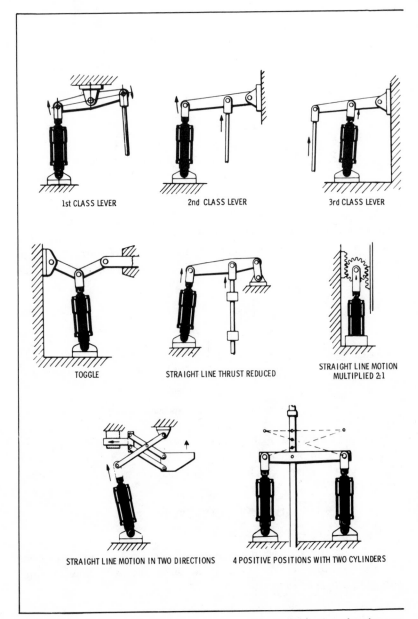

1st CLASS LEVER　　　　2nd CLASS LEVER　　　　3rd CLASS LEVER

TOGGLE　　　STRAIGHT LINE THRUST REDUCED　　　STRAIGHT LINE MOTION MULTIPLIED 2:1

STRAIGHT LINE MOTION IN TWO DIRECTIONS　　　4 POSITIVE POSITIONS WITH TWO CYLINDERS

Fig. 2. Applications for the non-

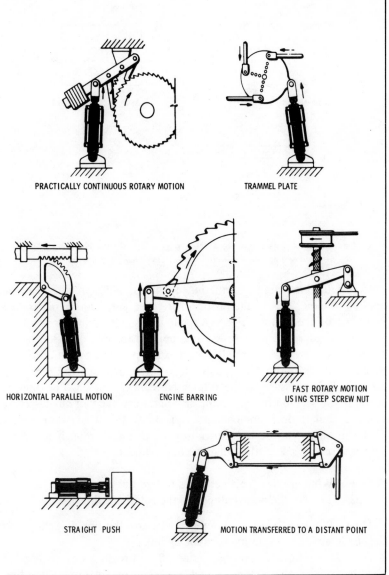

PRACTICALLY CONTINUOUS ROTARY MOTION

TRAMMEL PLATE

HORIZONTAL PARALLEL MOTION

ENGINE BARRING

FAST ROTARY MOTION
USING STEEP SCREW NUT

STRAIGHT PUSH

MOTION TRANSFERRED TO A DISTANT POINT

Courtesy Hanna Company

rotating type of hydraulic cylinder.

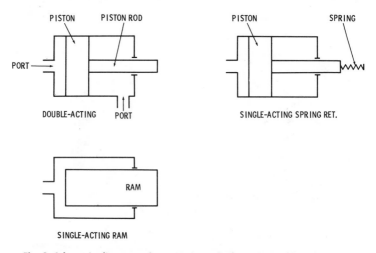

Fig. 3. Schematic diagrams of nonrotating cylinders: (A) Double-acting; (B) Single-acting, spring-return; and (C) Single-acting ram-type.

In the double-acting nonrotating cylinders, fluid pressure can be applied to either side of the piston; therefore, work can be performed in either direction (see Fig. 3A). In the single-acting nonrotating type of cylinder, the fluid pressure is applied to only one side of the piston. The piston is returned to its starting position by action of the spring in the spring-return type of single-acting cylinder (see Fig. 3B) after the fluid pressure has been released from the piston. The plunger or ram-type of nonrotating cylinder is another type of single-acting cylinder, but it does not contain a piston. Either gravity or a mechanical means can be used to return the piston or ram, if a spring-return is not used in the single-acting cylinder.

Ques. What are the two chief types of hydraulic cylinders?
Ans. They are the nonrotating and the rotating cylinders.

Ques. What is the basic difference between the double-acting and the single-acting nonrotating hyraulic cylinders?
Ans. In the double-acting cylinders, fluid pressure can be applied to either side of the piston, so that work can be performed in either direction; fluid pressure can be applied to only one side of the piston in the single-acting cylinder.

356

Ques. How is the piston returned to its starting position in the single-acting nonrotating cylnder?

Ans. Spring action returns the piston in the spring-return type of single-acting cylinder. Either gravity or a mechanical means can be used to return the piston if a spring-return is not used.

Names of Parts

A cutaway view of a double-acting cylinder is shown in Fig. 4, and a view of a disassembled double-acting nonrotating cylinder is shown in Fig. 5. These cylinders can be used for either pneumatics or medium-pressure hydraulics. To understand the operation of a cylinder, it is necessary to study the names of the parts and their functions.

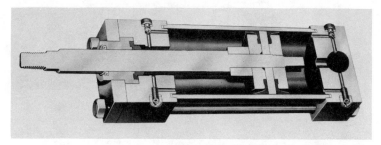

Courtesy Miller Fluid Power Div., Flick-Reedy Corp.

Fig. 4. Double-acting nonrotating cylinder with cushioning device.

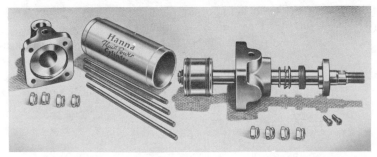

Courtesy Hanna Company

Fig. 5. View of a disassembled double-acting nonrotating cylinder.

357

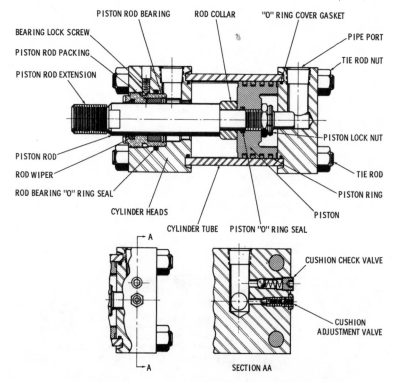

Courtesy Logansport Machine Co., Inc.

Fig. 6. Names of parts of a heavy-duty hydraulic cylinder.

The names of the parts of a heavy-duty hydraulic cylinder are illustrated in Fig. 6. The most important parts are:

1. *Piston rod.* One end of the piston rod is connected to the piston, and the opposite end of the rod is connected to a device that does work, depending on the job requirement. The piston rods are usually made of a good grade of steel that is ground and polished to an extremely smooth finish; they may be hardened and chromeplated to resist wear. Stainless steel material is often used to resist corrosion.

2. *Rod wiper.* The rod wiper is used to remove foreign material from the rod as it is drawn backward into the packing. It is usually made of a durable synthetic material. A metallic

358

scraper (Fig. 7) is sometimes needed to remove severe residues.

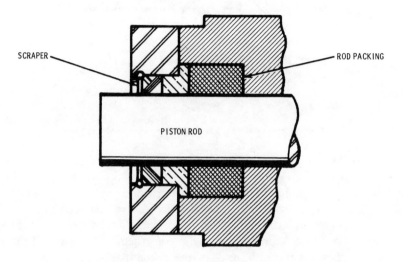

Fig. 7. Use of a metallic scraper to remove residue from the piston rod.

3. *Cylinder covers.* Each cylinder is provided with two covers—the front (rod-end) cover and the blank (blind-end) cover. The blind-end cover is sometimes a part of the tube or cylinder body. The covers are used for several purposes: (1) to seal the ends of the cylinder tubes; (2) to provide a means for mounting; (3) to provide a housing for seals, rod bearings, and rod packing (front cover); (4) to provide for ports of entry for the fluid; (5) to absorb the impact of the piston; and (6) to provide space for a cushioning arrangement. The cylinder covers may be made of iron, steel, bronze, or aluminum, and their dimensions are well standardized.

4. *Cylinder tube.* The cylinder tube may be constructed of cold-drawn seamless steel, brass, or aluminum tubing, which is held to a close tolerance and honed to an extremely smooth finish. The sealing action is dependent largely on the finish provided in the cylinder tube. The covers are usually fastened to the cylinder tube with cover screws (Fig. 8).

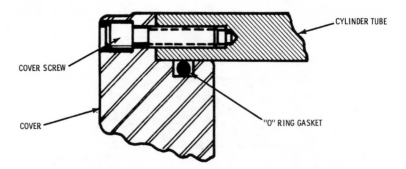

Fig. 8. Cover screws are used to fasten the cover to the cylinder tube.

5. *Piston assembly.* The function of the piston assembly in a hydraulic cylinder is similar to the function of the piston in an automobile. The piston must fit closely against the cylinder wall to provide a suitable bearing and to eliminate any possibility of extrusion of synthetic seals. Since the piston functions as a bearing, it must be constructed of a material that does not score the wall of the cylinder tube. Cast iron with high tensile strength performs well. One of the most common types of pistons for hydraulic service is illustrated in Fig. 9. The piston uses automotive-type rings which may be made of cast iron or bronze. The piston is designed with a relief at each end, so that small particles of dirt which may enter the system do not spring the end land, causing the piston rings to be crushed or frozen. Chevron-type packings, cup packings, and "O" rings are other types of sealing means that may be used.

6. *Piston lock nut.* The lock nut keeps the piston tightly secured to the piston rod. The need for setscrews, pins, and other locking means, which often work loose and drop into the cylinder to cause considerable damage, is eliminated.

7. *Tie rods.* The cylinder is held together by tie rods; they must be strong enough to absorb the shock loads that occur when the piston contacts the cover of the cylinder.

8. *Cushion collar and nose.* The function of the cushion collar and nose is to alleviate shock to the piston and cover as the piston approaches the cylinder cover. The cushioning device

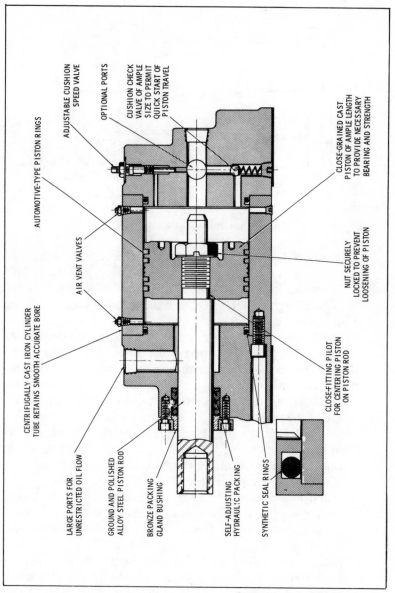

ADJUSTABLE CUSHION SPEED VALVE

AUTOMOTIVE-TYPE PISTON RINGS

OPTIONAL PORTS

CUSHION CHECK VALVE OF AMPLE SIZE TO PERMIT QUICK START OF PISTON TRAVEL

CLOSE-GRAINED CAST PISTON OF AMPLE LENGTH TO PROVIDE NECESSARY BEARING AND STRENGTH

AIR VENT VALVES

NUT SECURELY LOCKED TO PREVENT LOOSENING OF PISTON

CENTRIFUGALLY CAST IRON CYLINDER TUBE RETAINS SMOOTH ACCURATE BORE

CLOSE-FITTING PILOT FOR CENTERING PISTON ON PISTON ROD

LARGE PORTS FOR UNRESTRICTED OIL FLOW

GROUND AND POLISHED ALLOY STEEL PISTON ROD

BRONZE PACKING GLAND BUSHING

SELF-ADJUSTING HYDRAULIC PACKING

SYNTHETIC SEAL RINGS

Courtesy Logansport Machine Co., Inc.

Fig. 9. A piston with automotive-type rings in a hydraulic cylinder.

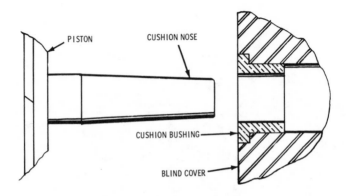

Fig. 10. Use of a tapered cushion nose.

on the rod-end side of the piston is the cushion collar, and the device on the blind side is the cushion nose (Fig. 10). Longer lengths of cushions may be required on cylinders that move a large mass on wheels, bearings, or other free-moving means at high speeds.

9. *Cushion adjustment valve.* This valve works with the cushion nose and collar, and is a part of the entire cushioning arrangement. When the trapped hydraulic oil (which occurs after the cushion closes the bushing) is metered out, it must pass by the needle of the cushion adjustment valve which determines the size of the exhausting orifice. The trapped oil cannot flow past the ball check, as it is blocked in that direction. Some designs are made with a fixed orifice; the chief advantage of the adjustable orifice is that it can be changed for different loadings and operating pressures.

10. *Piston rod bearing.* The piston rod bearing not only houses the rod packing but also acts as a bearing and as a guide for the piston rod. The rod bearings are made of cast iron or a good-quality bronze.

11. *Rod packing.* The rod packing seals the piston rod to prevent escape of the oil from around the rod. Various designs of piston rod packing are used, such as chevron, blocked vee, "O" ring, quad-ring, and *Sea* ring. Various materials, such as

362

Table 1. Force Developed By Nonrotating Cylinders

Cylinder Bore	Area of Cyl. Bore Rod	Rod Dia.	At 80 psi		At 100 psi		At 500 psi		At 1000 psi		At 1500 psi	
			Push#	Pull#	Push#	Pull#	Push#	Pull#	Push#	Pull#	Push#	Pull#
2	3.142	1	251	188	314	235	1571	1178	3142	2357	4713	3535
2½	4.909	1⅜	392	273	490	342	2454	1712	4909	3424	7363	5136
3	7.069	1⅜	565	443	706	558	3534	2792	7069	5584	10603	8376
3½	9.621	1⅜	769	650	962	813	4810	4068	9621	8136	14431	12204
4	12.566	1¾	1005	812	1256	1016	6283	5080	12566	10164	18849	15241
5	19.635	2	1570	1319	1963	1649	9817	8246	19635	16493	29457	24739
6	28.274	2	2261	2010	2827	2513	4137	12566	28274	25132	42411	37698
7	38.485	2½	3078	2686	3848	3357	19242	16788	38485	33576	57727	50364
8	50.265	2½	4021	3628	5026	4535	25132	22678	50265	45356	75397	68034

synthetic rubber, leather, *Teflon,* and nylon, are used in the packings, depending on the application.

12. *Cover gaskets.* These gaskets serve as a seal between the cylinder cover and the cylinder tube. When the "O" ring is placed as shown in Fig. 6, a perfect seal that is nearly indestructible is formed. The seal becomes tighter as the pressure is increased.

Ques. What is a rod wiper?

Ans. It is made of a durable synthetic material, and is used to clean foreign matter from the piston rod as it is retracted into the cylinder.

Ques. What is a rod scraper?

Ans. It is a metallic scraper that is sometimes used to remove residues from the piston rod.

Ques. What is the purpose of the rod packing?

Ans. It seals the piston rod, so that the fluid cannot escape from around the rod.

Force Developed in Nonrotating Cylinders

Tremendous forces can be developed in nonrotating cylinders (see Table 1). Their requirements should be realized before discussing the installation of these cylinders. The table is based on the formulas:

$$F = PA; \text{ and } F = P\,(A - A_1)$$

in which;

F is force (theoretical force, not including friction) developed
P is supply pressure, in *psi*
A is area, in sq. in., of cylinder bore
A_1 is area, in sq. in., of cross section of piston rod

To determine the force developed when fluid pressure is applied to the blind end (the end opposite the piston rod) of the cylinder, the formula, $F = PA$, is used, and the formula, $F = P\,(A - A_1)$, is used to determine the force created when fluid pressure is applied to the rod end of the cylinder. When the same force is applied either to the fluid end or to the rod end of a cylinder, the higher force is always exerted by the blind end, because it has a greater area.

Nonrotating cylinders can be specially designed to operate at pressures as high as 10,000 pounds per square inch; however, these applications are rare. Standard nonrotating hydraulic cylinders are designed for the different pressure ranges, and they should be used for applications within those ranges. These operating ranges are designated in pounds per square inch of operating pressure for hydraulic oil, as 0-150; 0-750; 0-1500 (Fig. 11); 0-2000 (Fig. 12); and 0-3000.

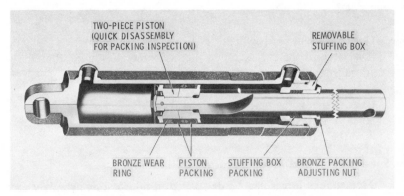

TWO-PIECE PISTON
(QUICK DISASSEMBLY
FOR PACKING INSPECTION)

REMOVABLE
STUFFING BOX

BRONZE WEAR
RING

PISTON
PACKING

STUFFING BOX
PACKING

BRONZE PACKING
ADJUSTING NUT

Photo furnished by Commercial Shearing & Stamping Company of Youngstown, Ohio

Fig. 11. Cutaway view of hydraulic cylinder (1500 psi).

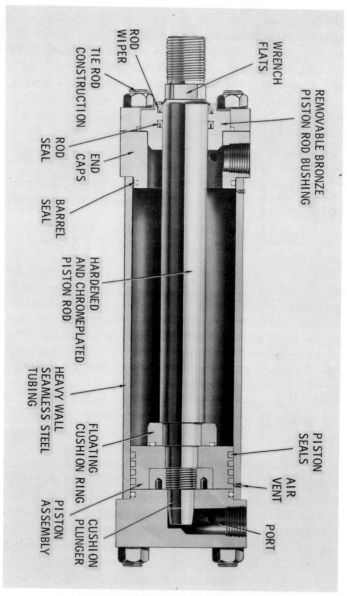

Fig. 12. Cutaway view of hydraulic cylinder (2000 psi).

Installation

Since installation is an important factor in the performance of a cylinder, the different mounting styles should be studied to obtain the best results. Of course, all mountings should be fastened securely.

Flange-Mounted—Front-flange mounted hydraulic cylinders are

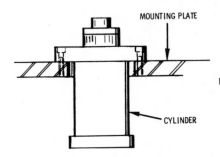

Fig. 13. Reverse-flange mounting of a hydraulic cylinder for press applications.

adapted to "pulling" applications. The front cover bears against the mounting plate, which relieves the pressure on the mounting screws. Reverse-flange mounting (Fig. 13) is preferred for press applications, because the strain on the mounting screws is relieved. The blind-end flange mounting (Fig. 14) is usually desirable where it is necessary to mount the cylinder in the base of a machine; this is the only type of mounting that can be used on some machines.

Centerline Mounted—The chief advantage of the centerline mounted cylinder (Fig. 15) is that the mounting feet or lugs are in a direct line with the center line of the thrust. If the mounting bolts are keyed, full thrust on the mounting bolts is eliminated.

Foot-Mounted—The foot-mounted method (Fig. 16) is commonly used for mounting nonrotating cylinders. Some torque is created, because the mounting lugs are in a different plane from that of the center line of the thrust; therefore, the mounting lugs should be keyed to reduce the thrust on the mounting bolts. Ample support for the piston rod should be provided on this type of cylinder, especially on cylinders with long strokes. The same type of guide should be provided for the end of the rod to prevent sagging which causes wear on the rod bearing or damage to the piston and cylinder walls. A center support (Fig. 17) should be provided for extra-long cylinders

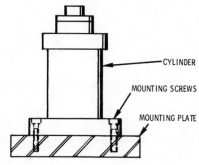

Fig. 14. The blind-end flange mounting is usually desirable where it is necessary to mount the cylinder in the base of a machine.

CYLINDER

MOUNTING SCREWS

MOUNTING PLATE

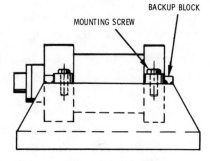

BACKUP BLOCK

MOUNTING SCREW

Fig. 15. Hydraulic cylinder with mounting lugs at the center line.

to reduce sagging of the cylinder tube. This support should be aligned perfectly with the mountings at the front and rear of the machine.

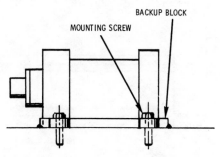

BACKUP BLOCK

MOUNTING SCREW

Fig. 16. A commonly used foot-mounting style.

367

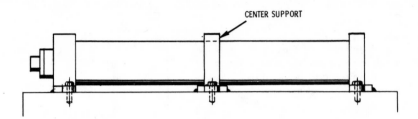

Fig. 17. A center support should be providel for long-stroke foot-mounted cylinders.

A loading problem always exists with nonrotating cylinders. If possible, these cylinders should be loaded concentrically. If this is impossible, provisions for eccentric loading should be made. The use of heavy guide rods and bearings (Fig. 18) is one method of compensating for eccentric loading.

Causes of Failure

Several causes contribute to failure of nonrotating cylinders. The major causes are:

1. *Dirt*. More failures can be attributed to dirt than to any other single problem. Particles of dirt may lodge between the piston and cylinder tube, scoring the tube; then the piston seal becomes defective, and excessive leakage past the piston occurs. The piston may "freeze" to the tube if the scoring is deep enough. Dirt particles settling on the piston rod may score the rod as it is drawn into the cover and, leaks may develop.

2. *Heat*. Excessive heat may cause deterioration of the packings,

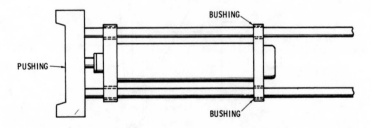

Fig. 18. Method of providing for eccentric loads.

causing packing and gasket leaks. The temperature at the cylinder should not exceed 140°F. A heat-resistant shield should be provided if a cylinder is subjected to excessive external heat. Heat-resistant packings are now available for temperatures up to 500°F.

3. *Misapplication.* This factor, rather than faulty design, contributes to a high percentage of cylinder failures. For example, cylinders with cast iron covers should not be used for applications that involve high shock impact and eccentric loads. A cylinder may fail after a few days in a heavy-duty application, but the same cylinder may provide satisfactory service on a medium-duty application for several years.

4. *Misalignment, side thrust, and improperly supported eccentric loading are factors that can cause cylinder failure.* Excessive wear on one side of the piston rod, leaks in the rod packing, and wear on one side of the rod bearing are early indications of the factors that lead to cylinder failure. A bent piston rod, a broken packing gland, a scored cylinder tube, a broken cylinder cover, or a broken piston may result in serious damage.

5. *Faulty mountings.* If the mounting is not secure or is not strong enough to withstand the load produced by the cylinder, the cylinder may break loose and damage the mounting or the application with which it is connected.

Repair and Maintenance

Suggestion for dismantling, repairing, and assembling nonrotating cylinders are as follows:

1. Drain all oil from the cylinder, and dismantle in a clean location. Do not attempt to dismantle a cylinder when pressure is applied to the cylinder.

2. Each part should be cleaned. Metal parts that are to be reused should be coated with a good preservative and placed in protected storage if the cylinder is to remain dismantled.

3. The piston rod should be checked for straightness. If the rod is bent, it can be straightened by placing it in vee-blocks in a press. The piston rod also should be examined for scores, indentations, and scratches. If the blemishes are not too deep, they can be removed with a fine emery cloth; however, if it is

369

necessary to grind the rod, it can be chromeplated to restore the diameter to its original size.

4. The cover and cushion bushings should be examined for wear and finish, and they should be replaced if they are not in first-class condition.

5. The cylinder tube should be repaired or replaced if it is damaged. Deep scores are difficult to repair; and it may be necessary to chromeplate the tube.

6. All the seals and gaskets should be replaced in reassembly of a cylinder. If metal piston rings are used, the manufacturer's specifications should be checked for gap clearance. If synthetic or leather seals are used on the piston, care should be exercised in placing the piston in the tube, so that the sealing surfaces are not damaged. When installing the packings, a light grease makes assembly much easier.

7. If a metal piston with rings is to be replaced, grind the piston concentrically with the piston rod after assembly to the rod. Grind the piston to fit the tube closely.

8. Cylinders with foot-mounted covers should be assembled on a surface plate. The mounting pads of both covers should make full contact with the surface plate; otherwise, a binding action may occur after mounting, or a mounting foot may be broken.

9. The cover bolts should be tightened evenly. If O ring or quad-ring gaskets are used to seal the tube and cover, tension on the cover screw is reduced to a minimum.

After assembly of a cylinder has been completed, it should be tested at low operating pressure for freedom of movement of the piston and rod and to make sure that they are not being scored or bound. Then the pressure should be increased to the full operating range, and the cylinder checked for both internal and external leakages. To check for internal leakage, place fluid pressure in the blind-end port of the cylinder, forcing the piston to the rod end; then check the amount of fluid coming from the rod and cover port. Place fluid pressure in the rod-end port, moving the piston to the blind-end cover, and check for leakage at this position. If leakage is to be checked at other positions, use an external means to block the ports at these positions and check as described above. When excessive leakage occurs, the cylinder must be disassembled to make corrections. If metal piston rings are used in a hydraulic cylinder, the leakage varies with the operating pressure, the cylinder bore, and the oil temperature and vicosity. Leakage should be nearly nonexistent if the piston is sealed with synthetic or leather seals.

A cylinder should be mounted securely when it is reattached to a machine or fixture. It should always be remembered that these cylinders are capable of delivering considerable force. Cylinder bores may range from 1 inch in diameter to more than 30 inches in diameter. The strokes may range from less than 1 inch to more than 30 feet.

ROTATING CYLINDERS

A study of the names of the parts and their functions is necessary to understand the operation of a rotating cylinder. A rotating hydraulic cylinder is diagrammed in Fig. 19.

Names of Parts

The important parts of a rotating cylinder are discussed as follows:

1. *Body.* The cylinder body is usually made of either cast iron or aluminum and it must be pressure tight. The body is usually machined on both the inside and the outside surfaces—on the inside surface to provide a smooth surface for the packing and on the outside surface for the sake of appearance. The body contains passages for directing the fluid to the front side of the piston; it also contains the housing for the rod packing, and provides a bearing for the piston rod. A number of tapped holes are provided in the open end of the body to receive the cover bolts. The closed end of the body is provided with an adaptation designed to meet either American Standards or the manufacturer's specifications. The body also may anchor one end of the drive pin.

   If the cylinders are designed with a stroke that is longer than the standard stroke, the body often consists of two sections—the cylinder tube and the rod-end cover. This design aids in reducing porosity, which is often a problem on long-stroke rotating cylinders with a one-piece body.

371

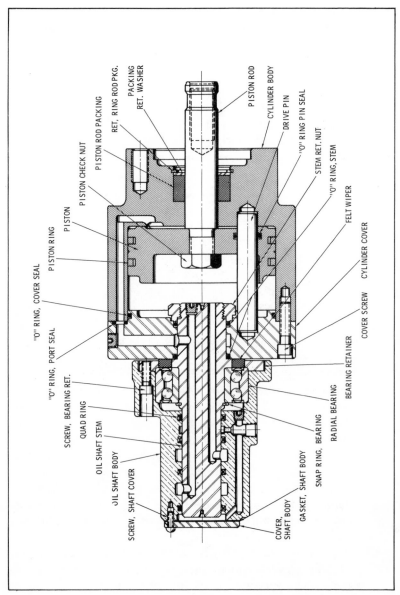

Fig. 19. Parts of a rotating hydraulic cylinder.

2. *Cylinder cover.* The cover is fastened to the body by cover screws, and it encloses the cylinder. The cylinder cover carries the oil shaft assembly, and may anchor one end of the drive pin. The cover carries a fluid passage which connects to the fluid passage in the cylinder body.

3. *Piston rod.* The piston rod is made of a ground and polished alloy steel, and is the connector between the piston and the driven means. The end of the piston is usually tapped with female threads, but some applications may require male threads.

4. *Piston assembly.* An automotive-type piston ring is used in the piston assembly of the hydraulic cylinder shown in Fig. 19. Other designs use various types of seals, such as "V" packing or blocked vees. The piston may be made of either cast iron or aluminum. The piston has three chief functions: (1) to provide an area for the fluid pressure to exert force, thereby developing a force to act on a load; (2) to provide a seal which prevents leaking or escaping of fluid to the exhaust side; and (3) to act as a guide or bearing.

5. *Drive pins.* These pins prevent rotation of the piston in relation to the cylinder body. Drive pins are needed, because brakes are provided on many machines with rotating spindles. Without the drive pins, a sudden stopping of the spindle may cause the piston to rotate within the cylinder body, causing the piston rod to become loosened or disconnected from its connecting part. This often causes considerable trouble, and considerable time is consumed in correcting it.

6. *Rod packing.* Since most of the work is usually done on the instroke and fluid pressure is exerted on the rod packing most of the time, the rod packing is extremely important in a rotating cylinder. The efficiency on the instroke is reduced greatly by any leakage past the packings. On rotating cylinders, it is a quite difficult job to make a packing change; therefore, the packings must be durable. Synthetic rubber, impregnated leather, *Teflon,* and other materials are used for packings. Several designs, such as chevron, *Sea* rings, and hat, are used for packings.

7. *Cover gasket.* This gasket seals the cylinder body and the cylinder cover, and it contains holes for the cover screws and

373

for the fluid passages between the body and the cover. Although the cover gasket can be made of a thin sheet of gasket material, it must be strong enough to prevent escape of the fluid.

8. *Oil shaft stem.* This is an important part in the action of the rotating cylinder. The shaft stem must be sturdy enough to provide proper support to the remainder of the oil shaft assembly and to withstand external force that results from the weight of the flexible hoses and pipe connectors. The oil shaft stem is made of a hardened alloy steel and ground to a high finish, so that the packing is provided a smooth bearing surface. An oil shaft assembly is often referred to as an oil distributor.

9. *Distributor body.* The distributor body functions as a housing for the shaft packing, as a housing for the means of lubrication, to provide ports of entry, and to retain the bearing. The body may be made of such materials as cast iron, cast aluminum, or cast bronze. It should be arranged to dissipate as much heat as possible from the packings and the shaft, and the body must be rugged enough to withstand the strain of the pipe lines and connectors. Water-cooled distributor bodies containing large-cored passages are often necessary to effect a better cooling action where hollow oil shafts are used.

10. *Shaft packing.* As little friction as possible must be created by the shaft packing; however, it must provide an effective seal at shaft revolutions up to five thousand revolutions per minute, and higher. Shredded lead, lead and graphite, asbestos, and other materials are used to combat the heat condition. Various packing shapes, such as formed-wedge, vee, and hat types, are used.

11. *Bearing.* A bearing is required to provide support between the shaft body and the shaft stem. Depending on the shaft design, various types of bearings, such as ball bearings, sleeve, and thrust bearings, are used. These bearings must be able to withstand considerable heat, and lubrication to the bearings is extremely important.

A number of minor parts are important in the functioning of a

374

rotating cylinder. Some of these parts are: retainer rings, spacers, O-ring gaskets and screws. Incorrect assembly of these minor parts or failure to replace worn or damaged seals, gaskets, etc., may cause the cylinder to malfunction or to fail to operate properly, resulting in increased maintenance and repair costs.

Installation

The pressure chart (see Table 1) should be studied before actual installation of a rotating cylinder is begun, if one is to visualize the great force that these cylinders can develop. Although the pneumatic rotating cylinders are seldom operated at more than 90 pounds of air pressure, the hydraulic rotating cylinders may be operated at pressures as high as 1000 *psi*.

Since the rotating cylinder may be subjected to high revolving speeds, installation is an extremely important factor. As mentioned previously, rotating cylinders are constructed with the mounting as a part of the cylinder body. On the small-diameter cylinders, the mounting is usually threaded; a number of tapped holes for mounting purposes are used on the larger cylinders.

Rotating cylinders are not mounted directly onto the machine spindle; they are mounted on an adapter which has previously been mounted onto the machine spindle. Adapters are used, because the manufacturers of lathes and other machines with spindles use different end designs on the cylinder end of the machine spindle. If a manufacturer produces a dozen, or more, different spindle sizes (depending on the range of sizes of his machine), each spindle end may have different dimensions. The adapter is usually made of the same material as the body of the rotating cylinder; therefore, an aluminum adapter is used for an aluminum cylinder.

Before installing the cylinder, it is important that the adapter is mounted properly. The adapter should bottom against the end of the spindle and then it should be locked securely. The locking action is accomplished by tightening the locking screws on a split-type adapter. On a threaded-type adapter, bronze plugs are forced inward against the threads on the spindle, and locked in place with setscrews. Two plugs spaced at a 90° angle from each other are often used (Fig. 20). After the adapter is locked securely in place, the pilot on the cylinder end should be checked for runout with an indicator. If the runout is more than 0.002 in., the adapter should be corrected. Since nearly

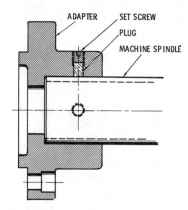

Fig. 20. Diagram illustrating an adapter
for a rotating type of cylinder.

all rotating cylinders need a draw bar to make a connection to the
mechanism which they operate, the draw bar is screwed into the end
of the piston rod of the cylinder (Fig. 21). Then the cylinder is
mounted onto the adapter, using the mounting screws. The adapting
surfaces on the cylinder should be clean and free of burrs, since they
may cause trouble. Also, the mounting screws should not be long
enough to bottom in the mounting holes in the cylinder. Otherwise,
the cylinder does not fit tightly on the adapter. After the cylinder has
been mounted, the indicator should be used to check the outside
diameter of the cylinder for runout. If the runout is more than 0.003
in., the cylinder mounting should be corrected.

Failure

The major causes of failure in rotating cylinders are:

1. *Lack of lubrication.* Improper lubrication to the bearings causes
   a hydraulic rotating cylinder to fail. An increase in friction
   caused by lack of lubrication causes piston and rod packing
   failure in air cylinders.
2. *Dirt.* Dirt inside the cylinder causes packing and bearing failure, scoring of the piston rod, shaft stem, and cylinder body,
   and the fouling of the passages within the cylinder.
3. *Misapplication.* If the rotating cylinders are used at speeds far
   in excess of their designed speeds, packing and bearing failure
   usually results.

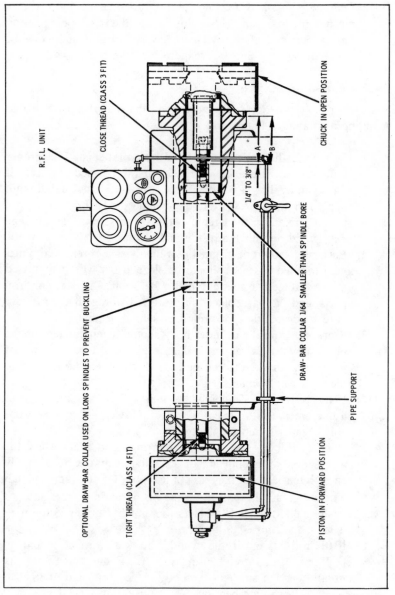

Courtesy Logansport Machine Co., Inc.

Fig. 21. Installation of power-operated chucking equipment on a machine.

377

4. *Poor installation.* If a cylinder is not mounted solidly or if it is not mounted concentrically with the spindle, a whipping action on the rear end of the cylinder may soon result in leakage of the shaft packing and in breakdown of the bearings.

Repair and Maintenance

Some important practices and suggestions that can be used in dismantling a rotating cylinder are:

1. Dismantle the cylinders on a clean workbench. Use proper tools; do not use a pipe wrench on the finished surfaces. If the cylinder is placed in a vise, use soft pads and do not apply too much pressure to the cylinder body. Loosen the rod packing retainer; then remove the cover screws, take off the cover, and remove the piston and piston rod.

2. Each part should be cleaned thoroughly as it is removed. Parts with internal passages should be cleaned out with compressed air. A protective coating should be applied to steel or iron parts, and the parts placed in protected storage if the cylinder is to be dismantled for prolonged length of time.

3. Score marks in the cylinder body should be eliminated, or the body should be scrapped if the scores are too deep. In a cast iron body, the marks can be brazed, and then the interior of the body can be refinished.

4. If the piston rod is scored, the marks may be removed with a fine emery cloth, unless they are too deep. Then it is probably cheaper to replace the rod.

5. It is advisable to replace all packings and seals when the cylinder is disassembled. In installing cup packings, apply enough tension that they do not leak, but do not apply enough tension to turn in the lips. If the piston parts are designed to make metal-to-metal contact, too much cam pressure may damage the cups.

6. If the rod bearing in the cylinder body is worn, it should be replaced. If the rod bearing is part of the body, there is usually enough stock in the body to bore out and press in a bronze sleeve-type bearing. The bearing must be tight.

7. A worn or scored oil shaft should be replaced, because this

is a vital part of the cylinder; any rough portions on the shaft can be a source of trouble.

8. In reassembly, all screws should be tightened securely. Tighten the cover screws evenly. Care should be exercised to prevent cuts in the packings and gaskets as they are placed.

9. After the cylinder has been reassembled and before applying pressure, lubricate and rotate the distributor body to be sure that it moves freely and without any binding action.

10. Then apply fluid pressure to one port of the distributor body, and check piston movement. Place a finger over the pipe port to check for leaks. Then shift the pressure connection to the second port, let the piston move to the end of its travel, and place a finger over the first port to check for leaks. Slight packing leaks that are caused by a slight blow of the shaft can usually be taken care of after the cylinder has been run in, by pulling upward on the shaft packing. If excessive leakage occurs, the cylinder should be dismantled.

SUMMARY

The hydraulic cylinder receives the fluid, under pressure, from a supply line. The oil in the cylinder acts on a piston to do work in a linear direction. The work that is performed is the product of the fluid pressure and the area of the cylinder bore. The chief types of hydraulic cylinders are: (1) *nonrotating;* and (2) *rotating.*

Three types of nonrotating cylinders are available. They are: (1) *double-acting;* (2) *single-acting;* and (3) *plunger* or *ram-type.* In the double-acting cylinders, fluid pressure can be applied to either side of the piston; therefore, work can be performed in either direction. Fluid pressure is applied to only one side of the piston in a single-acting cylinder. The piston is returned to its starting position by action of the spring in a spring-return type of single-acting cylinder. The plunger or ram-type cylinder is another type of single-acting cylinder.

Tremendous forces can be developed in nonrotating cylinders. To determine the force developed when pressure is applied to the blind end (the end opposite the piston rod) of the cylinder, the formula, $F = PA$, is used. The formula, $F = P (A - A_1)$, is used to determine the force created when fluid pressure is applied to the rod end of the cylinder.

Nonrotating cylinders can be specially designed to operate at pressures as high as 10,000 pounds per square inch; however, these applications are rare. Standard nonrotating hydraulic cylinders are designed for the different pressure ranges, and they should be used for applications within these ranges. These operating ranges are designated in pounds per square inch of operating pressure, as: 0-150; 0-750; 0-1500; 0-2000; and 0-3000.

Installation is an important factor in the performance of a nonrotating cylinder. The different styles of mounting these cylinders are: (1) *flange-mounted* (2) *centerline-mounted;* (3) *foot-mounted.*

Installation of rotating cylinders is extremely important, because these cylinders often revolve at high speeds. These cylinders are not mounted directly onto the machine spindle. They are mounted on an adapter that has previously been mounted onto the spindle. Therefore, it is important that both the adapter and the cylinder are installed correctly.

REVIEW QUESTIONS

1. What is the chief difference between a single-acting and a double-acting hydraulic cylinder?
2. What is an application for a nonrotating cylinder? A rotating cylinder?
3. What is the purpose of a cushion collar and nose?
4. List three factors that may cause a nonrotating cylinder to fail.
5. Name at least five types of seals that are used on the pistons

CHAPTER 11

Control Valves

The control valves that are used in fluid power systems can be divided into three categories: (1) *pressure* controls; (2) *flow* controls; and (3) *directional* controls. The pressure controls regulate the pressure intensity in the various portions of the system. Flow controls regulate the speed at which the fluid medium (air, oil, or water) is permitted to flow; this, in turn, controls the piston speed in the cylinders, the movements of the valve spools, the rotation speeds of the shafts of fluid motors, and the actuation speeds of other devices. The directional controls are used to direct the fluid medium to the various passages in the system. Many types of directional controls are available—from the simple shutoff valves (similar to those used on sillcocks in the home) to the six- and eight-way control valves that are used to control automatic machinery.

The size of its external openings determines the size of a control valve—or the amount of fluid that can pass through the opening with minimum back pressure. For example, a control valve with external openings or pipe ports threaded for 1/2-in. pipe should be capable of passing the same amount of fluid that can be passed normally by a 1/2-in. pipe. Generally, the flow of hydraulic fluid does not exceed 15 ft. per second; however, in some instances, the oil velocity far exceeds this rate, and it may be nearly twice this rate. Excessive velocities of hydraulic fluid create heat in the system, and they contribute to control problems that arise from undesirable pressure drops.

Subplate mountings (Fig. 1) and manifold-type mountings are often used for control valves. Then the control valve can be replaced without disturbing the piping.

CONTROL VALVES

Fig. 1. Showing a control valve with subplate mounting.

Fig. 2. A large hydraulic valve with flange connections, used for high-pressure service.

382

MEETS STANDARDS OF MS 16142 (SHIPS)

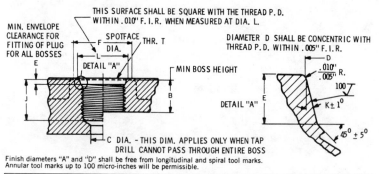

Finish diameters "A" and "D" shall be free from longitudinal and spiral tool marks. Annular tool marks up to 100 micro-inches will be permissible.

tube outside diameter	Th'd. Size UNF-2B	STRAIGHT THREAD "T"				B Min. Th'd. Depth	C Min. Dia.	D +.005 −.000 Dia.	E +.015 −.000 Dia.	F Dia.	J Min.	K ±1°	L Min. Dia.
		Pitch Dia.		Minor Dia.									
		Min.	Max.	Min.	Max.								
1/8	5/16-24	.2854	.2902	.267	.277	.390	.062	.358	.074	.672	.468	12°	.438
3/16	3/8-24	.3479	.3528	.330	.340	.390	.125	.421	.074	.750	.468	12°	.500
1/4	7/16-20	.4050	.4104	.383	.395	.454	.172	.487	.093	.828	.547	12°	.563
5/16	1/2-20	.4675	.4731	.446	.457	.454	.234	.550	.093	.906	.547	12°	.625
3/8	9/16-18	.5264	.5323	.502	.515	.500	.297	.616	.097	.969	.609	12°	.688
1/2	3/4-16	.7094	.7159	.682	.696	.562	.391	.811	.100	1.188	.688	15°	.875
5/8	7/8-14	.8286	.8356	.798	.814	.656	.484	.942	.100	1.344	.781	15°	1.000
3/4	1 1/16-12	1.0084	1.0158	.972	.990	.750	.609	1.148	.130	1.625	.906	15°	1.250
7/8	1 3/16-12	1.1334	1.1409	1.097	1.115	.750	.719	1.273	.130	1.765	.906	15°	1.375
1	1 5/16-12	1.2584	1.2659	1.222	1.240	.750	.844	1.398	.130	1.910	.906	15°	1.500
1 1/4	1 5/8-12	1.5709	1.5785	1.535	1.553	.750	1.078	1.713	.132	2.270	.906	15°	1.875
1 1/2	1 7/8-12	1.8209	1.8287	1.785	1.803	.750	1.312	1.962	.132	2.560	.906	15°	2.125
2	2 1/2-12	2.4459	2.4540	2.410	2.428	.750	1.781	2.587	.132	3.480	.906	15°	2.750

Courtesy Imperial-Eastman Corporation

Fig. 3. Hydraulic control valves with straight pipe threads are commonly used on military and mobile applications.

Flange-type connections (Fig. 2) are used on many of the larger control valves. These connections are usually used for ports that are larger than 2 inches, and they are used mostly in hydraulics for military or mobile applications (Fig. 3).

Materials that are used in construction of a control valve depend largely on the fluid medium, the operating pressure, and the ambient temperature. The bodies of pneumatic valves are made of aluminum, brass, bronze, or cast iron, and the internal parts are made of brass, aluminum, stainless steel, or plated steels. The bodies of hydraulic valves are made of high-tensile cast iron, cast steel, or plate steel, and the alloy steels are used for the interior parts.

Many of the interior parts are heat-treated to Rockwell C55 or 60. Bronze or cast iron alloys are used for the bodies of high-pressure water valves, and heat-treated steels or stainless steels are used for the interior parts. Care should be exercised in selecting valves for high-pressure water systems, because high-velocity water erodes some types of materials. The damage that results is called "wire-drawing effect" or "termite effect," and it can render a control valve completely inoperable in a relatively short period of time.

The packings for control valves are made in various configurations and materials. Some of these configurations are: cups, "O" rings, quad rings, "Vee" packings, "U" packings, etc. Some of the materials used are *Teflon, Viton,* Buna N, treated leather, and asbestos.

Ques. What are the three categories of control valves?
Ans. The three categories are: (1) pressure controls; (2) flow controls; and (3) directional controls.

Ques. What determines the size of a control valve?
Ans. The size of the external openings—or the amount of fluid that can pass through the opening with minimum back pressure.

Ques. How are the control valves usually mounted?
Ans. Subplate mountings and manifold-type mountings are often used for control valves; this permits replacement of the valve without disturbing the piping.

PRESSURE CONTROLS

The pneumatic control valves are generally designed for pressures up to 150 *psi*; hydraulic control valves are designed for much higher pressures—1000, 2000, 3000, and 5000 *psi*, and even higher pressures. The pneumatic pressure controls are: (1) *pressure regulators,* including the relieving and nonrelieving types; (2) *sequence;* and (3) *safety valves.* The hydraulic pressure control valves are: (1) *pressure relief;* (2) *pressure reducing;* (3) *sequence;* (4) *counterbalance;* and (5) *unloading.*

In the same manner that the air *pressure regulator* safeguards the pneumatic system, the *pressure relief valve* (Fig. 4) safeguards the hydraulic system. The pump and the means of driving the pump are kept from overloading. The other components of the hydraulic system

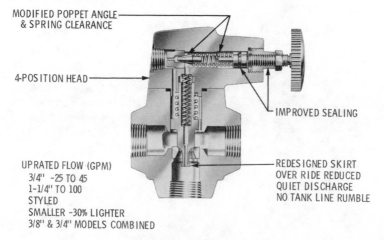

MODIFIED POPPET ANGLE
& SPRING CLEARANCE

4-POSITION HEAD

IMPROVED SEALING

UPRATED FLOW (GPM)
3/4" -25 TO 45
1-1/4" TO 100
STYLED
SMALLER -30% LIGHTER
3/8" & 3/4" MODELS COMBINED

REDESIGNED SKIRT
OVER RIDE REDUCED
QUIET DISCHARGE
NO TANK LINE RUMBLE

Courtesy Vickers Incorporated, Division of Sperry Rand Corporation

Fig. 4. A hydraulic pressure-relief valve.

are also protected from excessive pressure. When the preset operating pressure is reached, the operating mechanism in the relief valve causes the oil to spill through to the exhaust port, thus relieving the pressure.

Several different types of pressure relief valves are used: (1) the *direct-acting* type, with a spool or piston acting against a heavy spring; (2) the *direct-operated pilot* type, which is pilot operated, with the piston acting against a small spring; and (3) the *remote-actuated pilot* type, which is controlled through a remote valve. In the latter valve type, the remote valve may be located at a distance from the relief valve, and connected to the relief valve by piping.

Sequence valves are used for either air or oil and for the same purpose—to set up a sequence of operations. In several instances, a second four-way directional control valve can be eliminated by using one or two sequence valves. The sequence valves may be either the direct-acting type or the direct-operated pilot type of valve. The direct-acting valve (Fig. 5) can be used either for air or for low-pressure hydraulic service, but the direct-operated pilot-type valve

Fig. 5. A direct-acting sequence valve used for either pneumatic or low-pressure hydraulic service.

Courtesy Logansport Machine Co., Inc.

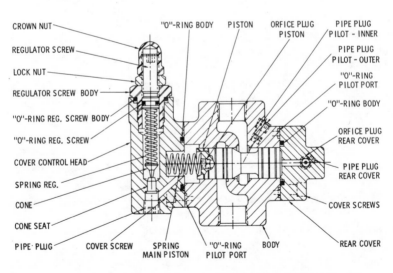

CROWN NUT
REGULATOR SCREW
LOCK NUT
REGULATOR SCREW BODY
"O"-RING REG. SCREW BODY
"O"-RING REG. SCREW
COVER CONTROL HEAD
SPRING REG.
CONE
CONE SEAT
PIPE PLUG

"O"-RING BODY   PISTON   ORFICE PLUG PISTON

PIPE PLUG PILOT - INNER
PIPE PLUG PILOT - OUTER
"O"-RING PILOT PORT
"O"-RING BODY
ORFICE PLUG REAR COVER
PIPE PLUG REAR COVER
COVER SCREWS
REAR COVER

COVER SCREW   SPRING MAIN PISTON   "O"-RING PILOT PORT   BODY

Courtesy Logansport Machine Co., Inc.

Fig. 6. A direct-operated pilot-type sequence valve used for hydraulic service.

386

(Fig. 6) is used only for hydraulic service. By building the check valve into the sequence valve body to provide free-flow return, piping and fittings can be eliminated at that point.

The *pressure reducing valves* are commonly used in hydraulic systems where more complicated system requirements demand more than one operating pressure. Pressure reduction from the upstream side of the valve to the downstream side of the valve can be as much as 10 to 1. If the pressure on the upstream side of the valve is 1000 *psi*, the pressure on the downstream side of the valve can be reduced conceivably to 100 *psi*. The hydraulic pressure reducing valves are of two types: (1) the *direct-acting* valve (Fig. 7); and (2) the *direct-operated pilot-type* valve.

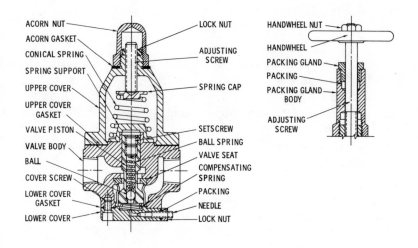

Fig. 7. A direct-acting pressure-reducing valve used for hydraulic service.

Hydraulic valves, such as the *counterbalance* valve and the *unloading valve*, have fewer applications than the previously mentioned valves. The counterbalance valve can be used either to restrict a movement or to balance a load that is being held in position by a cylinder, a motor, or an actuator. The unloading valve is used to unload either a pump or an accumulator; it is actuated from an external signal.

The pressure control valves that receive the operating signal from the upstream side are the sequence, safety, pressure relief, and counterbalance valves. The pressure regulating valves and the pressure reducing valves receive the operating signal from a downstream source. The source of the operating signal is significant primarily either in identifying a valve in a circuit diagram or in determining its specific function. This information can also be quite helpful in troubleshooting a malfunctioning system or component.

Ques. What is the chief difference in design of pneumatic and hydraulic pressure controls?

Ans. Pneumatic controls are generally designed for pressures up to 150 *psi*; hydraulic control valves are designed for much higher pressures—1000, 2000, 3000, and 5000 *psi*.

Ques. What pressure controls are used in pneumatic systems? In hydraulic systems?

Ans. The pneumatic system pressure controls are: (1) pressure regulator, including the relieving and nonrelieving types; (2) sequence; and (3) safety valves. The hydraulic system pressure control valves are: (1) pressure relief; (2) pressure reducing; (3) sequence; (4) counterbalance; and (5) unloading.

Ques. How are the pneumatic and hydraulic systems safeguarded?

Ans. The pressure regulator safeguards the pneumatic system, and the pressure relief valve safeguards the hydraulic system.

Ques. Which pressure control valves receive the operating signal from the upstream side, and which valves receive the operating signal from the downstream side? Why is this important?

Ans. The sequence, safety, pressure relief, and counterbalance valves receive the operating signal from the upstream side and the pressure regulating and pressure reducing valves receive the signal from the downstream source. This is significant either in identifying a valve in a circuit or in determining its function, and can also be quite helpful in troubleshooting a malfunctioning system or component.

FLOW CONTROLS

The valves which control the amount of flow of fluid in a pneumatic system are called *speed controls*; in a hydraulic system they are called *flow controls*. The *noncompensating* type of control that is designed for pneumatic service can also be used for low-pressure hydraulic service. The various types of flow controls are:

Hydraulic	*Pneumatic*
needle	needle
noncompensating	noncompensating
	pressure compensating
	pressure-temperature
	compensating

Three methods of controlling the flow (Fig. 8) from a relatively constant source of fluid are: (1) *meter-in*; (2) *meter-out*; and (3) *bleed-off*. In the "meter-in" method, the fluid is throttled before it reaches the device that is to be controlled. In the "meter-out" method, the fluid is throttled after it leaves the device; here the exhausting fluid is throttled. In the "bleed-off" method, a portion of the hydraulic fluid is bled off before it reaches the device. The devices mentioned may be cylinders, fluid motors, actuators, or large controls.

Needle valves (Fig. 9) are used in both pneumatic and hydraulic systems to meter fluid. The design of the needle is important where fine metering is required. Accuracy problems can be caused by dirty fluid where fine metering must be accomplished.

The *noncompensating-type flow controls* are used most commonly because of their low price and their availability. Although the noncompensating-type flow control cannot provide sufficient accuracy for extremely fine machine tool feeds, they perform satisfactorily in most installations. A speed control valve that can be used for both pneumatic service and low-pressure oil is shown in Fig. 10. A hydraulic flow control valve that can be used for high-pressure oil is shown in Fig. 11.

The *temperature- and pressure-compensated flow controls* are often found on machine tool applications where accurate feed rates are essential. A constant feed rate is provided for any temperature setting by the automatic temperature-compensating throttle, even though

"METER-IN" CONTROL

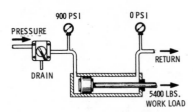

Recommended for feeding grinder tables, welding machines, milling machines, and rotary hydraulic motor drives.

"BLEED-OFF" CONTROL

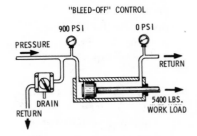

Recommended for reciprocating grinder tables, broaching machines, honing machines, rotary hydraulic motor drives.

"METER-OUT" CONTROL

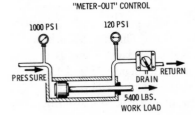

Recommended for drilling, reaming, boring, turning, threading, tapping, cut-off, and cold sawing machines.

Courtesy Vickers Incorporated, Division of Sperry Rand Corporation

Fig. 8. Three methods of controlling flow in hydraulic cylinders are: meter-in (top); bleed-off (center); and meter-out (bottom).

temperature changes occur in the hydraulic oil. The pressure-compensating device is a built-in pressure hydrostat that automatically compensates for any changes in loads. In each instance, compensation is achieved by automatically varying the size of the orifice to meet the demands of the changing load or condition (Fig. 12). In this type of valve there is a reverse free-flow from the outlet port to the inlet port. Pressure-compensated flow controls are available without the temperature compensator, and they are also built with an overload relief valve (Fig. 13). By using the overload relief valve, the only load that

Fig. 9. High-pressure needle valve for service at 5000 psi.

Courtesy Imperial-Eastman Corporation

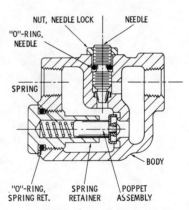

NUT, NEEDLE LOCK   NEEDLE

"O"-RING, NEEDLE

SPRING

"O"-RING, SPRING RET.   SPRING RETAINER   POPPET ASSEMBLY

BODY

Courtesy Logansport Machine Co., Inc.

Fig. 10. A speed-control valve used for both pneumatic service and low-pressure hydraulic service.

is imposed on the pump is the load that is needed to overcome the work resistance. This reduces the input power and the heat losses in applications where the loads may vary considerably. By turning the dial on the face of the control to the "zero" setting, the pump can be unloaded completely. The pressure-compensated flow control assures accurate flow despite the varying loads. These valves are available as either port-in-body type or subplate mountings, with the latter being used more commonly.

391

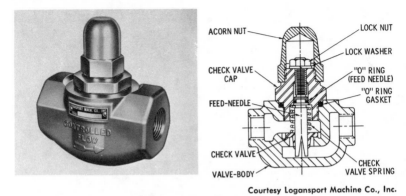

Courtesy Logansport Machine Co., Inc.

Fig. 11. A hydraulic flow-control valve.

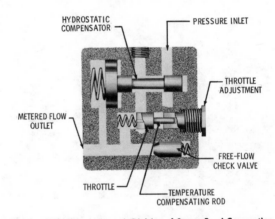

Courtesy Vickers Incorporated, Division of Sperry Rand Corporation

Fig. 12. Temperature- and pressure-compensated flow-control valve with check valve.

Ques. What is the difference between a speed control and a flow control?

Ans. They perform the same function—to control the amount of fluid flow. In a pneumatic system, the valves are called "speed controls"; they are called "flow controls" in a hydraulic system.

Ques. Where are the temperature- and pressure-compensated flow controls found?

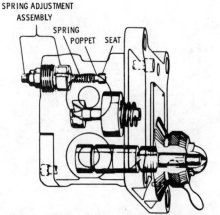

SPRING ADJUSTMENT
ASSEMBLY

SPRING
POPPET   SEAT

Courtesy Vickers Incorporated, Division of Sperry Rand Corporation

Fig. 13. Flow-control and overload relief valve.

Ans. Usually, they are used on machine tool applications where accurate feed rates are required.

Ques. How do the flow controls compensate for temperature and pressure?

Ans. In each instance, compensation is achieved by automatically varying the size of the orifice to meet the demands of the changing load or condition.

DIRECTIONAL CONTROLS

The *directional control valves* may be spool-type, piston-type, poppet-type, disk-type, or plug-type valves. The *two-way directional control valve* is one of the most common directional control valves that can be found in either a pneumatic or a hydraulic system. This valve can be used: (1) to close or to open a portion of a system; (2) to close or to open an entire system; or (3) to close or to open the passage to a single component, such as a pressure gauge. There are two ports in a *two-way valve*. In the normal position of the valve actuator, the two ports may be connected; or they may be closed to each other. If the two ports are connected, the valve is called a "normally-open" valve; it is called a "normally-closed" valve (Fig. 14) if the two ports are closed to each other.

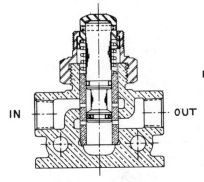

Courtesy Logansport Machine Co., Inc.

Fig. 14. A two-way normally-closed directional control valve.

Three port connections are found in the *three-way directional* control valves, and they may be "normally open" or "normally closed" when the valve actuator is in the normal or "at-rest" position. In a "normally-open" three-way valve, the inlet is connected to the cylinder port, and the exhaust port is blocked. When the actuator is moved to the second position, the inlet port is blocked, and the cylinder port is connected to the exhaust port. In a "normally-closed" valve, the inlet port is blocked, and the cylinder port is connected to the exhaust port when the actuator is in the normal position. When the actuator is moved to the second position, the inlet port is connected to the cylinder port, and the exhaust port is blocked. In some types of three-way valves there are three operating positions; this type of valve is called a *three-position, three-way directional control valve.* In the center operating position, all three ports can be blocked. This control is often used to actuate a single-acting cylinder (spring-return or gravity-return). The center position is a "hold" position, so that the piston of the cylinder can be positioned and stopped at any point in its range of travel. Three-way valves are employed to actuate single-acting cylinders, large control valves, fluid motors, fluid actuators, and regenerative systems. Two three-way valves can be used to actuate a double-acting cylinder.

The *four-way directional control valves* have four port connections —one inlet port, two cylinder ports, and one exhaust port. Some pneumatic four-way valves are built with two exhaust ports—one for each cylinder port. Speed controls are sometimes inserted in the

Fig. 15. A hydraulic four-way directional control valve.

exhaust ports. This arrangement can be quite satisfactory when used with an internally balanced valve. The hydraulic four-way directional control valves (Fig. 15) may be two-position or three-position valves. In the *two-position four-way* directional control valve, there are two positions for the actuator, and the *three-position four-way* valve has three positions for the actuator. The directional device (spools, pistons, etc.) in these valves may be spring-centered, spring-offset, or without springs.

Some of the spool configurations that are found in hydraulic valves are shown in Fig. 16. The pneumatic valves use many of these configurations, except for those arrangements in which the pressure is exhausted in neutral position, thus permitting considerable waste of energy.

The four-way control valves are used to actuate double-acting cylinders, fluid motors, fluid actuators, intensifiers, large control valves, etc. The *five-way directional control valves* are built with two inlet ports, two cylinder ports, and one exhaust port.

Specialty-type valves, such as the six- and eight-way directional control valves, are found in directional controls. A six-way directional control valve is built with one inlet port, four cylinder ports, and one exhaust port. The eight-way control valves are constructed with two inlet ports, two exhaust ports, and four cylinder ports, with an actuator of the "joy-stick" type. This type of valve can be used to control two cylinders at the same time.

A wide range of controls is now available. The designers and the maintenance personnel can avail themselves of quite a wide selection

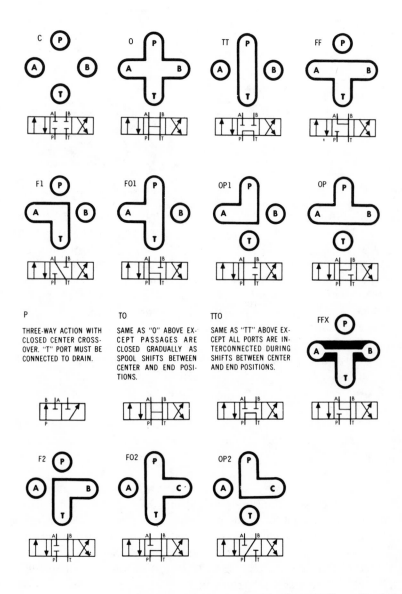

Fig. 16. Spool configurations of hydraulic valves.

in choosing valves to fulfill the demanded type of performance or control that an application requires.

Ques. What are the various types of directional control valves?
Ans. They may be spool-type, piston-type, poppet-type, disk-type, or plug-type valves.

Ques. How many ports are found in a two-way directional control valve?
Ans. There are two ports. In the normal position of the valve actuator, the two ports may be connected; or they may be closed to each other. If they are connected, the valve is called a "normally-open" valve, and it is a "normally-closed" valve if the two ports are closed to each other.

Ques. How many ports are found in a three-way directional control valve?
Ans. There are three port connections. When the valve actuator is in the normal or "at-rest" position, the valve may be "normally open" or "normally closed." In the "normally-open" valve, the inlet is connected to the cylinder port, and the exhaust port is blocked. When the actuator is moved to the second position, the inlet port is blocked, and the cylinder port is connected to the exhaust port. In a "normally-closed" valve, the inlet port is blocked, and the cylinder port is connected to the exhaust port when the actuator is in the normal position. When the actuator is moved to the second position, the inlet port is connected to the cylinder port, and the exhaust port is blocked. In a three-position, three-way directional control valve, all three ports can be blocked in the center operating position.

SUMMARY

The control valves that are used in fluid power systems can be divided into three categories: (1) *pressure* controls; (2) *flow* controls; and (3) *directional* controls. The *pressure controls* regulate the pressure intensity in the various portions of the system. *Flow controls* regulate the speed at which the fluid medium (air, oil, or water)is permitted to flow; this, in turn, controls the piston speed in the cylinders, the movements of the valve spools, the rotation speeds of the shafts of fluid motors, and the actuation speeds of other devices. The *directional controls* are used to direct the fluid medium to the various passages in the system.

The packings for control valves are made in various configurations and materials. Some of these configurations are: cups, "O" rings, quad rings, "Vee" packings, "U" packings, etc. Some of the materials used are *Teflon, Viton,* Buna N, treated leather, and asbestos.

In general, pneumatic control valves are designed for pressures up to 150 *psi;* hydraulic control valves are designed for much higher pressures—1000, 2000, 3000, and 5000 *psi,* and even higher pressures.

The pressure controls for pneumatic systems are: (1) *pressure regulators,* including the relieving and nonrelieving types; (2) *sequence;* and (3) *safety valves.* The hydraulic pressure control valves are: (1) *pressure relief;* (2) *pressure reducing;* (3) *sequence;* (4) *counterbalance;* and (5) *unloading.*

The valves which control the amount of flow of fluid in a pneumatic system are called *speed controls*; in a hydraulic system they are called *flow controls.* Three methods of controlling the flow from a relatively constant source of fluid are: (1) meter-in; (2) meter-out; and (3) bleed-off.

The directional control valves may be spool-type, piston-type, poppet-type, disk-type, or plug-type valves. The *two-way directional control valve* is one of the most common valves that can be found in either a pneumatic or a hydraulic system. Many types of directional control valves are available—ranging from the simple shutoff valve to the six- and eight-way control valves that are used to control automatic machinery.

REVIEW QUESTIONS

1. List the three-types of control valves that are used in fluid power systems.
2. What configurations are used in making the valve packings?
3. List the hydraulic pressure control valves.
4. List three uses for a two-way directional control valve.
5. Describe the basic operation of a two-way directional control valve.

CHAPTER 12

Control Valve Operators

The various control valves that are used in pneumatic and hydraulic systems were discussed in the preceding chapter. A means of operating these control valves must be provided if they are to function. In most instances, the pressure controls and the flow controls utilize valve operators that are different from those used on directional controls. In general, many different types of valve operators are available as standard equipment for directional control valves. It is important to select a suitable valve operator, because a poor choice may lead to problems in creating and maintaining the desired efficiency and controllability in a given fluid system.

PRESSURE CONTROL VALVE OPERATORS

The pressure control operators are made in relatively few general types. Among these operators can be found the direct-acting screw, the direct-acting cam roller, the offset cam roller, and the pilot types.

Nearly all types of pneumatic and hydraulic pressure control valves use a *screw-type operator* for setting the correct spring tension at which the valve is to function. A screw-type operator used on an air pressure regulator is shown in Fig. 1. As the screw is advanced, the downstream pressure is increased; as it is retracted, the downstream pressure is decreased.

A direct-acting spring-operated hydraulic relief valve is shown in Fig. 2. As the screw-type operator is advanced, spring tension is placed on the spool to increase the operating pressure of the system.

The *direct or offset cam roller type* of operator is often employed on valves for special applications. For example, this type of operator

CONTROL VALVE OPERATORS

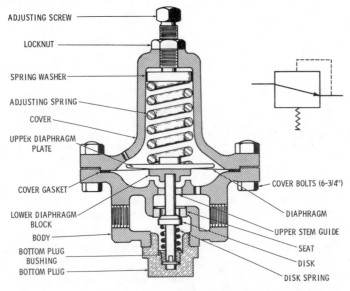

Courtesy The Clark-Reliance Corp.

Fig. 1. A diaphragm-type pressure regulator with a screw-type operator.

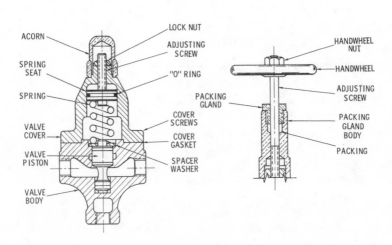

Courtesy Logansport Machine Co., Inc.

Fig. 2. Hydraulic pressure-relief valve with a screw-type operator.

400

on a relief valve may be advantageous if a considerable increase in pressure must occur at a given point in the travel of the piston in a cylinder. At that point, a cam can be placed on the machine table or other moving member; at the correct position, the cam depresses the cam roller type of operator on the relief valve, causing an increase in operating pressure.

The cam-type operators are also found on hydraulic pressure relief valves used for testing applications where the cams have an extremely shallow angle. The cam roller is depressed gradually and pressure readings are recorded.

Ques. What general types of valve operators are used on the pressure control valves?

Ans. The direct-acting screw, the direct-acting cam roller, the offset cam roller, and the pilot-type operators are used.

SPEED OR FLOW CONTROL OPERATORS

In nearly all instances, the speed control valve operator (in pneumatic systems) and the flow control valve operator (in hydraulic systems) utilize a screw-type or threaded mechanism to open and to

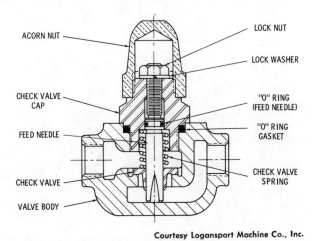

ACORN NUT

LOCK NUT

LOCK WASHER

CHECK VALVE CAP

"O" RING (FEED NEEDLE)

FEED NEEDLE

"O" RING GASKET

CHECK VALVE SPRING

CHECK VALVE

VALVE BODY

Courtesy Logansport Machine Co., Inc.

Fig. 3. Illustrating a hydraulic flow-control valve with a screw-type operator.

401

close the control orifice in the flow control valve. The screw-type mechanism may be in the form of a needle with slots, as shown in the diagram of the hydraulic valve in Fig. 3, which is used for pressures up to 3000 pounds per square inch. After the correct flow is achieved, the needle is locked in position by means of a lock nut.

A threaded mechanism is used in the pneumatic speed control valve shown in Fig. 4. As the threaded mechanism is advanced, the orifice through which the metered air passes is reduced. The check arrangement permits a free-flow return of the air through the valve. The threaded mechanism is locked in place with a lock nut.

A screw-type mechanism in the form of a needle is used in the air speed control valve diagrammed in Fig. 5, which is also suitable for low-pressure hydraulic oil. The needle in the valve is installed in such a way that the major diameter cannot be backed out beyond the retaining pin, which is a safety feature. The screw or threaded mechanism may be equipped with a handwheel, a micrometer-type knob, a locking device, or some other device for controlling it.

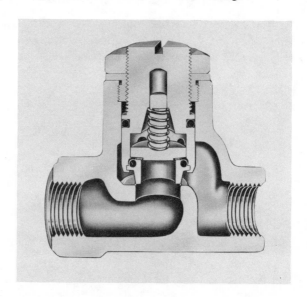

Courtesy Schrader Division, Scovill Manufacturing Company

Fig. 4. Illustrating a threaded mechanism used in a pneumatic speed-control valve.

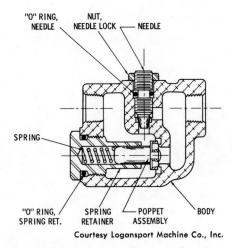

Fig. 5. Screw-type operator used in a speed- or flow-control valve.

Ques. What is the most common type of operator used on speed or flow control valves?

Ans. The screw-type or threaded mechanism is most common.

DIRECTIONAL CONTROL VALVE OPERATORS

The directional control valve operators can be classified in a number of different categories, and each category may consist of several different types of operators. Some of these categories are manual, solenoid, mechanical, automatic-return, and pilot operators. Various combinations of these different types of valve operators are also available.

Manual Operators

In most instances, the manual type of valve operator is considered to be the most positive and the least expensive. The manual-type operator is actuated by means of the hand, foot, or some other part of the body. A hand-type operator for a hydraulic directional control valve is shown in Fig. 6. The *hand-type valve operator* must be rugged, because a workman often uses a wrench or a piece of bar stock, instead of his hand, to actuate the valve operator.

403

Fig. 6. A hydraulic directional control valve
with a hand-type operator.

Courtesy Logansport Machine Co., Inc.

A *foot-operated* directional control valve that is used for pneumatic service is shown in Fig. 7. A latch mechanism causes the valve spool to be held in either of two positions—even though the foot is removed from the valve operator.

Fig. 7. A foot-operated directional control
valve assembly.

Courtesy Logansport Machine Co., Inc.

Knee-type operators are sometimes utilized, especially on pneumatic directional control valves. These valves can be operated easily when the worker is in a sitting position, thereby freeing the hands for positioning of the work, etc. If there is a possibility that the worker's hands may be endangered, the foot- or knee-type operators should be replaced with a hand-type operator in a no-tie-down circuit.

The hand-type operators may be of the spring-offset type (Fig. 8), the spring-centered type (Fig. 9) or the detent type (Fig. 10). A two-position directional control valve without friction stops is shown in Fig. 11.

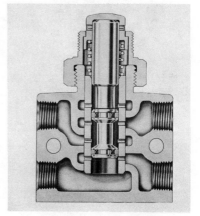

Fig. 8. Spring-offset type of operator for a directional control valve.

Courtesy Logansport Machine Co., Inc.

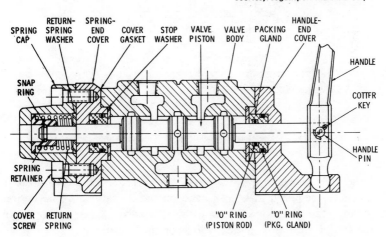

Courtesy Logansport Machine Co., Inc.

Fig. 9. Spring-centered hand-type operator used on a hydraulic directional control valve assembly.

405

Fig. 10. Illustrating a hand-type valve operator with detent.

Courtesy Logansport Machine Co., Inc.

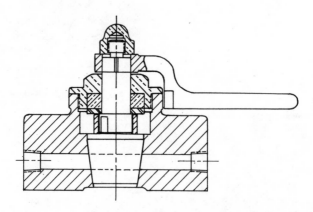

Courtesy Logansport Machine Co., Inc.

Fig. 11. A two-position directional control valve without friction stops.

When the *spring-offset valve operator* (see Fig. 8) is used, a workman is required to keep a hand on the operator until he desires to change the direction of flow within the valve. When the operator is released, it shifts automatically to its original position.

When the *spring-centered valve* operator (see Fig. 9) is used, a workman must apply force to the handle in either outward position to prevent the handle returning to the neutral position. When a detent on the valve operator is used to locate and to hold the spool position, a workman needs only to move the handle until he can "feel" the handle drop into the detent. The handle remains in place until it is moved to another position. Detents are used in two-position and three-position directional control valves.

A directional control valve sometimes requires two valve operators; one of the valve operators is used to shift the valve spool manually in one direction, and the other valve operator is used to reverse the valve spool by means of a solenoid or some mechanical means. With this arrangement, a workman can move some distance from the directional control valve and perform another task while the fluid power equipment is going through its normal operating cycle. A hydraulic four-way directional control valve in which the spool is reversed by a mechanical means is shown in Fig. 12.

Fig. 12. Illustrating a hydraulic four-way directional control valve with a mechanical reversing mechanism.

Courtesy Logansport Machine Co., Inc.

Ques. What are the different types of manual operators for directional control valves?

Ans. The manual directional control valve operators are hand-operated, foot-operated, and knee-operated. These may be spring-offset, spring-centered, or detent type operators.

Solenoid Operators

The solenoid operators consist of three general types: (1) the direct-acting solenoid; (2) the solenoid using a mechanical linkage; and (3) the solenoid pilot operators. The *direct-acting solenoid*

407

operator is found on both pneumatic and hydraulic directional control valves. In these controls, the solenoid plunger acts directly against the end of the valve spool in order to shift it. A pneumatic directional control valve with two direct-acting solenoid operators is shown in Fig. 13. The directional control valve does not function unless the

Courtesy Logansport Machine Co., Inc.

Fig. 13. Directional control valve with two direct-acting solenoid operators.

valve covers are in place. This feature protects the solenoids from dirt, which reduces the possibilities of malfunction of the solenoids. The solenoids are also protected from any moisture that may be collected in the exhaust of the valve by the "O" ring on the valve stem. Manual push pins are utilized in conjunction with the solenoid operator, so that the valve spool can be shifted before the electric wiring is connected to the valve. This permits the system to be cycled and checked thoroughly before the electrical connection is made.

The inrush and holding currents of solenoids used on the different sizes of hydraulic valves with direct-acting solenoid operators are shown in Table 1. The large direct-acting solenoid operators cause considerable noise when they are energized, due to the weight of the solenoid plungers. These large operators are not generally employed on high-cycling operations, due to the harsh and severe impact.

The direct-acting solenoid operators are available in various voltages, such as 115 volts, 230 volts, etc., for alternating current; in

Table 1. Inrush and Holding Current of Solenoids Used on Hydraulic Valves (Volt-Amperes)

Valve size Ports	60 cycle		50 cycle	
	Inrush	Holding	Inrush	Holding
⅜″	1970	165	1650	150
¾″	5450	390	4450	325
1″	6900	510	5750	460
1½″	12600	715	10500	590
2″	31200	1760	37000	1460

$$\text{Amperes} = \frac{\text{volt-amperes}}{\text{volts}}$$

most instances, they are suitable for continuous duty. This means that the solenoid coil may be energized for an indefinite length of time. Solenoids of this type are also available for direct-current applications and are usually equipped with a cut-out mechanism, often referred to as a "mouse trap." Direct-current solenoids normally are not recommended for continuous service.

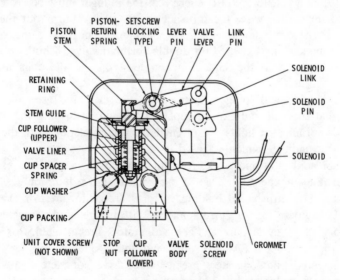

Courtesy Logansport Machine Co., Inc.

Fig. 14. Solenoid with mechanical linkage for operating the directional control valve.

A solenoid that uses a mechanical linkage is shown in Fig. 14. A mechanical advantage is produced by the linkage. This permits the use of a smaller solenoid than can be used in a direct-acting solenoid operator, but a longer stroke is usually required.

The two-position directional control valves that use a direct-acting solenoid operator on one end of the valve and a spring-return type of operator on the other end of the valve are widely used in both pneumatic and hydraulic service. This eliminates one solenoid, which reduces the cost of the control valve. The combination is commonly used in the design of "fail-safe" circuits. A disadvantage is that the solenoid plunger works against the spring, and it must be kept energized in order to maintain the spool in position against the spring. Where the two direct-acting solenoid operators are used, except on three-position spring-centered valves, the solenoid needs only to be energized momentarily in order to shift the valve spool. A solenoid operator which uses the mechanical linkage can also use a spring-return operator. Here again, when the spool is working against the spring, the solenoid must be kept energized.

When a solenoid coil is energized, the plunger must be seated immediately; otherwise, the inrush current quickly burns out the coil. If dirt becomes lodged between the plunger head and the seat, a malfunction may result. In a double solenoid valve, if both solenoids are energized at the same time, at least one of the coils may be burned out.

Solenoids with plug-in connections are available (see Fig. 13), so that the solenoid can be replaced without disturbing the electric wiring. Indicator lights are often used in conjunction with the solenoid to indicate which solenoid is energized.

Solenoid pilot operators are common, and, in most instances, they are quite inexpensive. They are compact and require only a small space. The inrush and holding currents are quite low; for example, 0.290 ampere inrush current and 0.210 ampere holding current for 115-volt, 60-cycle current. These operators are available for either alternating current (AC) or direct current (DC).

Solenoid pilot operators are available as a complete two-way or three-way valve (Fig. 15) used to control pilot-operated valves or as a subassembly. Solenoid pilot operators are available with explosion-proof housings for use in hazardous locations.

410

Fig. 15. A solenoid pilot operator for a directional control valve.

Courtesy Schrader Division, Scovill Manufacturing Company

Ques. What types of solenoid operators are available?

Ans. The solenoid control valve operators may be direct-acting, use a mechanical linkage, or be solenoid pilot operators.

Mechanical Operators

Mechanical operators on directional control valves play an important role on automatic equipment. The most commonly used mechanical operators are the direct-acting cam-roller type, the toggle lever type, the mechanical lever type with roller, the pin type, and the mechanical link type.

In the *direct-acting cam-roller type of operator*, more force is usually required to depress the roller, since it is acting against a spring. The angle on the cam should not be too abrupt, to avoid placing an excessive side load against the cam roller and the bearing in the valve cover.

The direct-acting cam-roller type of operator is found on some of the smaller directional control valves, but it is more commonly used on the larger more rugged valves for both pneumatic and hydraulic service. This type of operator requires a rather short stroke to complete an actuation. The cam roller should not be overstroked, although most of these valves provide for some overtravel. The cam is usually attached either to a machine table or to the piston rod of a cylinder. If it is attached to the piston rod of a cylinder, the rod should be supported near the contact point to eliminate deflection of the piston rod. Rotary cams are often used to actuate the cam roller.

411

The *toggle lever type of operator* requires only slight effort to actuate it. An inexpensive trip mechanism can be employed. This may be attached to a machine slide, to a feed mechanism, to a piston rod of a cylinder, or to some other moving mechanism. A workpiece moving down a conveyor can be used to trip the toggle mechanism.

The *mechanical lever type of operator* is similar in operation to the direct-acting cam operator, except that the line of action is offset and a mechanical advantage is created. This reduces the effort required to actuate the valve, although it does require a longer stroke to actuate the spool or flow director.

Return-type operators for directional controls can be of the spring type. The spring returns the spool or flow director to the neutral position, as in a three-position directional control valve; or it may return the spool or flow director to the end opposite the spring, as in a two-position directional control valve. A valve in which the spool is returned to the neutral position when the spring is released is shown in Fig. 9. The spring-return type of operator is used in conjunction with manual, solenoid, mechanical, and pilot types of operators.

Ques. What are the most commonly used types of mechanical operators?

Ans. The direct-acting cam roller, the toggle lever, the mechanical lever with roller, the pin, and the mechanical link are the most commonly used types.

Pilot Operators

Pilot types of operators are of the direct-acting, bleed, or differential types, and they are found on valves where high cycling, safety interlocks, and automatic sequencing are required. A direct-acting pilot operator used on a four-way hydraulic control valve is shown in Fig. 16. The medium which actuates the pilot operator is hydraulic fluid. To provide for better control of the spool as it shifts, chokes are often employed between the pilot operator and the spool. If two direct-acting pilot operators are employed (one at each end of the spool assembly), two chokes are usually used. Adjustable orifices in these chokes are controlled by a needle, and, in some instances, one choke may be set differently from the other choke, so that the spool shifts faster in one direction of travel.

412

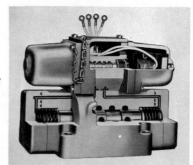

Fig. 16. Pilot-operated hydraulic four-way
directional control valve.

Courtesy Logansport Machine Co., Inc.

Although most hydraulic directional control valves which use direct-acting pilot operators make use of hydraulic fluid as the medium for shifting the main valve spool, more applications are now being found for compressed air as the shifting medium. There are several advantages in using compressed air as the medium. The controls which direct the fluid to the direct-acting pilot operators are less expensive, are more compact, and are manufactured in greater variety. Compressed air provides for faster spool shifting. Interlocks can be set up between a pneumatic system and a hydraulic system, permitting the use of air pressure for clamping and the use of hydraulic pressure for a heavy work cycle. Also, the necessary piping between the directional control and the operator is less expensive than when an all-hydraulic system is used.

Air-actuated direct-acting pilot operators are now manufactured in which the diameter of the operator is sufficient for permitting an air pressure of three to five *psi* to shift the spool in the directional control valve, although the valve itself is subjected to an oil pressure of 3000 *psi*.

Compressed air is usually the operating medium for the direct-acting pilot operators that are used on pneumatic directional control valves. In the differential-pressure type of operator (Fig. 17), pressure is placed on both ends of the spool operating mechanism, but the larger area of one mechanism causes the spool to travel toward the end with the smaller area. When the pressure is released from the larger area, the spool shifts to that end of the valve. The pressure differential action is similar to that of a spring, but it has the advantage of eliminating spring breakage caused by fatigue.

413

CONTROL VALVE OPERATORS

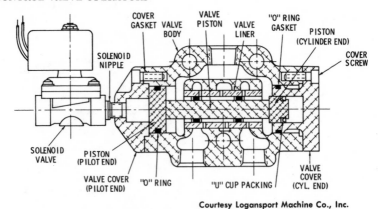

Courtesy Logansport Machine Co., Inc.

Fig. 17. Differential-pressure type of operator for a four-way directional control valve.

Fig. 18. Bleed-type operator for a four-way directional control valve.

Bleed-type pilot operators are most often utilized to control a pneumatic directional control valve, as shown in Fig. 18. The bleed-type pilot operators are pressurized at all times through internal passages in the body of the valve. Whenever the pressure is released from either pilot chamber, an unbalanced condition exists, and the

414

spool is shifted toward the pilot chamber where the air pressure has been released. The advantages of the bleed-type pilot operators are: external piping is eliminated; controls can be attached directly to the pilot operators; controls are inexpensive (only two-way controls are required); and high cycling is possible without excessive shock, because small orifices are used for pressurizing the operators. The chief disadvantages of the bleed-type operator are the limitation of distance of the control from the operator (usually no more than 8 feet) and malfunction due to leakage. Excessive distance between the control station and the bleed-type operator can produce sluggish and undependable response of the valve; leakage in the piping between the bleed operator and the control, or leakage in the control itself, may cause premature shifting of the valve with unfortunate results.

Although bleed-type pilot operators can conceivably be employed on hydraulic directional control valves, their use is not normally recommended, because sluggishness may be encountered in shifting of the spool, and seal problems may occur within the valve.

Ques. What are the pilot-type valve operators?

Ans. These are direct-acting, bleed, and differential types of pilot operators.

SUMMARY

The control valve operators provide a means of operating the control valves. In most instances, the valve operators for the pressure control and flow control valves are different from those used to operate the directional control valves.

Nearly all types of the pneumatic and hydraulic pressure control valves use a *screw-type operator* for setting the spring tension at which the valve is to function. The general types of valve operators used on the pressure control valves are the direct-acting screw, the direct-acting cam roller, the offset cam roller, and the pilot-type operators.

In nearly all instances, the speed control valve operator (in pneumatic systems) and the flow control valve operator (in hydraulic systems) utilize a screw-type or threaded mechanism to open and to close the control orifice in the valve. The screw or threaded mechanism may be equipped with a handwheel, a micrometer-type knob, a locking device, or some other device for controlling it.

Several different types of operators are used for the directional control valves. They are classified as manual, solenoid, mechanical, automatic-return, and pilot operators. Various combinations of these types of valve operators are also available.

REVIEW QUESTIONS

1. What is the purpose of the valve operator?
2. List three types of pressure control valve operators.
3. What type of operator is used for nearly all speed or flow control valves?
4. List four types of directional control valves.
5. What applications are most suitable for pilot operator directional control valves?

CHAPTER 13

Hydraulic Fluids

In hydraulics, hydraulic fluids are usually divided into three categories—petroleum-base fluids, synthetic-base fluids, and water. The first two fluids are used in "packaged-power devices." Water is generally used as the hydraulic fluid in central hydraulic systems.

The function of a good hydraulic fluid is threefold: (1) it is a means of transmission of fluid power; (2) it is a means of lubrication of the components of the fluid power system; and (3) it acts as a sealant. The selection of the proper hydraulic fluid is important, as it has a direct bearing on the efficiency of the hydraulic system, on the cost of maintenance, and on the service life of the system's components.

PETROLEUM-BASE FLUIDS

Three basic types of mineral oils are used: (1) Pennsylvania, or paraffin-base oils; (2) Gulf Coast, or naphthenic- and asphaltic-base oils; and (3) Mid-Continent, or mixed-base oils. These contain both naphthenic and paraffin compounds.

To obtain certain characteristics, chemicals are added to an oil. These chemical are called *additives*. Additives cannot make an inferior oil perform as well as a good oil, but they can make a good oil perform even better. An additive may be in the form of an antifoam agent, a rust inhibitor, a film-strengthening agent, or an oxidation stabilizer.

The user should not attempt to place additives in a hydraulic oil. That job is primarily for the oil manufacturer or refiner.

SYNTHETIC-BASE FLUIDS

Since fire hazards are prevalent around certain types of hydraulically operated machines, especially where open fires are present, much research has been done to develop fire-resistant hydraulic fluids. These fluids are divided into two classifications—synthetic-base mixtures and water-base fluids. Not all synthetic-base fluids are fire resistant.

Synthetic-base fluids include chemical compounds, such as the chlorinated biphenyls, phosphate esters, or mixtures containing each. These hydraulic fluids are fire resistant, because a large percentage of phosphorous and chloride materials are included.

Water-base fluids depend on a high percentage of water to effect the fire-resistant nature of the fluid. In addition to water, these compounds contain antifreeze materials, such as glycol-type thickeners, inhibitors, and additives.

Synthetic-base fluids have both advantages and disadvantages. Some of the advantages are: (1) they are fire resistant; (2) sludge or petroleum gum formation is reduced; and (3) temperature has little effect on the thickening or thinning of the fluid. A disadvantage of many synthetic fluids is their deteriorating effect on some materials, such as packings, paints, and some metals used in intake filters.

QUALITY REQUIREMENTS

Certain qualifications are demanded in a good hydraulic oil—an oil should not break down and it should give satisfactory service. Some of these requirements are:

1. Prevent rusting of the internal parts of valves, pump, and cylinders.
2. Prevent formation of a sludge or gum which can clog small passages in the valves and screens in filters.
3. Reduce foaming action which may cause cavitation in the pump.
4. Properties that provide a long service life.
5. Retain its original properties through hard usage—must not deteriorate chemically.
6. Qualities which resist changing the flow ability or viscosity as the temperature changes.

7. Form a protective film which resists wear of working parts.
8. Prevent pitting action on the parts of pumps, valves, and cylinders.
9. Does not emulsify with the water that is often present in the system either from external sources or from condensation.
10. Has no deteriorating effect on gaskets and packings.

MAINTENANCE

Proper maintenance of a hydraulic oil is often forgotten. Too often, hydraulic oil is treated as matter-of-fact. A few simple rules regarding maintenance are:

Courtesy Logansport Machine Co., Inc.

Fig. 1. Store hydraulic oil in a clean container.

1. Store oil in a clean container (Fig. 1). The container should not contain lint or dirt.
2. Keep lids or covers tight on the oil containers (Fig. 2), so that dirt or dust cannot settle on the surface of the oil. Oil should never be stored in open containers.
3. Store oil in a dry place; do not allow it to be exposed to rain or snow (Fig. 3).
4. Do not mix different types of hydraulic oils. Oils having different properties may cause trouble when mixed (Fig. 4).
5. Use a recommended hydraulic fluid for the pump (Fig. 5).

419

Fig. 2. Keep covers tight on oil containers.

6. Use clean containers for transporting oil from the storage tank to the reservoir.

7. Make sure that the system is clean before changing oil in the power unit; do not add clean oil to dirty oil.

8. Check the oil in the power unit regularly. Have the oil supplier check a sample of the oil from the power unit in his laboratory. Contaminants often cause trouble—these can be detected by frequent tests, which may aid in determining their source. On machines that use coolants or cutting oil, extreme caution should be exercised to keep these fluids from entering the hydraulic system and contaminating the oil.

9. Drain the oil in the system at regular intervals. It is difficult to set a hard and fast rule as to the length of the interval. In some instances, it may be necessary to drain the oil only every two

420

Fig. 3. Store hydraulic oil in a dry place.

Courtesy Logansport Machine Co., Inc.

Fig. 4. Do not mix different types of hydraulic oils.

421

Courtesy Logansport Machine Co., Inc.

Fig. 5. Use a factory recommended hydraulic fluid for the hydraulic pump.

years; however, one each month may be necessary for other operating conditions. This depends on operating conditions and on the original quality of the hydraulic oil. Thus, several factors should be considered in determining the length of the interval.

Before placing new oil in the hydraulic system, it is often recommended that the system be cleaned with a hydraulic system cleaner. The cleaner is placed in the system after the oil has been removed. The hydraulic system cleaner should be used while the hydraulic system is in operation, and usually requires 50 to 100 hours to clean the system. Then, the cleaner should be drained; the filters, strainers, and oil reservoir cleaned; and the system filled with a good hydraulic oil.

If hydraulic oil is spilled on the floor in either changing or adding oil to the system, it should be cleaned up at once. Good housekeeping procedure is important in reducing fire and other safety hazards.

CHANGE OF FLUIDS IN A HYDRAULIC SYSTEM

If the fluid in a hydraulic system is to be changed from a petroleum-base fluid to a fire-resistant fluid—or vice versa, the system should be drained and cleaned completely.

In changing from a petroleum-base fluid to a water-base fluid

1. Drain out all the oil—or at least as much as possible, and clean the system.
2. Either remove lines which form pockets, or force the oil out with a blast of clean, dry air.
3. Strainers should be cleaned thoroughly. Filters should be cleaned thoroughly and the filter element replaced.
4. Check the internal paint in all components; it is likely that the paint should be removed.
5. Check the gaskets and packings; those that contain either cork or asbestos may cause trouble.
6. Flush out the system. Either a water-base fluid or a good flushing solution is recommended. Carbon tetrachloride is not recommended, because it tends to form hydrochloric acid by reacting with the water. This generally can result in a corrosive action.
7. Since hydraulic fluids are expensive, the system should be free of external leaks.

In changing from a water-base fluid to a petroleum-base fluid

1. Remove all of the water-base fluid. This step is very important. A small quantity of water-base fluid left in the system can cause considerable trouble with the new petroleum-base fluid.
2. The reservoir should be scrubbed and cleaned thoroughly. If the interior of the reservoir is not painted, it should be coated with a good sealer that is not affected by hydraulic oil.
3. The components should be dismantled and cleaned thoroughly. Cleaning with steam is effective.
4. Flush the system with hydraulic oil and then drain.
5. Fill the system with a good hydraulic oil.

A similar procedure should be used in changing from synthetic-base fluids to petroleum-base fluids—and vice versa. If phosphate-base fluids are used, the packings should be changed. If satisfactory performance from a hydraulic fluid and a hydraulic system is expected, use a good grade of hydraulic fluid, keep it clean, change at regular intervals, do not allow it to become overheated, and keep contaminants out of the system.

SELECTION OF A HYDRAULIC FLUID

The main functions of the hydraulic fluid are to transmit a force applied at one point in the fluid system to some other point in the system and to reproduce quickly any variation in the applied force. Thus, the fluid should flow readily, and it should be relatively incompressible. The choice of the most satisfactory hydraulic fluid for an industrial application involves two distinct considerations: (1) the fluid for each system should have certain essential physical properties and characteristics of flow and performance; and (2) the fluid should have desirable performance characteristics over a period of time. An oil may be suitable when initially installed; however, its characteristics or properties may change resulting in an adverse effect on the performance of the hydraulic system.

The hydraulic fluid should provide a suitable seal or film between moving parts, in order to reduce friction. It is desirable that the fluid should not produce adverse physical or chemical changes while in the hydraulic system. The fluid should not promote rusting or corrosion in the system, and it should act as a suitable lubricant to provide film strength for separating the moving parts to minimize wear between them.

Certain terms are required to evaluate the performance and suitability of a hydraulic fluid. Important terms are discussed in the paragraphs that follow.

Specific Weight

The term *specific weight* of a liquid indicates the weight per unit of volume. For example, water at 60°F. weighs 62.4 pounds per cubic foot. The "specific gravity" of a given liquid is defined as *the ratio of the specific weight of the given liquid divided by the specific weight of water*. For example, if the specific gravity of an oil is 0.93, the specific weight of the oil is (0.93 × 62.4), or approximately 58 pounds per cubic foot. For commercially available hydraulic fluids, the specific gravity may range from 0.80 to 1.45.

Viscosity

Viscosity is a frequently used term. In many instances, the term is used in a general, vague, and loose sense. To be definite and specific, the term "viscosity" should be used with a qualifying term.

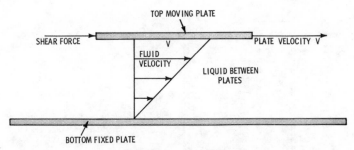

Fig. 6. Shearing action of a liquid.

The term *absolute or dynamic viscosity* is a definite specific term. As indicated in Fig. 6, the hydraulic fluid between two parallel plates adheres to the surface of each plate, which permits one plate to slide with respect to the other plate (as playing cards in a deck); this results in a "shearing" action in which the fluid layers slide with respect to each other. A "shear" force acts to "shear" the fluid layers at a certain velocity, or rate of relative motion, to provide the shearing action between the layers of fluid. The term "absolute or dynamic viscosity" is a physical property of the hydraulic fluid, which indicates the ratio of the shear force and the rate or velocity at which the fluid is being sheared.

To simplify, a very *viscous* fluid or a fluid having a high dynamic viscosity is a fluid that does not flow freely, or fluid having a low dynamic viscosity flows freely. The term *fluidity* is the reciprocal of "dynamic viscosity." A fluid having a high dynamic viscosity has a low fluidity, and a fluid having a low dynamic viscosity has a high fluidity. In general, the dynamic viscosity of a liquid decreases as temperature increases; therefore, as an oil is heated, it flows more freely. Because of pressure effects, it is difficult to draw general, firm conclusions for all oils. It is possible for an increase in fluid pressure to increase the viscosity of an oil.

Saybolt Universal Viscosimeter

The term "dynamic viscosity" is sometimes confused with the reading taken from the Saybolt Universal Viscosimeter. In actual industrial practice, this instrument has been standardized arbitrarily for testing of petroleum products. Despite the fact that it is called a viscosimeter, the Saybolt instrument does not measure "dynamic vis-

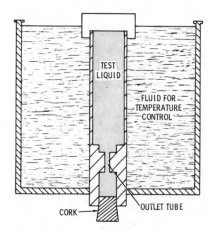

TEST LIQUID

FLUID FOR TEMPERATURE CONTROL

Fig. 7. Basic operating principle of the Saybolt viscosimeter.

CORK

OUTLET TUBE

cosity." A diagram illustrating the Saybolt viscosimeter is shown in Fig. 7.

In operating the instrument, the liquid to be tested is placed in the central cylinder, which is a short, small-bore tube having a cork at its lower end. Surrounding the central cylinder, a liquid bath is used to maintain the temperature of the liquid that is being tested. After the test temperature has been reached, the cork is pulled, and the time in seconds that is required for 69 milliliters of the test fluid to flow out of the cylinder is measured with a stop watch. This measured time, in seconds, is called the *Saybolt Universal Reading*.

The *S.A.E.* (Society of Automotive Engineers) has established standardized numbers for labeling of the oils. For oils tested at 130°F. in a standard Saybolt Universal instrument, Table 1 indicates *S.A.E.* numbers for the corresponding ranges of Saybolt Universal readings.

For example, if an oil is labeled "SAE 10," the Saybolt Universal reading at 130°F. is in the range from 90 to less than 120 seconds.

Table 1. Range Of Saybolt Readings, Seconds

SAE Numbers	Minimum	Maximum
10	90	less than 120
20	120	less than 185
30	185	less than 255

Viscosity Problems

If the viscosity of the hydraulic fluid is *too high* (fluid does not flow as freely as desired), the following undesirable actions may result:

1. Internal resistance, or fluid friction, is high, which means a high resistance to flow through the valves and pumps.
2. Power consumption is high, because fluid friction is high.
3. Fluid temperature is high, because friction is high.
4. Pressure drop through the system may be higher than desired, which means that less useful pressure is available for doing useful work.
5. The motion and operation of the various parts may be slow and sluggish as a result of the high fluid resistance.

If the viscosity of the hydraulic fluid is *too low* (fluid flows more freely than desired), the following undesirable actions may result:

1. More leakage may occur in the clearance space than is desired.
2. A lower pressure than is desired may occur in the system.
3. An increase in wear may occur because of the lack of a strong fluid film between mechanical parts that move in relation to each other.
4. Pump leakage may increase, resulting in reduced pump delivery and efficiency.
5. A loss of control may occur because fluid film strength is reduced.

With respect to Saybolt readings, the viscosimeter readings of oils in service should not exceed 4000 seconds, and they should not read less than 45 seconds.

Viscosity Index

Ideally, the dynamic viscosity of an oil should change only slightly, as the temperature changes. In the automobile engine, the oil in the crankcase is operated over a wide range of temperatures. On a very cold winter morning, after the car has been operated for some length of time, the temperature of the oil may be very low, and the dynamic viscosity of the oil may be very high. If the dynamic viscosity of the oil is excessively high, large forces and large amounts of power may be required to "shear" the oil films. Also, after the engine has been operated for a period of time on a hot summer day, the temperature of the oil may be very high, and the dynamic viscosity of the oil may be too low; therefore, the oil may not form a suitable lubricating film between the sliding surfaces. A breakdown of the oil film may result in excessive wear of the metal surfaces and a loss of power in the engine.

The term *viscosity index* is an arbitrarily defined ratio; it indicates the relative change in Saybolt Universal reading, with respect to temperature. The most desirable oils are those that have a high viscosity index; that is, the change in Saybolt reading is relatively small as the temperature changes. Oils having a small viscosity index register a relatively large change in Saybolt reading as the temperature changes.

Lubricating Value

The terms *oiliness and lubricity* are used to refer to the lubricating value of an oil. These terms are most often used when the moving surfaces are relatively close and may make metal-to-metal contact. At the same pressure and temperature, an oil *A* may be a better lubricant than another oil *B*; therefore, oil *A* possesses more "oiliness" or "lubricity" than oil *B*. The lubricating value of a fluid depends on its chemical structure and its reaction with various metal surfaces when the metal surfaces are relatively close to each other. Thus, oiliness and lubricity are extremely important in the performance of an oil.

Pour Point

The *pour point* of a fluid is defined as the lowest temperature at which the fluid flows when it is chilled under given conditions. The pour point is important when the hydraulic system is exposed to low temperatures. As a general rule, the most desirable pour point should be approximately 20°F. below the lowest temperature to which the fluid will be exposed.

Oxidation and Contamination

Oxidation is a chemical reaction in which oxygen combines with another element. As the air contains oxygen, the oxygen that is involved in fluid oxidation comes from exposing or mixing the fluid with air. The oxidation reaction increases with the increased exposure of the oil to air.

Undesirable quantities of air in hydraulic systems can be due to mechanical causes, such as air leakage into the oil suction line, low fluid level in the oil reservoir, and leakage around the packing. Air leakage may result in the erratic motion of mechanical parts, and it also may cause the fluid to oxidize more rapidly. All oils contain some air in solution, which may not cause any trouble. If the air is not in solution, a foaming action may result. If trapped in a cylinder, air that is not in solution is highly compressible; however, the oil is not as highly compressible as the air. Irregular action of a cylinder, for example, may result if a significant quantity of air becomes undissolved.

Ferrous metals are destroyed by rust. Rust can develop in a hydraulic system if moisture is present; this moisture may be the result of condensation from air that enters through leaks on the intake (low pressure) side of a pump.

The "oxidation stability" of an oil refers to the inherent ability of an oil to resist oxidation. Oxidation increases with increases in temperature, pressure, and agitation. Oxidation also increases as the oil becomes contaminated with such substances as grease, dirt, moisture, paint, and joint compound. Various metals also promote oil oxidation, and the various fluids have different oxidation characteristics. Table 2 lists the essential properties of the commercially available hydraulic fluids.

Table 2. Properties of Available Hydraulic Fluids

Petroleum-Base Fluids
Viscosity range, Saybolt Universal reading, in
    seconds, at 100°F .... 40 to 5000
Operating temperature, in °F .... −75 to 500
Minimum viscosity index .... 76 to 225

Fire-Resistant Fluids (Water-oil emulsions, water-glycol, phosphate-ester, chlorinated hydrocarbon, silicate ester, silicon)
Viscosity range, Saybolt Universal reading, in
    seconds, at 100°F .... 20 to 5000
Operating temperature, in °F .... −100 to 600

HYDRAULIC FILTERS

Hydraulic filters are needed to aid in eliminating many of the potential causes of hydraulic system failures. Proper filters and proper filter maintenance are important in obtaining satisfactory results in a hydraulic system.

Although most hydraulic systems are considered to be the "closed" type, they are not free from contaminants. Four sources of contaminants are common in hydraulic systems. These are:

1. *Wear.* As the sliding members of components move, small particles of metal and seals enter the fluid. A typical example of this action is the movement of a cast-iron piston within a steel cylinder tube. Wear begins as soon as the cylinder is placed in operation, although it may not be visible to the eye for a long period of time.

2. *Formation of sludge and acids due to fluid breakdown.* When extreme heat and pressure are encountered, chemical reaction within the fluid causes sludge and acids which are harmful to the precision parts of the components to form. For example, resinous coatings may cause a valve spool to "freeze" within the valve body by forming on moving parts; or small orifices may become clogged. Acids cause pitting and corrosive conditions.

3. *Built-in contaminants in the manufacture of components.* In castings with intricate cored passages, core sand is difficult to remove, and small quantities of sand can enter the system as the fluid flows through the cored passages under high pressure. Lint and small metal chips are also encountered.

4. *Contaminants from outside the system.* Lint may enter the system if the filler cap on the oil reservoir is not replaced. Dirt that clings to the piston rod of a cylinder or to the stem of a valve may enter the system. Water or coolant may enter a system.

Factors that should be considered in selecting a hydraulic filter are: flow rate, pressure drop, degree of filtration, capacity, ease of servicing, compatibility with the fluid in the system, and pressure to which the filter is subjected. The filter in a hydraulic system can be located in a number of places. Some of these locations are:

Fig. 8. A sump-type filter equipped with magnetic rods for collecting minute particles of steel and iron.

Courtesy Marvel Engineering Company

1. *In the sump or oil reservoir.* This is a sump-type filter (Fig. 8). The filter should have a capacity twice that of the hydraulic pump in order to keep pressure drop at a minimum and to eliminate the possibility of cavitation in the pump.

2. *In the discharge line from the relief valve.* Since, in most systems, a considerable quantity of fluid passes through the discharge of the relief valve, a low-pressure filter with fine filtration is recommended. The filter should be equipped with a low-pressure by-pass valve to avoid filter or system failure. The capacity of the filter should be large enough to handle the full flow of the pump without imposing a back-pressure on the relief valve. Back-pressure on the exhaust of the relief valve can cause malfunctions within the system.

3. *In the by-pass line from the pump.* In by-pass line filtration, a small percentage (approximately 10 percent) of the flow from the pump passes through the by-pass filter, and returns to the reservoir as clean oil. A pressure-compensated flow control should be installed between the pump and the filter to maintain constant flow at minimum pressure through the filter. An internal by-pass valve in the filter is recommended to avoid filter failure if the filter becomes clogged completely.

4. *In the pressure line between the pump and the directional control valve.* To protect the components of the system that are

431

located beyond the pump, a high-pressure filter which can handle full pump pressure and flow is often employed. Although 25-micron filtration is an often-used standard in industry, a 5-micron, or less, filter is sometimes desirable if close-fitting parts are to be protected. The flow capacity through the filter should be as high as possible (four to five times pump capacity). A built-in by-pass relief valve should be incorporated within the filter, because the filter may become overloaded with contaminants. A high-pressure filter equipped with a warning switch that provides a signal when the filter requires cleaning is shown in Fig. 9.

Fig. 9. A high-pressure filter equipped with a warning switch that provides a signal when the filter requires cleaning.

Courtesy Marvel Engineering Company

5. *In the intake line between the sump and the pump.* The intake line filter is similar to the sump-type filter, except that it is encased and is mounted outside the reservoir. A 100-mesh filter is commonly used for hydraulic oils, and a 60-mesh filter is usually specified for aqueous-base fluids. The filter elements can be replaced without disturbing the piping (Fig. 10).

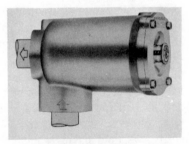

Courtesy Marvel Engineering Company

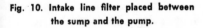

Fig. 10. Intake line filter placed between the sump and the pump.

6. *In the exhaust line between the four-way directional control valve and the reservoir.* The exhaust line filter is helpful when the bulk of the fluid is returned to the reservoir through the four-way directional control valve. However, if most of the fluid is returned through the relief valve or by-pass valve, this type of filter is of little value. When the return-line filter is used, it should have more capacity than the maximum flow of the return line to reduce back-pressure to a minimum on the exhaust of the control valve. Sudden surges and shock can have a detrimental effect on the element in this type of filter.

SUMMARY

Hydraulic fluids are usually divided into three categories—petroleum-base fluids, synthetic-base fluids, and water. The function of a good hydraulic fluid is threefold: (1) it is a means of transmitting fluid power; (2) it is a means of lubricating the components of a fluid power system; and (3) it acts as a sealant.

To obtain certain desired characteristics, chemicals called *additives* are added to an oil. An additive may be in the form of an antifoam agent, a rust inhibitor, a film-strengthening agent, or an oxidation stabilizer.

The main functions of a hydraulic fluid are to transmit a force applied at one point in a system to some other point in the system and to reproduce quickly any variation in the applied force. Thus, the fluid should flow readily, and it should be relatively incompressible. The choice of the most satisfactory hydraulic fluid for an industrial application involves two distinct considerations: (1) the fluid should

433

have certain essential physical properties and characteristics of flow and performance; and (2) the fluid should have desirable performance characteristics over a period of time.

A very *viscous* fluid or a fluid having a high dynamic viscosity is a fluid that does not flow freely; or a fluid having a low dynamic viscosity flows freely. The term *fluidity* is the reciprocal of "dynamic vis- and its reaction with various metal surfaces when the surfaces are relatively close to each other.
cosity." A fluid having a high dynamic viscosity has a low fluidity, and a fluid having a low dynamic viscosity has a high fluidity.

The terms *oiliness* and *lubricity* refer to the lubricating value of an oil. The lubricating value of a fluid depends on its chemical structure

Hydraulic fitlers are needed to aid in eliminating many of the potential causes of failures in hydraulic systems. Proper filters and proper filter maintenance are important factors in obtaining satisfactory results in a hydraulic system. In selecting a hydraulic filter, factors that should be considered are: flow rate, pressure drop, degree of filtration, capacity, ease of servicing, compatibility with the fluid in the system, and the pressure to which the filter is subjected.

REVIEW QUESTIONS

1. List three disadvantages of using water in a fluid power system.
2. What may be the cause of hydraulic oil becoming overheated in a hydraulic system?
3. In what ways can air enter a hydraulic system?
4. In what ways can dirt get into a hydraulic system, despite the fact that a suitable filter is employed in the system?
5. What precautions should be taken in changing the oil in a hydraulic system?
6. In storing hydraulic fluids, what precautions should be exercised?
7. What hazards are presented when hydraulic oil remains on the floor?
8. List three types of commonly used hydraulic fluids.
9. What is the effect of some fire-resistant fluids on packing, gaskets, and filters?
10. What is the purpose of the filter in a hydraulic system?

CHAPTER 14

Fluid Lines and Fittings

The efficiency of a fluid power system is often limited by the lines (fluid carriers) which carry the fluid operating medium from one fluid power component to another. The purpose of these carriers is to provide leakproof passages at whatever operating pressure may be required in a system. A poorly planned system of fluid carriers for the system often results in component malfunctions due to: restrictions which create back pressure in the components: loss of speeds which reduce efficiency; and broken carriers (especially in high-pressure systems), which create fire hazards and other problems. Selection of the proper carrier is as important as the proper selection of the fluid components.

Fluids may be directed through either lines or manifolds. Fluid lines or piping fall into three categories: (1) *rigid;* (2) *semirigid,* or *tubing;* and (3) *flexible,* or *hose.* In many instances, all three categories are employed in a single fluid system. The pressures involved and the fluid medium used determine, to a great extent, the type of carrier and the connectors and fittings.

RIGID PIPE

Steel pipe is the original type of carrier used in fluid power systems, and it is available in four different weights, as follows:

1. *Standard (STD), or Schedule 40.* This pipe (seamless) is designed for test pressure of 700 *psi* in the 1/8″ size to 1100 *psi* in the 2″ size.
2. *Extra strong (XS), or Schedule 80.* This weight of pipe is used in the medium pressure range of hydraulic systems. This pipe

(seamless) is designed for test pressures of 850 *psi* for 1/8″ size to 1600 *psi* in the 2″ size (Grade B).

3. *Schedule 160.* This pipe is designed for test pressures up to 2500 *psi*.
4. *Double extra heavy (XXS).* This pipe is also used for test pressures up to 2500 *psi*, even though the wall thickness is somewhat heavier.

Sizes of pipe are listed by the nominal inside diameter (I.D.) which is actually a misnomer. The sizes are nearly equivalent to Schedule 40, but there is a difference. For example, the inside diameter of a 1/4″ Schedule 40 pipe is 0.364″, and the I.D. of a 1/2″ Schedule 40 pipe is 0.622″.

As the schedule number of the pipe increases, the wall thickness also increases. This means that the inside diameter of the pipe for each nominal size is smaller, but the O.D. of the pipe for each nominal size remains constant (Table 1).

Some of the fittings that are used with steel pipe are tees, crosses, elbows, unions, street elbows, etc. Pipe fittings are listed in nominal pipe sizes.

Steel pipe is one of the least expensive of the fluid carriers for hydraulic fluid so far as the materials costs are concerned, but the installation costs often consume considerable man-hours in comparison to installation costs of some types of fluid carriers. Pipe is applicable to handling large fluid volumes and to running long lines of fluid carriers. Pipe is commonly used on suction lines to pumps and for short connections between two components. It is also useful on piping assembles that are seldom disassembled. Pipe provides rigidity for holding various components in position, such as the valves that are designed for "in-line mounting" with no other method of support. Pipe should be cleaned thoroughly before it is installed in a fluid power system.

SEMIRIGID (TUBING)

Two types of steel tubing are utilized in hydraulic systems, as recommended by *USASI* hydraulic standards. These types of tubing are *seamless* and *electric-welded*. Tubing sizes are measured on the out-

Table 1. Sizes of Steel Pipe

Nominal Pipe Size in.	Outside Diameter of Pipe in.	Schedule 40 (Standard)		Schedule 80 (Extra Heavy)		Schedule 160		Double Extra Heavy	
		Pipe ID-in.	Burst Press-psi	Pipe ID-in.	Burst Press-psi	Pipe ID-in.	Burst Press-psi	Pipe ID-in.	Burst Press-psi
1/8	0.405	—	—	—	—	—	—	—	—
1/4	0.540	0.364	16,000	0.302	22,000	—	—	—	—
3/8	0.675	0.493	13,500	0.423	19,000	—	—	—	—
1/2	0.840	0.622	13,200	0.546	17,500	0.466	21,000	0.252	35,000
3/4	1.050	0.824	11,000	0.742	15,000	0.614	21,000	0.434	30,000
1	1.315	1.049	10,000	0.957	13,600	0.815	19,000	0.599	27,000
1 1/4	1.660	1.380	8,400	1.278	11,500	1.160	15,000	0.896	23,000
1 1/2	1.900	1.610	7,600	1.500	10,500	1,338	14,800	1.100	21,000
2	2.375	2.067	6,500	1.939	9,100	1.689	14,500	1.503	19,000
2 1/2	2.875	2.469	7,000	2.323	9,600	2.125	13,000	1.771	18,000
3	3.500	3.068	6,100	2.900	8,500	2.624	12,500	—	—

side diameter (O.D.) of the tubing. Seamless steel tubing is manufactured from a highly ductile, dead-soft, annealed, low-carbon steel, with a chemical percentage of: carbon, 0.08-0.18; manganese, 0.30-0.60; phosphorous, 0.50 maximum; and sulfur, 0.55 maximum. The physical properties include: a tensile strength of 55,000 *psi*, maximum; Rockwell Hardness B65, maximum; and an elongation in 2 inches of 35 percent, minimum. In tubes with an O.D. 3/8″ and/or a wall thickness of 0.035, a minimum elongation of 30 percent is permitted. The diameter of the tubing shall not vary from that specified by more than the limits shown in Table 2.

Table 2. Specifications For Tubing Diameters

Nominal, O.D.	O.D. (Inches)	I.D. (Inches)
¼ to ½ in., incl.	±0.003	———
Above ½ to 1½ in., incl.	±0.005	±0.005
Above 1½ to 3½ in., incl.	±0.010	±0.010

The process used for making steel tubing is the cold drawing of pierced or hot-extruded billets. Table 3 shows the nominal sizes of seamless steel tubing that are readily available for hydraulic systems.

Electric-welded steel tubing is manufactured by shaping a cold-rolled strip of steel into a tube and then performing a welding and drawing operation. The chemical and physical properties of electric-welded steel tubing are similar to those of seamless steel tubing. In order to use steel tubing (or any other type of tubing) in a fluid power system, it is necessary to attach some type of fitting to each end of the tubing. Numerous methods are employed to accomplish this; but, in the final analysis, the fitting holds the tubing securely, providing a leakproof assembly that can withstand the pressures for which it was designed. In some instances, the fitting is welded to the tubing; in other applications (air systems), friction between the tubing and the fitting is sufficient to hold the pressure. An assembly in which a sleeve is brazed to the tubing, and the nut is then screwed onto the fitting, is shown in Fig. 1. A sleeve that digs into the tubing wall when the nut is tightened on the fitting is shown in Fig. 2. Some of the fittings that are most commonly used, such as tees, elbows, crosses, and straights are shown in Fig. 3.

Table 3. Steel Tubing Sizes and Safety Factors (SAE 1010)

Tube O.D.	Fitting Size	4/1 SAFETY FACTOR Working Pressure in psi.				5/1 SAFETY FACTOR Working Pressure in psi.		
		1000	2000	3000	5000	1000	2000	3000
⅛	2	.020	.020	.020	.025	.020	.020	.020
3⁄16	3	.020	.020	.020	.035	.020	.020	.028
¼	4	.020	.020	.028	.049	.020	.022	.035
5⁄16	5	.020	.025	.035	.056	.020	.028	.042
⅜	6	.020	.028	.042	.072	.020	.035	.049
½	8	.020	.042	.056	.095	.025	.049	.065
⅝	10	.025	.042	.072	.120	.032	.058	.083
¾	12	.028	.058	.083	.134	.035	.072	.109
⅞	14	.035	.072	.095	.165	.042	.083	.120
1	16	.042	.083	.109	.180	.049	.095	.134
1¼	20	.049	.095	.134	.238	.058	.120	.165
1½	24	.058	.120	.165	.284	.072	.134	.203
2	32	.072	.148	.220	.375	.095	.180	.259

Tube O.D.	Fitting Size	7.5/1 SAFETY FACTOR Working Pressure in psi.				10/1 SAFETY FACTOR Working Pressure in psi.		
		1000	2000	3000	5000	1000	2000	3000
⅛	2	.020	.020	.025	.042	.020	.025	.035
3⁄16	3	.020	.025	.042	.065	.020	.035	.056
¼	4	.020	.035	.058	.095	.022	.049	.072
5⁄16	5	.022	.042	.065	.109	.028	.056	.083
⅜	6	.025	.058	.083	.134	.035	.072	.109
½	8	.035	.072	.109	.220	.049	.095	.134
⅝	10	.042	.095	.134	.220	.058	.120	.180
¾	12	.058	.109	.148	.259	.072	.134	.203
⅞	14	.065	.120	.180	.320	.083	.165	.238
1	16	.072	.134	.203	.350	.095	.180	.259
1¼	20	.095	.180	.259	.450	.120	.238	.350
1½	24	.109	.203	.320	.500	.134	.284	.450
2	32	.134	.284	.400	—	.180	.375	—

Courtesy Imperial-Eastman Corporation

Fig. 1. An assembly in which a sleeve is brazed to the tubing, and the nut is then screwed onto the fitting.

Other types of tubing employed in fluid power systems are:

1. *Copper tubing.* This type of tubing is often found on air circuits which are not subject to *USASI* standards. Due to its work-hardening when flared and since it is as an oil-oxidation catalyst, *USASI* standards restrict the use of copper tubing for

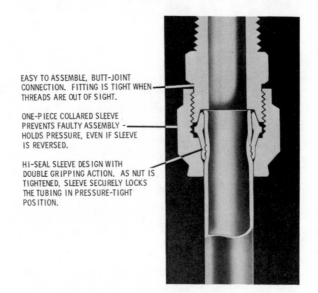

EASY TO ASSEMBLE, BUTT-JOINT CONNECTION. FITTING IS TIGHT WHEN THREADS ARE OUT OF SIGHT.

ONE-PIECE COLLARED SLEEVE PREVENTS FAULTY ASSEMBLY - HOLDS PRESSURE, EVEN IF SLEEVE IS REVERSED.

HI-SEAL SLEEVE DESIGN WITH DOUBLE GRIPPING ACTION. AS NUT IS TIGHTENED, SLEEVE SECURELY LOCKS THE TUBING IN PRESSURE-TIGHT POSITION.

Courtesy Imperial-Eastman Corporation

Fig. 2. A fitting for high-pressure tubing in which the sleeve of the fitting grips the tubing.

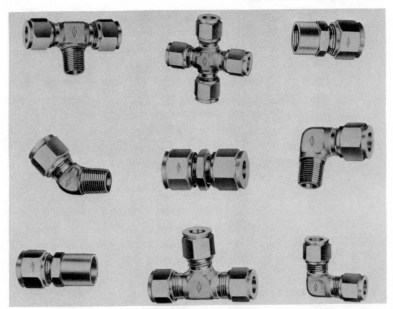

Courtesy Imperial-Eastman Corporation

Fig. 3. Tubing fittings used in fluid-power systems.

hydraulic service. Copper tubing can be worked easily in making bends, which reduces the fittings requirements.

2. *Aluminum tubing.* Seamless aluminum tubing is approved for low-pressure systems. This tubing has fine flaring and bending characteristics.

3. *Plastic tubing.* Plastic tubing for fluid power lines is made from several basic materials. Among these materials are nylon, polyvinyl, polyethylene, and polypropylene.

    a. *Nylon tubing.* This tubing is used on fluid power applications in the low-pressure range up to 250 *psi.* It is suitable for a temperature range of $-100°F$. to $225°F$. This tubing possesses good impact and abrasion resistance; it can be stored without deterioration or becoming brittle, and it is not affected by hydraulic fluids. One of the newer developments is the self-storing type of nylon tubing which looks like a coil spring, and is very popular for use on pneumatic tools.

441

b. *Polyvinyl chloride tubing.* For air lines with pressures up to 125 *psi,* this type of tubing may be used. Temperatures should not exceed 100° F continuously. It may be used intermittently for temperatures up to 160° F.

c. *Polyethylene tubing.* This is an ideal tubing for pneumatic service, and it is also used for other fluids at low pressures. It possesses great dimensional stability and resists most chemicals and solvents. Polyethylene tubing is manufactured in several different colors, which lends it readily to color coding. Tubing sizes are usually available up to, and including, ½″ O.D.

d. *Polypropylene tubing (Impolene TM).* This type of tubing is suitable for operating conditions with temperatures of −20° F. to + 280° F., and it can be sterilized repeatedly with steam. It possesses surface hardness and elasticity that provide good abrasion resistance. It is usually available in sizes up to, and including, ½″ O.D. and in natural or black colors.

FLEXIBLE PIPING (HOSE)

Hose is employed in a fluid power system in which the movement of one component of the system is related to another component. An example of this utilization is a pivot-mounted cylinder that moves through an arc while the valve to which the cylinder is connected with fluid lines remains in a stationary position. Hose may be used in either a pneumatic system or a hydraulic system.

Many different types of hose are used in fluid power systems, and nearly all of these types of hose have three things in common. They are:

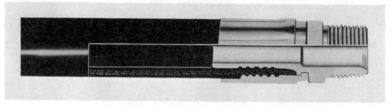

Courtesy Imperial-Eastman Corporation

Fig. 4. Section of hose assembly showing the layers of material, including the inner liner, reinforcement, and outer cover.

1. *A tube or inner liner which resists penetration by the fluid being used.* This tube should be smooth to reduce friction. Some of the materials used for the tube are neoprene, Buna N, synthetic rubber, etc.
2. *A reinforcement which may be in the form of rayon braid, fabric braid, wire braid, or spiral-wound wire.* The strength of the hose is determined by the number of thicknesses and type of reinforcement. If more than one thickness of reinforcement is used, a synthetic type of separator is utilized. A three-wire braid type of hose is made of three layers of wire braid.
3. *An outer cover to protect the inner portion of the hose and to enable the hose to resist heat, weather, abrasion, etc.* This cover can be made of synthetic rubber, neoprene, woven metal, or fabric.

The nominal size of hose is specified by inside diameter (I.D.), such as 3/16″, 1/4″, 3/8″, 1/2″, etc. The outside diameter of hose depends on the number of layers of wire braid, etc. Fluid power applications may require hose with working pressure ratings ranging from approximately 300 *psi* to 12,000 *psi*. Specifications for a typical two-wire braid hose can be found in Table 4. The hose and the

Table 4. Specifications For a Typical Two-Wire Braid Hose

SIZE		PRESSURE		BEND RADIUS
Hose I.D. In.	Hose O.D. In.	Recommended Maximum Working Pressure psi	Minimum Burst Pressure psi	Minimum Bending Radius In.
³⁄₁₆	⅝	5,000	20,000	4
¼	¹¹⁄₁₆	5,000	20,000	4
⁵⁄₁₆	¾	4,250	17,000	5
⅜	²⁷⁄₃₂	4,000	16,000	5
½	³¹⁄₃₂	3,500	14,000	7
⅝	1³⁄₃₂	2,750	11,000	8
¾	1¼	2,250	9,000	9½
⅞	1⅜	2,000	8,000	11
1	1⁹⁄₁₆	2,000	8,000	12
1¼	2	1,625	6,500	16½
1½	2¼	1,250	5,000	20
2	2¾	1,125	4,500	25

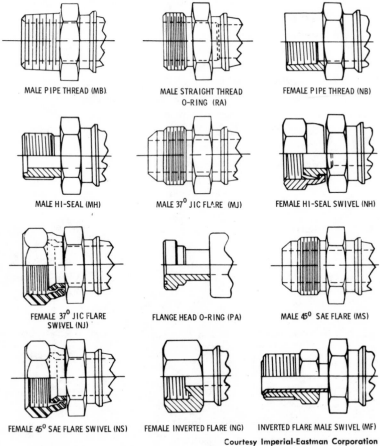

MALE PIPE THREAD (MB)

MALE STRAIGHT THREAD O-RING (RA)

FEMALE PIPE THREAD (NB)

MALE HI-SEAL (MH)

MALE 37° JIC FLARE (MJ)

FEMALE HI-SEAL SWIVEL (NH)

FEMALE 37° JIC FLARE SWIVEL (NJ)

FLANGE HEAD O-RING (PA)

MALE 45° SAE FLARE (MS)

FEMALE 45° SAE FLARE SWIVEL (NS)

FEMALE INVERTED FLARE (NG)

INVERTED FLARE MALE SWIVEL (MF)

Courtesy Imperial-Eastman Corporation

Fig. 5. Common types of ends used on hose couplings.

couplings that are attached at each end of the hose make up the hose assembly for fluid power applications. Several methods are used to attach these couplings to the hose. Some of these are:

1. *Pressed on* by a mechanical crimping action. Production machine can be used to make large quantities of the assemblies.
2. *Screwed on* by removing the outer cover of the hose for a required distance that is marked on the shell of the fitting; the

shell is then threaded onto the braid, and the male body can be screwed into the hose and shell assembly. In some types of couplings, it is unnecessary to remove the outer cover. Screwed on couplings can be disassembled and used again.

3. *Clamped on* by screwing the hose onto the coupling stem until it bottoms against the collar on the stem; then the hose clamp is attached with bolts. Some couplings require two bolts, and

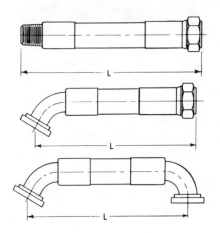

LENGTH TOLERANCE FOR HOSE ASSEMBLIES

LENGTH	TOLERANCE
UP TO 12"	± 1/8"
ABOVE 12" – UP TO 18"	± 3/16"
ABOVE 18" – UP TO 36"	± 1/4"
ABOVE 36"	± 1% OF LENGTH MEASURED TO NEAREST 1/8"

Courtesy Imperial-Eastman Corporation

Fig. 6. Method of measuring the length of a hose assembly.

others require four bolts for tightening the clamp onto the hose.

4. *Pushed on* by merely pushing the hose onto the coupling. This type of coupling is used in low-pressure applications up to 250 *psi*. No tools, except a knife to cut the hose to length, are needed to make this type of assembly. This type of coupling is reusable.

Various types of ends that are used on hose couplings are shown in Fig. 5. This permits the user a wide choice for his application.

Hose assemblies are measured with respect to their overall length from the extreme end of one coupling to the extreme end of the other coupling (Fig. 6). In applications using elbow couplings, the length is measured from the centerline of the sealing surface of the elbow end to the centerline of the coupling on the opposite end.

445

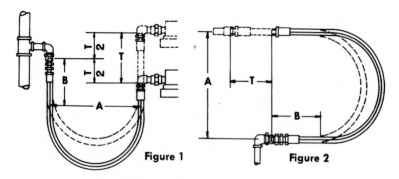

Figure 1   Figure 2

Typical Dimensions for One and Two Wire Braid Hose

If bending diameters other than those below are used, apply the following formulas:

Figure 1: Overall length $= B + 1.57A + \frac{1}{2}T$
Figure 2: Overal length $= B + 1.57A + T$

I.D. of Hose	"B" Constant for Straight Portion Including Coupling	Min. "A"	Minimum Overall Length	
			Fig. 1	Fig. 2
$\frac{3}{16}''$	10″	8″	$23'' + \frac{1}{2}T$	$23'' + T$
$\frac{1}{4}''$	10″	8″	$23'' + \frac{1}{2}T$	$23'' + T$
$\frac{3}{8}''$	10″	10″	$26'' + \frac{1}{2}T$	$26'' + T$
$\frac{1}{2}''$	12″	14″	$34'' + \frac{1}{2}T$	$34'' + T$
$\frac{3}{4}''$	14″	19″	$44'' + \frac{1}{2}T$	$44'' + T$
1″	16″	22″	$51'' + \frac{1}{2}T$	$51'' + T$
$1\frac{1}{4}''$	18″	32″	$68'' + \frac{1}{2}T$	$68'' + T$
$1\frac{1}{2}''$	20″	44″	$87'' + \frac{1}{2}T$	$87'' + T$
2″	20″	48″	$95'' + \frac{1}{2}T$	$95'' + T$

Courtesy Imperial-Eastman Corporation

Fig. 7. Typical dimensions for one-wire and two-wire braid hose in determining length.

The length of a hose assembly that is to be looped can be determined from Fig. 7. Also, the proper diameter of hose to assure proper performance of hose for hydraulic service can be determined in Fig. 8.

In applications in which it is desirable to disconnect one end of a hose assembly repeatedly, quick-disconnect couplings are recommended. These couplings not only save considerable time in making or breaking the connection, but a properly chosen coupling provides positive shut-off, so that the fluid is not lost. A quick-disconnect cou-

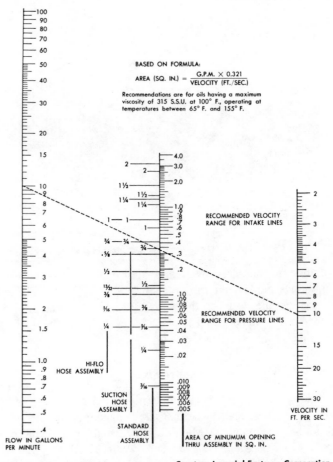

BASED ON FORMULA:

$$\text{AREA (SQ. IN.)} = \frac{\text{G.P.M.} \times 0.321}{\text{VELOCITY (FT./SEC.)}}$$

Recommendations are for oils having a maximum viscosity of 315 S.S.U. at 100° F., operating at temperatures between 65° F. and 155° F.

RECOMMENDED VELOCITY RANGE FOR INTAKE LINES

RECOMMENDED VELOCITY RANGE FOR PRESSURE LINES

FLOW IN GALLONS PER MINUTE

HI-FLO HOSE ASSEMBLY

SUCTION HOSE ASSEMBLY

STANDARD HOSE ASSEMBLY

AREA OF MINUMUM OPENING THRU ASSEMBLY IN SQ. IN.

VELOCITY IN FT. PER SEC.

Courtesy Imperial-Eastman Corporation

Fig. 8. Method of determining the correct size of hose.

pling with double shut-off is shown in Fig. 9; when the coupling is disconnected, the valved nipple and the valved coupler prevent the escape of fluid. Quick-disconnect couplings are also furnished in various other combinations, such as a single shut-off coupling with a plain nipple and a valved coupler and a no-shut-off coupler with a plain nipple and a plain coupler. Quick-disconnect couplings are available in a wide range of sizes from 1/4″ to 4″ pipe size. Larger sizes are usually available as "specials." Various metals, such as

447

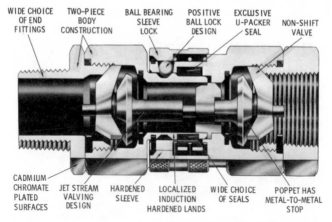

Fig. 9. Cutaway of "quick-disconnect" double shutoff.

brass, aluminum, stainless steel, and alloy steel are used. Seals in these couplings depend on the type of service involved. The fitting connections on the ends of the couplings are available in several forms, such as: Female (NPT), Male (NPT), Hose Shank, Female (SAE), Male Flare, Bulkhead, etc.

MANIFOLDS

Manifolds are designed to eliminate piping, to reduce joints which are often a source of leakage, to conserve space, and to help streamline modern-day equipment. Manifolds are usually one of the following types: (1) *sandwich;* (2) *cast;* (3) *drilled;* and (4) *fabricated-tube.* The sandwich type of manifold is made of flat plates in which the center plate or plates are machined for the passages, and the porting is drilled in the outer plates. The passages are then bonded together to make a leakproof assembly. The cast type of manifold is designed with cast passages and drilled porting. The casting may be steel, iron, bronze, or aluminum, depending on the fluid medium to be used. In the drilled type of manifold, all of the porting and passages are drilled in a block of metal. The fabricated-tube type of manifold is made of tubing to which the various sections have been welded. This makes an assembly which may contain welded flange connections, valve subplates, male or female pipe connectors, etc. These assemblies are usually produced in large quantities for use on the hydraulic systems of mobile equipment. The assemblies are held to close tolerances, as they are manufactured in fixtures. Although manifolds are used mostly on hydraulic systems, the demand for them in pneumatic systems is increasing.

SUMMARY

Fluid lines or piping fall into three categories: (1) *rigid;* (2) *semi-rigid,* or *tubing;* and (3) *flexible,* or *hose.* In many instances, all three categories of piping are employed in a single fluid system.

The size of rigid pipe is indicated by the nominal inside diameter (I.D.), which is actually a misnomer. For example, the inside diameter of a 1/4″ Schedule 40 pipe is 0.364 in., and the inside diameter of a 1/2″ Schedule 40 pipe is 0.622 in.

Two types of steel tubing are utilized in hydraulic systems, as recommended by *USASI* hydraulic standards; they are *seamless and electric-welded.* Tubing size is indicated by the nominal outside diameter (O.D.) of the tubing.

Flexible pipe (hose) is utilized in a fluid power system in which the movement of one component of the system is related to another component. The size of a hose is indicated by the nominal inside diameter (I.D.), such as 3/16 in., 1/4 in., etc.

Manifolds are designed to eliminate piping, to reduce joints which are often a source of leakage, to conserve space, and to help streamline modern-day equipment. Manifolds are usually one of the following types: (1) *sandwich;* (2) *cast;* (3) *drilled;* and (4) *fabricated-tube.*

REVIEW QUESTIONS

1. List the three types of fluid lines or piping.
2. What are the advantages of steel pipe as a fluid carrier?
3. What are three types of tubing commonly used in fluid power systems?
4. What is the chief advantage of hose in fluid power systems?
5. What is the chief advantage of manifolds in fluid power systems?

Index

450

AUDEL BOOKS *practical reading for profit*

APPLIANCES

Air Conditioning   (23159)

Domestic, commercial, and automobile air conditioning fully explained in easily-understood language. Troubleshooting charts aid in making diagnosis and repair of system troubles.

Commercial Refrigeration   (23195)

Installation, operation, and repair of commercial refrigeration systems. Included are ice-making plants, locker plants, grocery and supermarket refrigerated display cases, etc. Trouble charts aid in the diagnosis and repair of defective systems.

Air Conditioning and Refrigeration Library—2 Vols.   (23196)

Home Appliance Servicing—3rd Edition   (23214)

A practical "How-To-Do-It" book for electric & gas servicemen, mechanics & dealers. Covers principles, servicing and repairing of home appliances. Tells how to locate troubles, make repairs, reassemble and connect, wiring diagrams and testing methods. Tells how to fix electric refrigerators, washers, ranges, toasters, ironers, broilers, dryers, vacuum sweepers, fans, and other appliances.

Home Refrigeration and Air Conditioning (23133)

Covers basic principles, servicing, operation, and repair of modern household refrigerators and air conditioners. Automotive air conditioners are also included. Troubleshooting charts aid in trouble diagnosis. **A gold mine of essential facts for engineers, servicemen, and users.**

Oil Burners   (23151)

Provides complete information on all types of oil burners and associated equipment. Discusses burners—blowers—ignition transformers—electrodes—nozzles—fuel pumps—filters—controls. Installation and maintenance are stressed. Troubleshooting charts permit rapid diagnosis of system troubles and possible remedies to correct them.

AUTOMOTIVE

Automobile Guide   (23192)

New revised edition. Practical reference for auto mechanics, servicemen, trainees, and owners. Explains theory, construction, and servicing of modern domestic motorcars. FEATURES: All parts of an automobile—engines—pistons—rings—connecting rods—crankshafts—valves—cams—timing—cooling systems—Fuel-feed systems—carbureators — automatic choke — transmissions — clutches — universals — propeller shafts—dierentials—rear axles—running gear—brakes—wheel alignment—steering gear—tires—lubrication—ignition systems—generators and alternators—starters—lighting systems—batteries—air conditioning—cruise controls—emission control systems.

Auto Engine Tune-up   (23181)

New revised edition. This popular how-to-do-it guide shows exactly how to tune your car engine for extra power, gas economy, and fewer costly repairs. New emission-control systems are explained along with the proper methods for correcting faults and making adjustments to keep these systems in top operating condition.

Automotive Library—2 Vols.   (23198)

Diesel Engine Manual   (23199)

A practical treatise on the theory, operation and maintenance of modern Diesel engines. Explains Diesel principles—valves—timing—fuel pumps—pistons and rings—cylinders—lubrication—cooling system—fuel oil—engine indicator—governors—engine reversing—answers on operation—calculations. AN IMPORTANT GUIDE FOR ENGINEERS, OPERATORS, STUDENTS.

Gas Engine Manual   (23061)

A completely practical book covering the construction, operation and repair of all types of modern gas engines. Part I covers gas-engine principles; engine parts; auxiliaries; timing methods; ignition systems. Part II covers troubleshootng, adjustment and repairs.

BUILDING AND MAINTENANCE

Answers on Blueprint Reading   (23041)

Covers all types of blueprint reading for mechanics and builders. The man who can read blueprints is in line for a better job. This book gives you the secret language, step by step in easy stages. NO OTHER TRADE BOOK LIKE IT.

Building Construction and Design   (23180)

A completely revised and rewritten version of Audel's **Architects and Builders Guide.** New illustrations and extended coverage of material makes this treatment of the subject more valuable than ever. Anyone connected in any way with the building industry will profit from the information contained in this book.

Building Maintenance   (23140)

A comprehensive book on the practical aspects of building maintenance. Chapters are included on: painting and decorating; plumbing and pipe fitting; carpentry; calking and glazing; concrete and masonry; roofing; sheet metal; electrical maintenance; air conditioning and refrigeration; insect and rodent control; heating maintenance management; cutodial practices: A BOOK FOR BUILDING OWNERS, MANAGERS, AND MAINTENANCE PERSONNEL.

Gardening & Landscaping   (23229)

A comprehensive guide for the homeowner, industrial, municipal, and estate groundskeepers. Information on proper care of annual and perennial flowers; various house plants; greenhouse design and construction; insect and rodent control; complete lawn care; shrubs and trees; and maintenance of walks, roads, and traffic areas. Various types of maintenance equipment are also discussed.

Carpenters & Builders Library—4 Vols.   (23169)

A practical illustrated trade assistant on modern construction for carpenters, builders, and all woodworkers. Explains in practical, concise language and illustrations all the principles, advances and short cuts based on modern practice. How to calculate various jobs.

Vol. 1—(23170)—Tools, steel square, saw filing, joinery, cabinets.
Vol. 2—(23171)—Mathematics, plans, specifications, estimates.
Vol. 3—(23172)—House and roof framing, laying out, foundations.
Vol. 4—(23173)—Doors, windows, stairs, millwork, painting.

Carpentry and Building   (23142)

Answers to the problems encountered in today's building trades. The actual questions asked of an architect by carpenters and builders are answered in this book. No apprentice or journeyman carpenter should be without the help this book can offer.

Do-It-Yourself Encyclopedia   (23207)

An all-in-one home repair and project guide for all do-it-yourselfers. Packed with step-by-step plans, thousands of photos, helpful charts. A really authentic, truly monumental, home-repair and home-project guide.